WORKBOOK

S N A P

Student Notes and Problems

MATH 8
Alberta

CASTLE ROCK
RESEARCH CORP

Publisher
Gautam Rao

Contributors
Ruth Rancier
Bill Simpson

Rao, Gautam, 1961 –
STUDENT NOTES AND PROBLEMS – Math 8 Workbook Alberta
(Second Edition)

1. Math – Juvenile Literature. I. Title

Published by
Castle Rock Research Corp.
2340 Manulife Place
10180 – 101 Street
Edmonton, AB T5J 3S4

1 2 3 FP 13 12 11

CASTLE ROCK
RESEARCH CORP

Dedicated to the memory of Dr. V. S. Rao

STUDENT NOTES AND PROBLEMS WORKBOOKS

Student Notes and Problems (SNAP) workbooks are a series of support resources in mathematics for students in grades 3 to 12 and in science for students in grades 9 to 12. SNAP workbooks are 100% aligned with curriculum. The resources are designed to support classroom instructions and provide students with additional examples, practice exercises, and tests. SNAP workbooks are ideal for use all year long at school and at home.

The following is a summary of the key features of all SNAP workbooks.

UNIT OPENER PAGE

- summarizes the curriculum outcomes addressed in the unit in age-appropriate language
- identifies the lessons by title
- lists the prerequisite knowledge and skills the student should know prior to beginning the unit

LESSONS

- provide essential teaching pieces and explanations of the concepts
- include example problems and questions with complete, detailed solutions that demonstrate the problem-solving process

NOTES BARS

- contain key definitions, formulas, reminders, and important steps or procedures
- provide space for students to add their own notes and helpful reminders

PRACTICE EXERCISES

- include questions that relate to each of the curriculum outcomes for the unit
- provide practice in applying the lesson concepts

REVIEW SUMMARY

- provides a succinct review of the key concepts in the unit

PRACTICE TEST

- assesses student learning of the unit concepts

ANSWERS AND SOLUTIONS

- demonstrate the step-by-step process or problem-solving method used to arrive at the correct answer

Answers and solutions for the odd-numbered questions are provided in each student workbook. A *SNAP Solutions Manual* that contains answers and complete solutions for all questions is also available.

CONTENTS

Data Representation

Ratio, Rate, and Proportions

Pythagorean Relationships

Percent

Surface Area

Fraction Operations

Volume

Integer Operations

Patterns with Linear Relations

Linear Relations

Probability

Answers and Solutions

NOTES

DATA REPRESENTATION

When you are finished this unit, you will be able to…
- understand how different graphs can represent the same data
- show advantages and disadvantages of using different graphs
- understand how data can be distorted on graphs
- analyse graphs and critique their format, type, and accuracy of representation

Lesson	Page	Completed on
1. Graphical Representation	2	
2. Ways of Misrepresenting Data	14	
3. Analysis of Graphs and Data Representation	24	
Review Summary	30	
Practice Test	31	
Answers and Solutions	at the back of the book	

PREREQUISITE SKILLS AND KNOWLEDGE

Prior to starting this unit, you should be able to…
- do basic graphing

Lesson 1 GRAPHICAL REPRESENTATION

NOTES

Survey results can be visually displayed using a variety of graphs. **Bar graphs** are best for displaying data with distinct categories that are being compared with each other. **Line graphs** are used to graph data that show trends over time. **Pictographs** use pictures to compare two or more similar things. **Circle graphs** use percentages to show how much out of a whole circle is represented by each category.

BAR GRAPH

Bar graphs are best used to show data across different categories. These can be drawn either horizontally (left to right) or vertically (up and down). In a bar graph, all the bars need to be the same width, and they must be equally spaced. Label each axis with what it is representing, and always include the units. Be sure every graph has an appropriate title.

Here is an example of a bar graph showing the numbers of different types of animals found in a zoo.

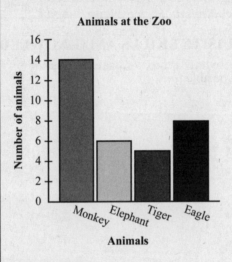

LINE GRAPH

Line graphs are best used to show continuous data over a certain period of time. With line graphs, it is standard to put the time on the x-axis and data you are graphing on the y-axis. Again, label each axis with what it is representing, and always include the units. Be sure every graph has an appropriate title.

Remember the x-axis on a graph is the horizontal axis and the y-axis is the vertical axis.

Here is an example of a line graph showing how many lawns can be mowed over a certain amount of time.

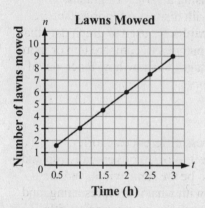

PICTOGRAPH

Pictographs have pictures that represent what is being displayed. The pictures on a pictograph usually give an estimate of the data being displayed instead of an exact number. Always include a legend showing what each picture represents. Be sure every graph has an appropriate title.

Here is an example of a pictograph showing the approximate number of each type of book found in a library.

Types of Books in the Library

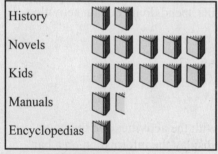

Each 📘 represents 150 books

CIRCLE GRAPH

Circle graphs represent data using percentages. To make a circle graph, find the portion of 360 (the number of degrees in a circle) that each event takes up. Do this by taking the percentage of 360, which will give you the angle measure for that event. Draw the angles using a protractor, and label the sections by percentage on the graph. All the sections must add up to exactly 360 degrees and 100 percent. Be sure every graph has an appropriate title.

To figure out the angle for each section of a circle graph, change the percent to a decimal and multiply by 360. Then, round to the nearest degree.

NOTES

Here is an example of a circle graph showing a group of Grade 8 students' favourite sports.

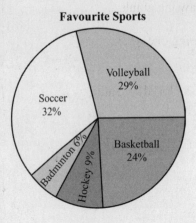

Favourite Sports

When given information and asked to display it on a graph, determine which graph would best represent the data, and be able to justify the answer. Use bar graphs for distinct categories with numbers, line graphs for trends over time, pictographs for approximate values, and circle graphs when given percentages.

Example

Determine the best type of graph on which to display the given information. Justify the answer and then draw the graph.

The number of hours junior high students spend doing certain activities in a day:

Sleeping—9   Eating—2.5
School—6   TV or Computer—3
Recreation—2   Other—1.5

Solution

Because this information is given with the activities and the hours spent on each activity, it is best to display the information on a bar graph. Each activity will be represented by one bar on the graph, and the height of each bar will represent the hours spent on each task.

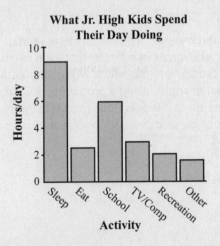

What Jr. High Kids Spend Their Day Doing

Your Turn 1

Determine the best type of graph on which to display the given information. Justify the answer and then draw the graph.

Packages of seeds a gardening store sold during one week.

Monday—45   Tuesday—40
Wednesday—30   Thursday—45
Friday—50   Saturday—0 (store is closed on Saturday)

Example

Determine the best type of graph on which to display the given information. Justify the answer and then draw the graph.

Percentage of people who listen to different types of music:

Country—19%   Rap—24%
Pop—42%   Rock—15%

Solution

Because the choices are given in percentages, it is best to display this information on a circle graph. To figure out the angle for each section, multiply the percentage (as a decimal) by 360, and then round to the nearest degree.

Country—$19\% = 0.19 \times 360 = 68.4°$
Rap—$24\% = 0.24 \times 360 = 86.4°$
Pop—$42\% = 0.42 \times 360 = 151.2°$
Rock—$15\% = 0.15 \times 360 = 54°$

Now, draw the angles on a circle, and label each section.

The angles may not always add up to exactly 360° because of rounding, but the percentages must add up to 100.

Favourite Music

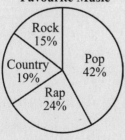

NOTES

Your Turn 2

Determine the best type of graph on which to display the given information. Justify your answer and then draw the graph.

Percentage of high school students who like certain types of movies.

Action—16%   Thriller—14%

Romance—25%   Comedy—31%

Horror—14%

Example

Determine the best type of graph on which to display the given information. Justify the answer and then draw the graph.

Each hour that Kyle works, he earns $7.50. Show how much he would earn each hour during an eight-hour shift.

Solution

Because this is an amount that Kyle is earning over a continuous time period (his eight-hour shift), this is best displayed on a line graph. Determine how much Kyle earns each hour by making a table.

Then, graph the time on the *x*-axis and the dollars earned on the *y*-axis.

Hours Worked	Dollars Earned
1	7.50
2	15.00
3	22.50
4	30.00
5	37.50
6	45.00
7	52.50
8	60.00

Plot each point and then join the points to make a line graph, as shown in the following diagram.

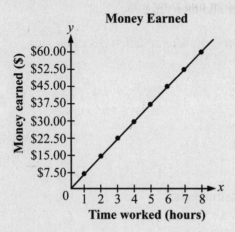

Money Earned

Your Turn 3

Melissa owns a bookstore. She has a book on sale for $10. Show on a line graph how much she will make if she sells five books.

PRACTICE EXERCISES

Determine which type of graph would best represent each situation and state why.

1. The favourite colours of people who live in Calgary.

2. Percentage of people who play different types of musical instruments.

3. Approximate number of people who read each section of the newspaper.

4. Amount of annual precipitation in six Canadian cities.

5. Number of hours of sleep needed over the course of someone's life.

Use the following graph to answer the next three questions.

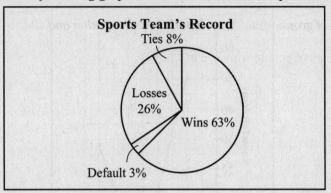

6. What is being represented by the given graph?

7. What is the angle of the losses section on the graph?

8. If the team played 25 games, how many did they tie?

Use the following graph to answer the next three questions.

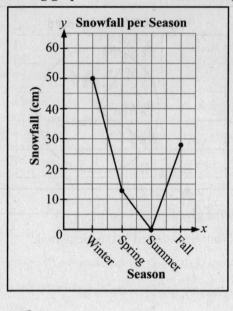

9. Which season has the most snow?

10. Approximately how much more snow falls in Fall compared with Spring?

11. Approximately how much snow falls in one year?

Use the following graph to answer the next three questions.

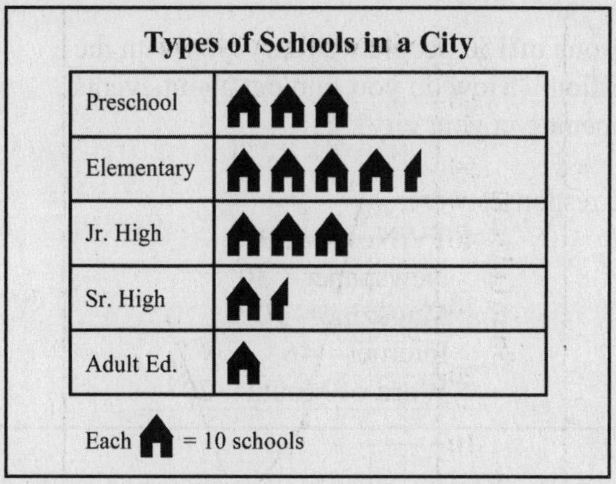

Types of Schools in a City

Preschool	🏠🏠🏠
Elementary	🏠🏠🏠🏠▲
Jr. High	🏠🏠🏠
Sr. High	🏠▲
Adult Ed.	🏠

Each 🏠 = 10 schools

12. How many elementary schools are represented in the pictograph?

13. If there are 32 pre-schools, why are there only 3 pictures drawn?

14. According to the pictogram, how many schools are there in total in the city?

Use the following data to answer the next question.

A group of 150 people was surveyed with the
question: "How do you find out about events
happening in your city?"

The responses were:
>   TV News—50
>   Newspaper—30
>   Magazine—10
>   Internet—46
>   Word of Mouth—20

15. Choose the best graph to display the data. Justify your choice and then draw the graph.

Use the following data to answer the next question.

Trina surveyed shoppers as they exited the mall.
She recorded the colour of each car leaving the
parking lot. Her data is as follows:
>   Silver—37%
>   White—22%
>   Black—20%
>   Blue—15%
>   Orange—6%

16. Choose the best graph to display Trina's data. Justify your choice and then draw the graph.

Use the following data to answer the next question.

Wayne recorded the number of cows at his dairy farm during the first five years of operation.

First year—26
Second year—48
Third year—103
Fourth year—240
Fifth year—512

17. Choose the best graph to display Wayne's data. Justify your choice and then draw the graph.

Lesson 2   WAYS OF MISREPRESENTING DATA

To distort means to change the appearance or alter the meaning of something in a manner that can be misleading.

As seen in Lesson 1, there are many ways of graphically representing data. However, these ways of representing data can be distorted so that the graphical representation may look different than expected, and may even lead to misinterpretations of the data. False conclusions can be made from such data. It is important to clearly understand how data is being represented so that the correct conclusions can be drawn.

DISTORTING THE SCALE

Graphs can be drawn using different scales to make the data look different.

Example

Consider the two line graphs A and B.

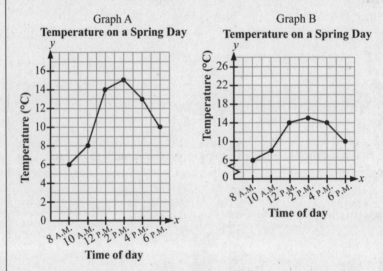

How are the graphs the same? How are they different?

Solution

The graphs are the same because they represent the same data.

A break in the *y*-axis of a graph means that the length of the axis has been shortened. It is shown by either a pair of short parallel lines or by a jagged line. This is sometimes done to alter the scale of a graph.

They are different because they each use a different scale to represent the data, and Graph B has a break in the *y*-axis, which shortens the length. Graph A seems to show a larger range of temperature change than Graph B does, even though the graphs are displaying the exact same data.

Your Turn 1

Consider the two line graphs. How are the graphs the same? How are the graphs different?

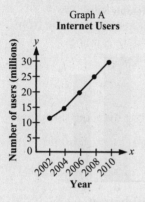

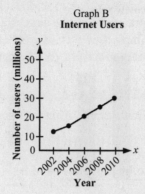

Your Turn 2

Consider the two bar graphs. How are the graphs the same? How are they different?

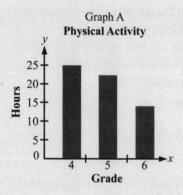

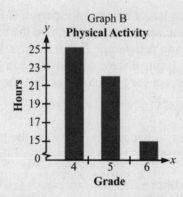

DISTORTING THE BAR SIZE

Bar graphs can also be drawn so that the sizes of the bars are different. For example, two graphs can show the same data using different sized bars. Using different sized bars can give the false impression that the differences are much larger than they actually are.

NOTES

Example

Consider the two bar graphs, A and B.

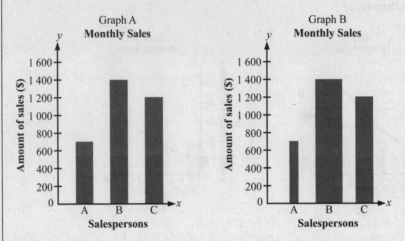

How are the graphs the same? How are they different?

Solution

The graphs are the same because they represent the same data.

They are different because the size of the bars is the same for all three salespersons in Graph A, but they are not the same for the salespersons in Graph B.

The much larger bar for Salesperson B in Graph B makes the sales for that person seem much larger, and the much smaller bar for Salesperson A in Graph B makes the sales for that person seem much smaller. Using different sized bars can give the false impression that the differences are much larger than they actually are.

Your Turn 3

Consider the two bar graphs. How are the graphs the same? How are the graphs different?

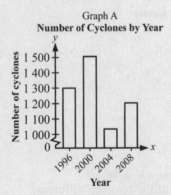
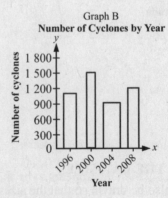

Your Turn 4

Compare the two bar graphs. How are the graphs the same? How are they different?

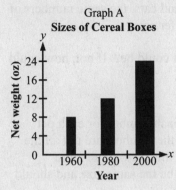

Graph A
Sizes of Cereal Boxes

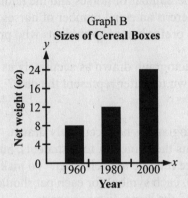

Graph B
Sizes of Cereal Boxes

DISTORTING THE VISUALS

Example

Examine the given pictograph.

Favourite Pets of Grade 7 Students

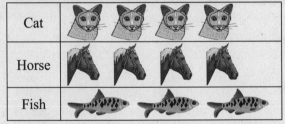

Cat	
Horse	
Fish	

 represents the choice of 4 students

 represents the choice of 4 students

 represents the choice of 4 students

a) At first glance which pet appears to be the most popular?

Solution
Fish seem to be the most popular since they have the largest symbol and produce the longest line on the graph.

NOTES

b) Do students like horses more than cats or cats more than horses?

Solution

Count the number of horses and the number of cats on the pictograph. Since there is an equal number of horses and cats, the same numbers of students prefer horses as students who prefer cats.

c) Is this pictograph drawn as accurately as it could be? If not, how could it be drawn to better represent the data?

Solution

The pictograph is not accurately drawn. Each symbol for each pet represents the choice of four students, but the symbols are not all the same size relative to each other. To make this pictograph more accurate, each symbol for each pet should be the same size and should be spaced the same distance apart.

Your Turn 5

Examine the given pictograph.

Favourite Sports

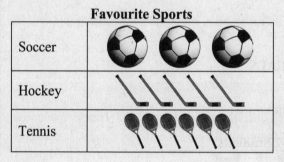

 Represents 5 students

 Represents 5 students

 Represents 5 students

a) At first glance, which sport appears to be the most popular?

b) Do more students actually like hockey or tennis?

c) Is this pictograph misleading? If yes, how should it be drawn to accurately represent the data?

18

Your Turn 6

Examine the given pictograph.

Tournament Victories at Riverside Secondary from 1977–2007

Basketball	
Soccer	
Hockey	
Tennis	
Swimming	
Rugby	
Football	

a) Which teams seem to have won the most tournaments?

b) Have more tournament victories been produced by swimming or football?

c) Is this pictograph drawn as accurately as it could be? If not, how could it be drawn to better represent the data?

PRACTICE EXERCISES

Use the following information to answer the next question.

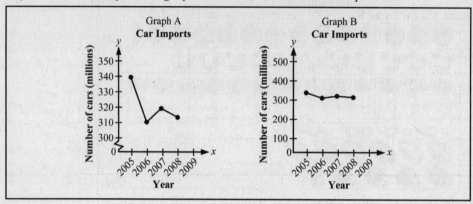

1. Consider the two line graphs. How are the graphs the same? How are the graphs different?

Use the following information to answer the next question.

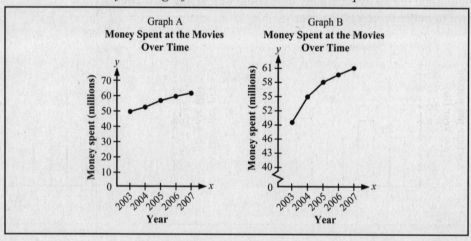

2. Consider the two line graphs. How are the graphs the same? How are the graphs different?

Use the following information to answer the next question.

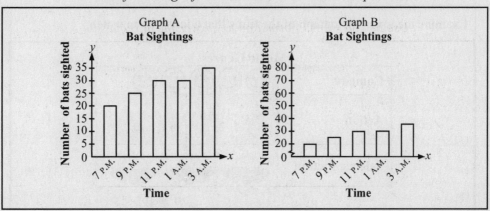

3. Consider the two bar graphs. How are the graphs the same? How are the graphs different?

Use the following information to answer the next question.

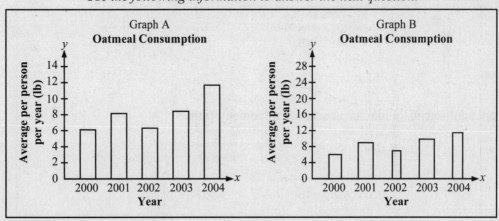

4. Consider the two bar graphs. How are the graphs the same? How are the graphs different?

Use the following information to answer the next three questions.

Examine the given pictograph of the films that adults like to watch.

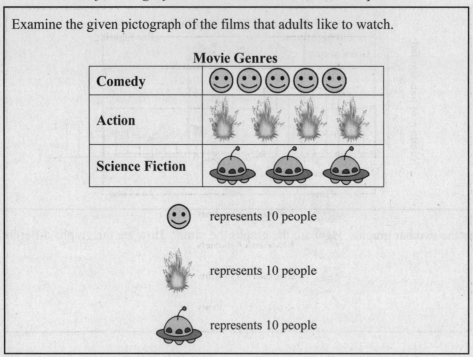

Movie Genres

represents 10 people

represents 10 people

represents 10 people

5. At first glance, which movie genre appears to be the most popular? Which appears to be the least popular?

6. Do more adults actually like science fiction or comedy films?

7. Is this pictograph misleading? If yes, how should it be drawn to accurately represent the data?

22

Use the following information to answer the next three questions.

Favourite Pizza Toppings

Green pepper	🍕🍕🍕
Pepperoni	🍕🍕🍕🍕
Sausage	🍕🍕🍕🍕🍕🍕
Mushroom	🍕🍕🍕

Represents 6 students

Represents 6 students

Represents 6 students

Represents 6 students

8. At first glance which topping appears to be the most popular? Which appears to be the least popular?

9. Do more students actually order pepperoni or mushroom pizza?

10. Is this pictograph misleading? If yes, how should it be drawn to accurately represent the data?

Lesson 3   ANALYSIS OF GRAPHS AND DATA REPRESENTATION

Critique means to review and analyse critically, making unbiased observations.

Graphs and data can be analysed to determine what is really being presented and if a graph representing data is portraying the information in an accurate way.

CRITIQUING STATISTICAL INFORMATION FROM THE MEDIA

The media often reports statistical data in a way that may be misleading. Sometimes, this is unintentional. Sometimes, in advertising for example, the statistical data is made to reflect only what the advertiser wants. For example, many car manufacturers advertise 0% financing for their cars, although the price at which they sell the car is higher with 0% financing than it would be if some other promotion was chosen.

Example

Identify whether or not the information in the following statements is misleading. Give reasons for your answers.

a)   In Edmonton in 2005, there were 500 accidents involving cars and 30 involving bicycles. It is safer to ride a bicycle than to drive a car.

   Solution

   This is misleading because there are more people driving cars than riding bikes, so more car accidents than bike accidents would be expected.

b)   At Marmot Basin ski hill in 2008, 60% of the snowboarding accidents happened to people who had taken snowboarding lessons. It is safer to go snowboarding without taking lessons.

   Solution

   This is misleading because most people who snowboard probably took lessons at one time or another. The population of snowboarders who took lessons includes almost all snowboarders. It is definitely not safer to snowboard without taking lessons.

Your Turn 1

State whether or not the information provided in the following statement is misleading. Give reasons for your answer.

In 2007, 127 people were injured bungee jumping and 5 367 were injured crossing the street. It is safer to bungee jump than to cross the street.

CRITIQUING A GRAPH

When critiquing a graph, it is important to keep some important factors in mind.

- Is the type of graph being used actually the best way of representing the data?
- Is the graph designed so that it accurately represents the data?
- Is the graph informative?
- Does the graph accurately support a claim?

Being aware of these factors will better allow the perception of any bias or misleading information that may be presented, and will allow more accurate conclusions to be drawn about the information that is presented.

Example

Amanda recorded the scores for two Grade 8 Math classes that wrote the same test on fractions.

Class 8A (28 Students)		Class 8B (30 Students)	
Score (%)	Frequency	Score (%)	Frequency
0–49	2	0–49	1
50–59	4	50–59	3
60–69	5	60–69	6
70–79	7	70–79	10
80–89	8	80–89	7
90–100	2	90–100	3

She decided to display the data using a double bar graph.

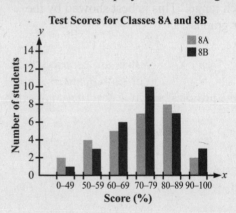

a) What conclusions can you make from the graph?

Solution

The largest group in each class was the group that scored in the 70–79% range. There were more students in Class 8B who scored in this range than there were in Class 8A. The next largest group in each class was the group that scored in the 80–89% range. There were more students in Class 8A who scored in this range than in Class 8B. The smallest group in each class was the group that scored in the 0–49% range, with more students in Class 8A scoring in this range than in Class 8B.

b) Draw two circle graphs to represent the data.

Solution

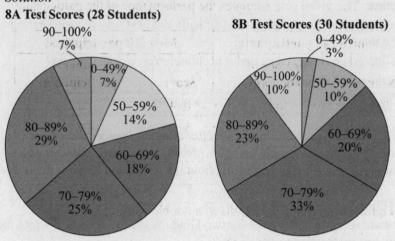

8A Test Scores (28 Students)

90–100%
7%
0–49%
7%
50–59%
14%
80–89%
29%
60–69%
18%
70–79%
25%

8B Test Scores (30 Students)

0–49%
3%
90–100%
10%
50–59%
10%
80–89%
23%
60–69%
20%
70–79%
33%

c) Which method of graphing is the best method of representing this data? Why?

Solution

The double bar graph shows only the number of students who scored in each range. The circle graphs show the percentages of students who scored in this range. The factor to keep in mind in this situation is that the number of students in each class is different. If there was the same number of students in each class, it would not matter which method of graphing was used. However, since the classes are not equal in size, the best way to compare test scores between the two classes is to show the percentage that scored in each range. This is best showed by the circle graphs, not the double bar graphs.

Your Turn 2

An online quiz on popular movies attracted 60 participants: 40 women and 20 men. The given data tabulates the performance of the participants.

Women (40 participants)		Men (20 participants)	
Score	Number of participants	Score	Number of participants
0–4	6	0–4	2
5–6	17	5–6	7
7–8	13	7–8	10
9–10	4	9–10	1

The quiz host declared the results as a double bar graph.

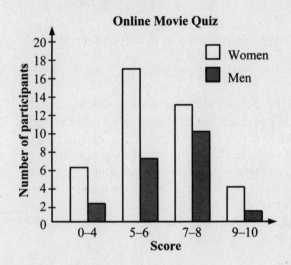

a) What conclusions can you make from the double bar graph?

b) Represent the data using two circle graphs.

c) Which of the two methods of graphing is more suited to represent the data? Give reasons.

PRACTICE EXERCISES

Use the following information to answer the next question.

An ad for sports cars claimed that there were close to 200 accidents on the Trans-Canada highway involving cars travelling less than 90 km/h, and only 25 accidents involving cars travelling at over 120 km/h. It is safer to drive at over 120 km/h than it is to drive below 90 km/h.

1. State whether or not the information provided in the given statement is misleading. Give reasons for your answer.

Use the following information to answer the next three questions.

The Edmonton Transit System collected the given data regarding the ages of passengers who purchased monthly passes for the months of August and February.

	August 2008		February 2009	
Age	Number of Pass Holders (in thousands)	Age	Number of Pass Holders (in thousands)	
10–19	39	10–19	44	
20–29	47	20–29	58	
30–39	40	30–39	53	
40–49	32	40–49	41	
50–59	18	50–59	24	

A double bar graph of the data is shown.

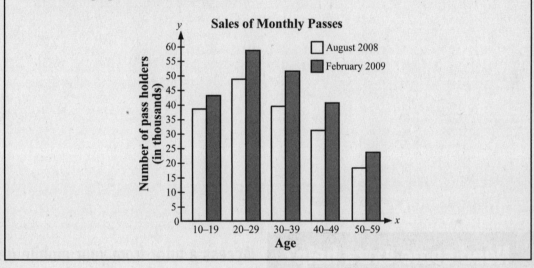

2. What conclusions can you make from the double bar graph?

3. Represent the data using two circle graphs.

4. Which of the two methods of graphing is more suited to represent the data? Give reasons to support this answer.

REVIEW SUMMARY

- Data can be represented in many ways, including line graphs, bar graphs, double bar graphs, circle graphs, and pictographs.
- Different types of graphs show information differently and some graphs display certain data better than other graphs.
- Data can be misrepresented based on the type of graph used to display it.
- Some ways data can be misrepresented on a graph include distorting the scale, distorting the bar size, and distorting the visuals.
- It is important to learn how to critique a graph and to determine if the information being presented is shown in the most effective and unbiased manner. Some factors to keep in mind while critiquing a graph include the type of graph, the design and format of the graph, whether or not the graph is informative, and does the graph accurately support the claim.

PRACTICE TEST

Use the following information to answer the next question.

> The data below shows the number of leaves on a young maple tree during the four seasons of the year.
>
> Spring—158
>
> Summer—574
>
> Fall—209
>
> Winter—15

1. Determine the best type of graph on which to display the data. Give reasons to support this answer, and then draw the graph.

Use the following information to answer the next question.

> Suzie jogs at a steady rate of 6 miles per hour. The table gives the distance she covers in intervals of 10 minutes.
>
> | Time (minutes) | Total Distance (miles) |
> |:---:|:---:|
> | 10 | 1 |
> | 20 | 2 |
> | 30 | 3 |
> | 40 | 4 |
> | 50 | 5 |
> | 60 | 6 |

2. Determine the best type of graph on which to display the data. Give reasons to support this answer, and then draw the graph.

Use the following information to answer the next three questions.

Consider the given circle graph of baby Asad's average day. Use the graph to answer the following questions.

Baby Asad's Day

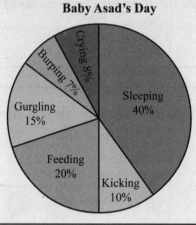

3. On which activity does Asad spend the least amount of time?

4. What is the angle for Asad's feeding?

5. How many hours a day does Asad sleep?

Use the following information to answer the next four questions.

Consider the given graph displaying the number of sunny days per month in London, England.

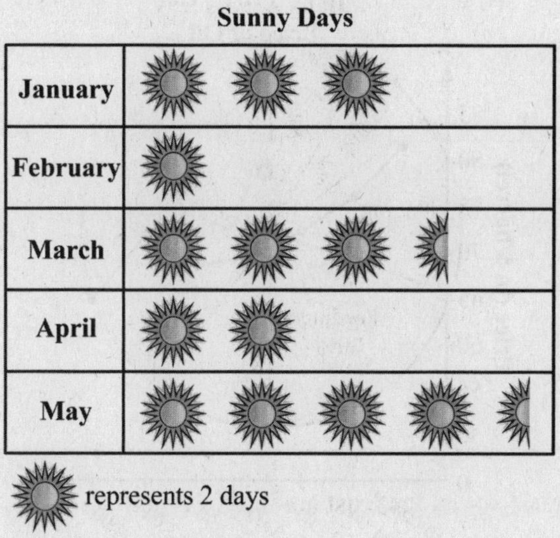

Sunny Days

January	☀ ☀ ☀
February	☀
March	☀ ☀ ☀ ☽
April	☀ ☀
May	☀ ☀ ☀ ☀ ☽

☀ represents 2 days

6. Which of the five months had most sunny days?

7. What does half a sun depict?

8. How many of the months had more than four sunny days?

9. How many sunny days in total did London experience over the five months?

Use the following information to answer the next three questions.

During the stock market crash of October 2008, the price of oil fell dramatically on the Toronto Stock Exchange. The given graph shows the change in the price of the stock for October 2, 2008.

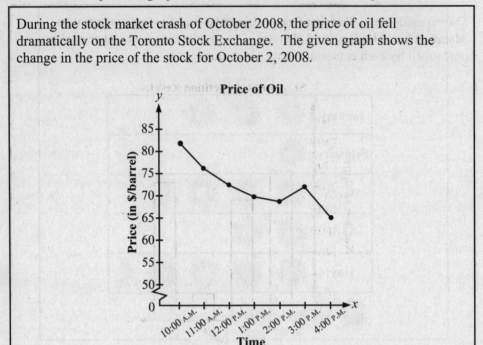

10. Describe the change in the stock price through the day.

11. At approximately what time was the price 74 dollars per barrel?

12. By approximately how much did the price change from the opening bell to the closing bell?

Use the following information to answer the next three questions.

During the Annual Skipping Competition, the final four contestants were Mahuli, Delna, Rashmi, and Hemant. The graph gives the number of skips performed by each contestant in the final round.

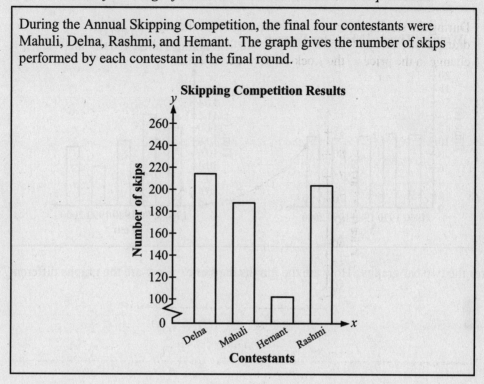

13. Who won the competition? Who came second?

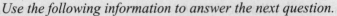

Use the following information to answer the next question.

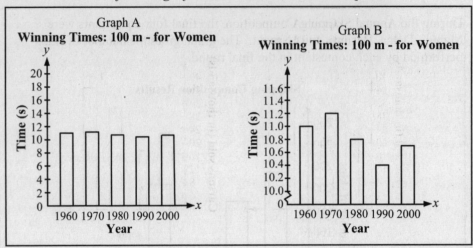

14. Consider the two bar graphs. How are the graphs the same? How are the graphs different?

Use the following information to answer the next question.

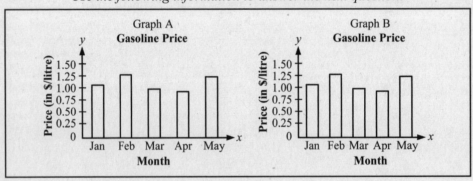

15. Consider the two bar graphs. How are the graphs the same? How are the graphs different?

Use the following information to answer the next question.

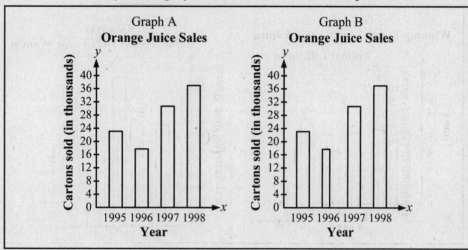

16. Consider the two bar graphs. How are the graphs the same? How are the graphs different?

37

Use the following information to answer the next question.

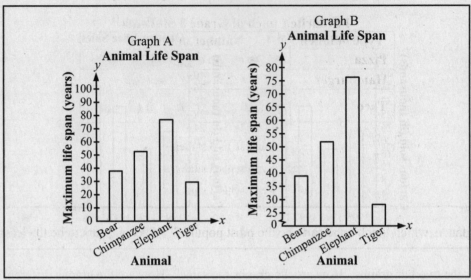

17. Consider the two bar graphs. How are the graphs the same? How are the graphs different?

Use the following information to answer the next three questions.

Favourite Lunch of Grade 8 Students

Type of lunch	Number of symbols
Pizza	🍕 🍕 🍕 🍕 🍕
Hamburger	🍔 🍔 🍔 🍔 🍔 🍔
Taco	🌮 🌮 🌮 🌮

🍕 Represents 3 students
🍔 Represents 3 students
🌮 Represents 3 students

18. At first glance, which lunch appears to be the most popular? Which appears to be the least popular?

19. Do more students actually like pizzas or tacos?

20. Is this pictograph misleading? If yes, how should it be drawn to accurately represent the data?

State whether or not the information provided in the following statements is misleading. Give reasons to support these answers.

21. In British Columbia in 2008, over 3 000 people suffered bites from their pet dogs, while less than 10 people suffered bites from their pet alligators. It is safer to have an alligator than a dog as a pet in British Columbia.

22. During a safari through India's Bandhavgarh Tiger Reserve, Kevin spotted 4 tigers but no dogs. Therefore, dogs are a more endangered species than tigers.

Use the following information to answer the next three questions.

The table gives the distribution of time spent on homework by students of Class 8A (40 students) and Class 8B (50 students).

Class 8A		Class 8B	
Time (minutes)	Number of students	Time (minutes)	Number of students
30–39	4	30–39	8
40–49	13	40–49	7
50–59	14	50–59	18
60–69	9	60–69	17

A double bar graph of the data is shown.

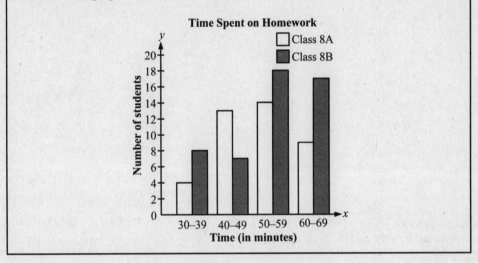

23. What conclusions can you make from the double bar graph?

24. Represent the data using two circle graphs.

25. Which of the two methods of graphing is more suited to represent the data? Give reasons to support this answer.

NOTES

RATIO, RATE, AND PROPORTIONS

When you are finished this unit, you will be able to…
- express two-term ratios in equivalent form
- express three-term ratios in equivalent form
- express ratios using different notations
- derive and apply unit rates
- solve proportions involving rates or ratios

PREREQUISITE SKILLS AND KNOWLEDGE

Prior to starting this unit, you should be able to…
- understand the meaning of ratios
- distinguish between rate and ratio
- understand proportion
- know how to reduce fractions to lowest terms

Lesson 1   RATIOS

NOTES

Since ratios compare quantities with the same units, the units are not written.

TWO-TERM RATIOS

A **ratio** compares two quantities with the same units. For example, there are 3 red balls and 5 green balls in the gym storage container. The ratio of red balls to green balls is 3 to 5.

Each number in a ratio is called a **term.** Expressions such as $3:5$, 3 to 5, or $\frac{3}{5}$ are called **two-term ratios** because the ratio has two numbers or terms.

THREE-TERM RATIOS

Three-term ratios compare three quantities with the same units. For example, there are 3 red balls, 5 yellow balls, and 4 green balls in the gym storage container. The ratio of red balls to yellow balls to green balls is 3 to 5 to 4 or $3:5:4$.

WRITING RATIOS

The order of the terms is important when writing ratios. Write the terms in the order they are given.

There are different forms for writing ratios:

Ratio form uses a colon (:) between the terms.
• Two-term ratio → $3:5$
• Three-term ratio → $3:5:4$

Word form uses the word *to* between the terms.
• Two-term ratio → 3 to 5
• Three-term ratio → 3 to 5 to 4

Fraction form places the first term in the numerator and the second term in the denominator.
• Two-term ratio → $\frac{3}{5}$

Three-term ratios cannot be represented using a single fraction.

Example

a) Write a ratio, in all forms, that compares the amount of shaded circles to unshaded circles in the given diagram.

Solution

There are 5 shaded circles and 4 unshaded circles. Since shaded circles were mentioned first in the question, the number of shaded circles will be the first term in the ratio.

Ratio form → 5 : 4

Word form → 5 to 4

Fraction form → $\dfrac{5}{4}$

b) What is the unit of the ratio?

Solution

Circles are being compared.

Your Turn 1

a) Write a ratio, in all forms, that compares the number of squares to circles in the given diagram.

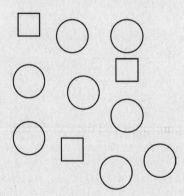

b) What is the unit of the ratio?

NOTES

Example

a) Write a ratio that compares the number of circles to squares to triangles in the given diagram.

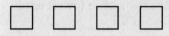

Solution
There are 5 circles, 4 squares, and 3 triangles. Keep the terms in the same order as given in the question.
Ratio form → 5 : 4 : 3
Word form → 5 to 4 to 3

b) What is the unit of the ratio?

Solution
Shapes are being compared.

Your Turn 2

a) Write a ratio that compares the number of squares to triangles to circles in the given diagram.

b) What is the unit of the ratio?

When writing ratios, the terms must be expressed using the same unit of measurement, which sometimes means converting the terms so they are all in the same units.

As well, similar to fractions, ratios are always reduced to lowest terms.

Lowest terms, also called simplest form, means the terms only share 1 as a common factor.

Example

Write 30 minutes to 2 hours in ratio form.

Solution

Since the terms of the ratio have different units (minutes and hours), the first step is to convert the terms into the same units. In this case, minutes are the easiest unit to use.
$1 \text{ h} = 60 \text{ min} \rightarrow 2 \text{ h} = 120 \text{ min}$

Rewrite the ratio $\rightarrow 30 \text{ min} : 120 \text{ min}$

Remove the units of measure $\rightarrow 30 : 120$

Reduce the ratio to lowest terms by dividing both terms by their common factor, 30.
$30 \div 30 : 120 \div 30$
$= 1 : 4$

Your Turn 3

Write 4 nickels to 3 dimes as a ratio in word form.

Example

Write 240 minutes to 2 hours to 1 day as a ratio in word form.

Solution

Convert the terms to the same unit. In this case, hours are the easiest unit to use.
$60 \text{ min} = 1 \text{ h} \rightarrow 240 \text{ min} = 4 \text{ h}$
$2 \text{ h} = 2 \text{ h}$
$1 \text{ d} = 24 \text{ h}$

Remove the units of measure.
4 to 2 to 24

Reduce to lowest terms by dividing all the terms by 2.
$4 \div 2 \text{ to } 2 \div 2 \text{ to } 24 \div 2$
$= 2 \text{ to } 1 \text{ to } 12$

NOTES

Your Turn 4

Write 6 nickels to 2 dimes to 2 quarters as a ratio in ratio form.

PART TO PART AND PART TO WHOLE

So far, when looking at ratios, parts have been compared to each other:

- Students $\rightarrow \dfrac{\text{boys}}{\text{girls}}$

- Time $\rightarrow \dfrac{\text{hours}}{\text{hours}}$

- Money $\rightarrow \dfrac{\text{dollars}}{\text{dollars}}$

These ratios compare part to part.

Ratio $\rightarrow \dfrac{\text{part}}{\text{part}}$

Ratios also compare parts to the whole; for example, 16 questions out of 20 were correct. The ratio is written $16:20$, 16 to 20, or $\dfrac{16}{20}$. In this example the number of correct questions on a test is compared to the total number of questions on the test. The phrase *out of* indicates part to whole.

Ratio $\rightarrow \dfrac{\text{part}}{\text{whole}}$

Example

The hockey team won 30 out of 50 games.

a) Write a ratio in ratio form comparing wins to total games.

Solution
The ratio 30 winning games to 50 total games is written $30:50$.

Reduce the ratio to lowest terms.
$30 \div 10 : 50 \div 10 \rightarrow 3:5$

The ratio is $3:5$.

b) Write a ratio in word form comparing losses to wins.

Solution

If the team won 30 games out of 50, it means they lost
50 – 30 = 20 games. This is written as 20 to 30. Once reduced,
the ratio is 2 to 3.

c) Write a ratio in fraction form comparing losses to total number
of games.

Solution

The ratio is 20 to 50.

In fraction form, this is written as $\dfrac{20}{50}$, which reduces to $\dfrac{2}{5}$.

d) Identify the ratios as part-to-part or part-to-whole.

Solution

The ratio in **b)** is a part-to-part ratio because it is comparing winning
games to losing games.

The ratios in **a)** and **c)** are part-to-whole because they are comparing
winning or losing games to the total number of games.

Your Turn 5

In a survey, 65 out of 80 Canadians said they owned a car.

a) Write the ratio in word form that represents the given statement.

b) Write the ratio comparing the Canadians who own a car to those who
do not. Show your answer in ratio form.

c) Identify the ratio that is part-to-part and the ratio that is part-to-whole.

Notice that ratios
comparing parts to a
whole always have the
first term smaller than
the second term.

Example

A formula for an orange, lemon, and apple juice mixture is $2:1:3$.

a) What is the ratio of orange juice to lemon juice in ratio form?

Solution

The orange juice is the first term. The lemon juice is the second term. The ratio of orange juice to lemon juice is $2:1$.

b) What is the ratio of orange juice to the juice mixture in ratio form?

Solution

Add all three terms to determine the whole ($2+1+3=6$).

The ratio of orange juice to juice mixture is
$$2:6 \xrightarrow{\text{reduce}} 2 \div 2 : 6 \div 2$$
$$=1:3$$

Your Turn 6

A cereal company makes a blend of wheat, flax, and oats in a ratio of $4:1:2$.

a) What is the ratio of wheat to oats?

b) What is the ratio of flax to the cereal blend in ratio form?

PERCENT

Percent is a ratio in which the part is compared to the whole, and the whole is always 100. Percent means hundredths or per 100. The percent symbol (%) means that a number is being compared to 100.

Think of the fraction line (—) as a division sign (÷) without the dots.

The terms 80 percent or 80% both represent the ratio $80:100$ or $\dfrac{80}{100}$.

$$85\% = \frac{85}{100} \rightarrow 85 \text{ out of a total of } 100$$

RATIOS AS A PERCENT

Ratios in which the part is compared to the whole can be expressed as a percentage. To change a part-to-whole ratio into a percentage, divide the first term by the second term, and then multiply by 100.

Example

a) A class has 18 girls and 12 boys. Write a ratio in fraction form comparing the part (girls) to the whole.

Solution
Calculate the whole by adding the parts.
$18 + 12 = 30$

The ratio is $\dfrac{18}{30}$.

b) What percent of the class is girls?

Solution
Divide the first term by the second term, and then multiply by 100.
$(18 \div 30) \times 100 = 60$

Girls make up 60% of the class.

Your Turn 7

Albert got 24 questions right and 16 questions wrong on an assignment. What percent did he earn on the test?

PRACTICE EXERCISES

Identify the unit in each of the following ratios.

1. There are 12 boys and 3 girls in a class.

2. A hockey team has 35 wins and 25 losses.

Use the following diagram to answer the next four questions.

Write the ratios in lowest terms. Identify each ratio as part-to-part or part-to-whole.

3. squares : circles

4. triangles to squares

5. squares : all shapes

6. shaded shapes : unshaded shapes

Write each ratio in all forms. Identify each ratio as part-to-part or part-to-whole.

7. Thirteen blonds to six red heads

8. Twenty correct questions on a test of thirty questions

9. Seven boys out of twenty

52

10. Number of vowels to number of consonants, including *y* as a vowel.

11. Six nickels to three pennies to six dimes

12. A box is 30 cm long, 20 cm wide and 40 cm high

Use the following table to answer the next two questions.

Class	Number of Boys	Number of Girls
Math	30	27
Science	15	30
French	25	15

13. What is the ratio of boys to girls in science class as a fraction?

14. What is the ratio of students in science class to students in French class?

Use the following information to answer the next two questions.

Alyssa received a mark of 28 out of 40 on her social studies test, while Joanne received a mark of 32 out of 40.

15. Write a ratio that expresses Joanne's score relative to Alyssa's score in ratio form.

16. What percent of the questions did each girl get correct?

Use the following information to answer the next two questions.

Fourteen out of twenty students passed the test.

17. What is the ratio of passes to failures in ratio form?

18. What percent of students passed the test?

Use the following information to answer the next two questions.

There are nine parts water to three parts bleach in a solution.

19. What is the ratio of water to total solution?

20. What percent of the solution is bleach?

54

Lesson 2   RATES

RATES

A **rate** is a comparison of two or more quantities with different units.
An example of a rate is travelling 300 km in 5 hours, in which the units are kilometres and hours. Another rate is $60.00 for 5 hours worked. In this case, the units are dollars and hours.

Rates are usually written as a **unit rate**, in which the relationship is reduced so that the value of the second term, or the denominator in the case of a fraction, is equal to 1. To change a rate into a unit rate, divide the numeric value of the first term by the numeric value of second term, and write the units of measurement beside the result. The units go behind the unit rate except for units in dollars, which go in front of the unit rate.

Example

Express $30.00/5 h as a unit rate.

Solution

The rate is written in words as *thirty dollars per five hours*. The word *per* indicates a rate.

The first term is in dollars. The second term is in hours. Divide the numeric value of the first term (30.00) by the numeric value of the second term (5) $\rightarrow$ $30 \div 5 = 6$.

Rates are written symbolically or in word form with the abbreviated units beside the result.

Symbolically $\rightarrow$ $6.00/h or $\dfrac{\$6.00}{h}$

The denominator's value, 1, does not need to be written. This rate is written in words as *six dollars per hour*.

Word form $\rightarrow$ $6.00 per h.

The / symbol is replaced by the word *per*.

Your Turn 1

John typed 375 words per 5 minutes. Express his typing speed as a unit rate symbolically and in word form.

Sometimes the terms are not presented in the order that they would be written in a rate. To figure out which term is first, look at the question. Usually, the question will ask for a specific rate, which will clearly indicate the first term.

NOTES

Example

Meghan rode her bike for 3 hours and travelled 24 km. What was her rate of speed?

Solution

The question asks for speed. Distance is the first term, and hours is the second term. The rate is 24 km/3 h.

To get the rate of speed (the unit rate), divide the numeric value of the first term by the numeric value of the second term $\rightarrow 24 \div 3 = 8$. Then, insert the units.

Meghan's rate of speed is 8 km/h (also written 8 km per h).

Your Turn 2

A plumber worked for 6 hours and charged $480.00 before taxes. What is her hourly rate?

Problems involving rates often require that the unit rate be calculated first. Use the unit rate with other given information to find the solution to a problem.

Example

The cost of 6 apples is $3.00. What is the cost of 15 apples?

Solution

The question is asking for cost. The rate is $3.00/6 apples.

Calculate the unit rate by dividing the numeric value of the first term by the numeric value of the second term. The unit rate is $3.00 \div 6 = \$0.50/$apple.

Now, multiply the unit rate by the number of apples that are being purchased.
$(\$0.50/\text{apple}) \times 15 \text{ apples} = \$7.50$

The cost of 15 apples will be $7.50.

Your Turn 3

A pipe 4 m long has a mass of 12 kg. What is the mass of a similar pipe that is 10 m long?

PRACTICE EXERCISES

1. Determine if $\dfrac{20}{46}$ is a rate or a ratio.

2. Determine if $\dfrac{16 \text{ km}}{2 \text{ h}}$ is a rate or a ratio.

3. Fatima paid $20.40 for 43 L of gasoline. What is the unit rate that she paid for the gas, rounded to the tenths place?

4. Lise can jog 6 miles in 1.4 hours. How many miles can she jog per hour, rounded to the tenths place?

5. A recipe calls for 450 mL of chocolate for 10 servings. How much chocolate is needed for 15 servings?

6. Cheryl can type 56 words per minute. At that rate, how many words can she type in 5 minutes?

7. Tomatoes are advertised at $9.45 for 5 kg. How much will it cost to purchase 20 kg of tomatoes?

8. A dog walker earns $14.25 for 5 hours of work. How much will she earn if she works for 3 hours?

Lesson 3   EQUIVALENT RATIOS AND PROPORTIONAL REASONING

EQUIVALENT RATIOS

Equivalent ratios are ratios that have the same value but use different numbers—they are multiples of a given ratio in lowest terms. Since ratios are reduced to lowest terms, the original ratio is a multiple of the reduced ratio.

Example

What is the ratio of vowels to consonants in the word *mathematic*?

Solution

There are 4 vowels and 6 consonants. The ratio of vowels to consonants is $\dfrac{4}{6}\xrightarrow[\div 2]{\div 2}\dfrac{2}{3}$.

The ratios $\dfrac{4}{6}$ and $\dfrac{2}{3}$ are equivalent because they have the same value.

The ratio $\dfrac{4}{6}$ is a multiple of $\dfrac{2}{3}$.

Your Turn 1

What is the ratio of consonants to vowels in the word *students*?

When a ratio is given, an equivalent ratio can also be made by multiplying the numerator and denominator by the same number.

Example

Write three equivalent ratios to $\dfrac{3}{4}$.

Solution

Choose any number to multiply the numerator and denominator by. The resulting fraction is an equivalent fraction.

$\dfrac{3}{4}\xrightarrow[\times 2]{\times 2}\dfrac{6}{8},\ \dfrac{3}{4}\xrightarrow[\times 3]{\times 3}\dfrac{9}{12},\ \dfrac{3}{4}\xrightarrow[\times 4]{\times 4}\dfrac{12}{16}$

The ratios $\dfrac{6}{8}$, $\dfrac{9}{12}$, and $\dfrac{12}{16}$ are all equivalent to each other and to $\dfrac{3}{4}$.

There are also other possible solutions.

Your Turn 2

Write three equivalent ratios to $\frac{2}{3}$.

Sometimes two ratios are given and you are asked to determine if they are equivalent. There are two strategies to use to determine the equivalency of the ratios.

Strategy 1: Equivalent fractions
Reduce each ratio to lowest terms to see if they are equivalent. If the ratios are the same, they are equivalent. If the ratios are different, they are not equivalent.

Strategy 2: Cross products
Multiply the numerator of the first ratio by the denominator of the second ratio. Then, multiply the numerator of the second ratio by the denominator of the first ratio. If the products are the same, the ratios are equivalent.

Example

Are the ratios $\frac{3}{15}$ and $\frac{5}{25}$ equivalent?

Solution

Strategy 1: Equivalent fractions
Reduce each ratio to lowest terms to see if they are equivalent.

$$\frac{3}{15} \xrightarrow[\div 3]{\div 3} \frac{1}{5} \text{ and } \frac{5}{25} \xrightarrow[\div 5]{\div 5} \frac{1}{5}$$

The ratios $\frac{3}{15}$ and $\frac{5}{25}$ are equivalent, since they reduce to the same ratio.

Strategy 2: Cross products
Multiply the numerator of the first ratio by the denominator of the second ratio. Then, multiply the numerator of the second ratio by the denominator of the first ratio.

$$\frac{3}{15} = \frac{5}{25}$$
$$3 \times 25 = 5 \times 15$$
$$75 = 75$$

The ratios $\frac{3}{15}$ and $\frac{5}{25}$ are equivalent.

Your Turn 3

Are $\dfrac{6}{14}$ and $\dfrac{21}{49}$ equivalent ratios? Use equivalent fractions and cross products to solve.

PROPORTIONS

A **proportion** is a statement of equality between two ratios.
When working with proportions, one complete ratio will be given along with a part or portion of another ratio. To solve a proportion, change the ratios that are in word or ratio form into fraction form, and set the fractions so they are equal to each other. Then, use one of the two following methods to solve.

Strategy 1: Equivalent fractions
Look at the portion of the fractions that are given. Use multiplication or division to establish the relationship between the two. Since both denominators are given, multiply or divide one to get the other.

Strategy 2: Cross products
Multiply the numerator of the first fraction by the denominator of the second fraction. Then, multiply the numerator of the second fraction by the denominator of the first fraction.

Example

Determine the missing number in the proportion $1:5 = x:20$.

Solution
Set the fractions so they are equal to each other.

$$\frac{1}{5} = \frac{x}{20}$$

Strategy 1: Equivalent fractions
Use multiplication or division to establish the relationship between the two.

The variable x is used to represent the unknown number.

Multiplication	Division
$\dfrac{1}{5} \xrightarrow{\times 4} \dfrac{x}{20}$	$\dfrac{1}{5} \xleftarrow{\div 4} \dfrac{x}{20}$
Multiply the numerator of the fraction by 4 to get the missing value.	Think, "What number divided by 4 equals 1?"
$\dfrac{1}{5} \xrightarrow[\times 4]{\times 4} \dfrac{\mathbf{4}}{20}$	$\dfrac{1}{5} \xleftarrow[\div 4]{\div 4} \dfrac{\mathbf{4}}{20}$

NOTES

Strategy 2: Cross products

$$\frac{1}{5} = \frac{x}{20}$$ $$1 \times 20 = 5x$$ $$20 = 5x$$	Multiply the numerator of the first fraction by the denominator of the second fraction. Then, multiply the numerator of the second fraction by the denominator of the first fraction.
$$\frac{20}{5} = \frac{5x}{5}$$ $$4 = x$$	Solve for x by dividing each term by 5.
$$\frac{1}{5} = \frac{4}{20}$$	Replace x with the solution to the cross products—in this case, 4. Therefore $x = 4$

Your Turn 4

Use equivalent fractions and cross products to determine the missing number in the following proportions.

a) $\dfrac{7}{8} = \dfrac{k}{16}$

b) 3 to 5 = 12 to m

Use equivalent fractions and cross products to solve proportion problems involving rates and ratios.

Example

A football team has a record of 5 wins to 4 losses. If their ratio of wins to losses stays the same, then out of 27 games, how many will they win?

Solution
The equivalent-fraction or cross-products strategy can be used to solve for w, the number of wins.

Choose an appropriate variable to represent the unknown.

Set up a proportion of number of wins (5) to games played ($5 + 4 = 9$).

$$\frac{5 \text{ wins}}{9 \text{ games}} = \frac{w}{27 \text{ games}}$$
$$\frac{5}{9} = \frac{w}{27}$$

Strategy 1: Equivalent fractions

$$\frac{5}{9} \xrightarrow[\times 3]{\times 3} \frac{\mathbf{15}}{\mathbf{27}}$$

If the multiple is not obvious, use cross products.

Strategy 2: Cross products

$$\frac{5}{9} = \frac{w}{27}$$
$$5 \times 27 = 9w$$
$$135 = 9w$$
$$\frac{135}{9} = \frac{9w}{9}$$
$$15 = w$$
$$\frac{5}{9} = \frac{\mathbf{15}}{\mathbf{27}}$$

If they play 27 games, the team will win 15 games.

Your Turn 5

To make 12 cupcakes, Alice needs 132 g of sugar. How much sugar does she need for 6 cupcakes? Use equivalent fractions and cross products to solve. Show your work.

Example

If 20% of a number is 60, what is the number?

Solution

You are given 20% of a number (60) and want to find the entire number or 100% of the number. Set up the proportion.

$$\frac{20}{60} = \frac{100}{n}$$

Equivalent fractions

$$\frac{20}{60} \xrightarrow[\times 5]{\times 5} \frac{100}{\mathbf{300}}$$

Cross products

$$\frac{20}{60} = \frac{100}{n}$$
$$20n = 100 \times 60$$
$$20n = 6\,000$$
$$\frac{20n}{20} = \frac{6\,000}{20}$$
$$n = 300$$
$$\frac{20}{60} = \frac{100}{\mathbf{300}}$$

60 is 20% of 300.

PRACTICE EXERCISES

Write three equivalent fractions for the following ratios.

1. $\dfrac{2}{2}$

2. $\dfrac{8}{3}$

3. $\dfrac{2}{7}$

Match the pairs of equivalent fractions.

4. $\dfrac{1}{2}$ _____   A. $\dfrac{15}{25}$

5. $\dfrac{2}{3}$ _____   B. $\dfrac{11}{22}$

6. $\dfrac{3}{5}$ _____   C. $\dfrac{8}{24}$

7. $\dfrac{2}{6}$ _____   D. $\dfrac{14}{21}$

Solve for the missing term using equivalent-fraction and cross-products strategies. Show your work.

8. $\dfrac{2}{3} = \dfrac{e}{9}$

9. $\dfrac{3}{7} = \dfrac{12}{r}$

10. $\dfrac{4}{n} = \dfrac{20}{25}$

11. $\dfrac{f}{8} = \dfrac{9}{24}$

Determine whether the following ratios are equivalent using the equivalent-fraction strategy.
Show your work.

12. $\dfrac{6}{14} \leftrightarrow \dfrac{18}{42}$

13. $\dfrac{3}{12} \leftrightarrow \dfrac{6}{32}$

Determine whether the following ratios are equivalent using the cross-products strategy.
Show your work.

14. $\dfrac{7}{11} \leftrightarrow \dfrac{28}{55}$

15. $\dfrac{3}{8} \leftrightarrow \dfrac{24}{64}$

Use the cross-products strategy to solve the following problems. Show your work.

16. The ratio of oil to vinegar in a salad dressing is $7:3$. The chef put 357 mL of oil into a decanter. How much vinegar did the chef have to add to maintain the ratio?

17. A video store has DVDs and Blu-ray discs in a ratio of $4:1$. If there are 440 total DVDs and Blu-ray discs in the store, how many Blu-ray discs are there?

18. Carlos is driving on the highway at a constant speed of 95 km per hour. How far will he drive in $6\frac{1}{2}$ hours?

19. The ratio of length to width of a picture frame is $3:5$. If the actual length of the picture is 12 cm, what is the perimeter of the picture?

20. In a particular school, 88% of girls in Grade 8 have their ears pierced. If 154 girls have their ears pierced, how many girls are in Grade 8?

21. The human body is made up of 75% water. If the mass of water in Samantha's body is 45 kg, what is her total mass?

REVIEW SUMMARY

- A ratio compares quantities with the same units, so the units are never written.
- Each number in a ratio is called a term.
  - A two-term ratio can be written in ratio form, word form, or fraction form.
  - A three-term ratio can be written in word form or ratio form.
- Before writing a ratio, all terms must be in the same units.
- Ratios are always reduced to lowest terms in the same manner as fractions.
- Ratios can compare a part to a part or a part to a whole.
- Ratios can be written as a percent
- A rate compares quantities with different units, so the units are always written.
- A unit rate is a rate in which the second term is always 1.
- Equivalent ratios have the same value but different numbers.
- A proportion states an equality between two ratios.
- Proportions can be used to solve problems involving rates and ratios.
- Proportion problems can be solved using either of two methods: equivalent fractions or cross products.

PRACTICE TEST

1. Write 45 minutes to 4 hours in ratio form.

2. Write 5 pennies to 3 nickels to 3 dimes in ratio form.

Use the following information to answer the next three questions.

> Sundeep surveyed all the students in his Grade 12 class and found out that 54 out of the 81 students planned to go to university next year.

3. Write the ratio that represents the given statement in word form.

4. Write the ratio comparing the students going to university to those who are not. Use ratio form to express your answer.

5. Identify the ratio that is part-to-part and the ratio that is part-to-whole.

68

Use the following information to answer the next three questions.

A formula for a science class experiment required a mixture of liquid 1, liquid 2, and liquid 3 in a ratio of $8:3:5$.

6. What is the ratio of liquid 1 to liquid 2?

7. What is the ratio of liquid 1 to liquid 3?

8. What is the ratio of liquid 2 to the entire mixture?

Write each ratio in each of the three forms. Identify each ratio as part-to-part or part-to-whole.

9. A team won 12 games out of 20 games played.

10. Months of the year that start with a vowel to total months of the year.

11. A car dealership that has 12 red cars to 6 yellow cars.

12. A math class that has 5 girls out of 16 students.

Write each ratio using word form and ratio form. Identify each ratio as part-to-part or part-to-whole.

13. A box that is 50 cm long, 25 cm wide, and 35 cm high.

14. A cash register contains 5 nickels to 2 pennies to 10 dimes.

Use the following table to answer the next three questions.

Workers in an Office Building		
Floor	**Number of Men**	**Number of Women**
Fifth	24	16
Sixth	10	25
Seventh	42	18

15. What is the ratio of men to women on the fifth floor as a fraction?

16. What is the ratio of women to men on the seventh floor in word form?

17. What is the ratio of men on the fifth floor to men on the sixth floor to men on the seventh floor?

18. Express 300 km/4.5 hours as a unit rate. Round to the nearest whole number.

Determine if each of the following is a rate or a ratio.

19. $\dfrac{12 \text{ km}}{3 \text{ h}}$

20. $\dfrac{11}{18}$

21. Write three equivalent ratios to $\dfrac{2}{5}$.

Solve for the missing term using the equivalent-fractions and cross-products strategies. Show your work.

22. $\dfrac{2}{5} = \dfrac{x}{20}$

23. $\dfrac{4}{7} = \dfrac{b}{28}$

24. $\dfrac{3}{n} = \dfrac{15}{35}$

25. $\dfrac{z}{6} = \dfrac{24}{36}$

Use the equivalent-fractions and cross-products strategies to solve the following problems. Show all your work.

26. Jin Soo is driving on the highway at a constant speed of 85 km per hour. How far will he drive in 6 hours?

27. Tank A has a capacity of 30 L. It is half-filled with water. The ratio of the volume of water in tank A compared to tank B is 3:5. How much water is in tank B?

PYTHAGOREAN RELATIONSHIPS

When you are finished this unit, you will be able to…
- represent exponents and square roots
- understand and identify perfect squares and square roots
- approximate square roots of numbers that are not perfect squares
- distinguish between square roots and decimal approximations using a calculator
- use concrete materials and diagrams to develop the Pythagorean relationship
- use the Pythagorean relationship to calculate the measure of the third side of a right triangle, given the measure of the other two sides
- apply the Pythagorean relationship to solve problems

PREREQUISITE SKILLS AND KNOWLEDGE

Prior to starting this unit, you should be able to…
- read and write numbers using a place value table
- understand what factors are
- perform calculations involving exponents
- explain the difference between right triangles and other types of triangles

Lesson 1 *EXPONENTS AND PERFECT SQUARES*

EXPONENTS

To find the area of a rectangle, the length and width are multiplied together.

Example

Solve for the area of the given shape.

7 cm

5 cm

Solution

$A = l \times w$
$\quad = 5 \text{ cm} \times 7 \text{ cm}$
$\quad = 35 \text{ cm}^2$

Notice that the unit in the final answer, called the **base**, now has an **exponent** with it. When calculating area, not only are the numbers multiplied together, but the units are as well, resulting in an answer with squared units.

The exponent, 2, means the base (the unit) was multiplied by itself ($\text{cm} \times \text{cm} = \text{cm}^2$) and is read as "centimetres squared."

Your Turn 1

Complete the following table.

Example	Read As	Base	Exponent	Factored	Perfect Square
25^2					
19^2					
4.2^2					

SQUARES

When finding the area of a rectangle, the length and width are multiplied. If the length and the width are the same measure, the resulting shape is always a square. The area formula for a square can be written as $A_{\text{square}} = s^2$. The variable s represents the side length. The exponent indicates that the length of a side, s, is multiplied by itself: $s \times s$. This is called **squaring a number** because the shape that results is a square. When a **whole number** is squared, the resulting number is called a **perfect square**.

Example

What is the area of the given shape.

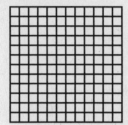

Solution

The shape looks like a square. Count the number of squares along the length and the width. Since both lengths are 12, substitute 12 into the area formula for a square.

$A_{\text{square}} = s^2$

$= 12^2 \leftarrow$ read as "twelve squared"

$= 12 \times 12 \leftarrow$ expanded multiplication (factored)

$= 144 \text{ units}^2 \leftarrow 144$ is a perfect square

If the correct units are added to the final answer, it is not necessary to write them throughout the calculations.

Your Turn 2

What is the area of the given shape, and label each step.

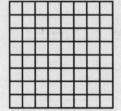

NOTES

Factors are numbers that, when multiplied together, make another number.

FACTORS OF PERFECT SQUARES

Perfect squares always have an odd number of factors. If the number of factors is even, the number is not a perfect square.

Example

Determine the factors of 15 and 16.

Solution

List the factors of the two numbers.

Factors of 15	Factors of 16
$1 \times 15 = 15$	$1 \times 16 = 16$
$3 \times 5 = 15$	$2 \times 8 = 16$
	$4 \times 4 = 16$

Order the factors from smallest to largest.

1, 3, 5, 15	1, 2, 4, 8, 16
Since 15 has four factors, it is not a perfect square.	Since 16 has five factors, it is a perfect square.

The number 15 has an even number of factors (4). This number is not a perfect square, as shown in the given model:

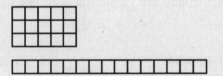

Perfect squares have an odd number of factors because the middle factor is squared, eliminating one factor when ordering the factors from smallest to largest.

The number 16 has an odd number of factors (5). This number is a perfect square, as shown in the given model:

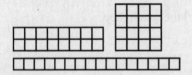

76

Your Turn 3

Determine if the following numbers are perfect squares based on their factors. Prove your conclusion with a model of all the factors, showing them on the grid provided.

a) 4

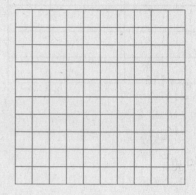

b) 6

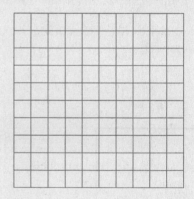

c) 9

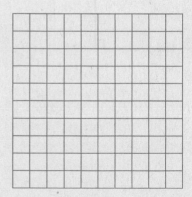

PRACTICE EXERCISES

1. Complete the following table.

	Read As	Base	Exponent	Factored	Perfect Square
23^2					
15^2					
12.9^2					
5.3^2					

Explain why the following areas are or are not perfect squares.

2. $21 \times 21 = 441 \text{ cm}^2$

3. $12 \times 13 = 156 \text{ m}^2$

4.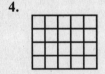

5.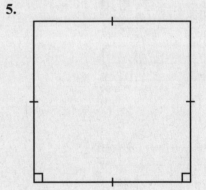

Match the perfect square with the correct side length.

6. 324 mm² ____

A. 23 mm

7. 1 024 mm² ____

B. 26 mm

8. 676 mm² ____

C. 18 mm

9. 529 mm² ____

D. 32 mm

Model the following numbers on graph paper to determine whether they are perfect squares. Show all the factored possibilities.

10. 36

11. 48

Lesson 2 SQUARES AND SQUARE ROOTS

SQUARE ROOTS OF PERFECT SQUARES

The **square root** of a number is the number that when multiplied by itself gives you the original number. For example, 6 is the square root of 36, because $6 \times 6 = 36$. **Taking the square root** of a number is expressed by writing a radical sign ($\sqrt{}$) over the number you wish to take the square root of (for example, $\sqrt{16}$).

Only perfect squares will be considered in this section. There are three methods used to solve for the square root of a perfect square.

Method 1

The square root of any perfect square is the middle factor when the factors of the perfect square are written in order from smallest to largest.

Example

Calculate $\sqrt{64}$.

> *Solution*
>
> The expression $\sqrt{64}$ means to find the number that when multiplied by itself (number × number) equals 64.
>
> Order the factors of 64 from smallest to largest: 1, 2, 4, **8**, 16, 32, 64
>
> Since 64 has seven factors, it is a perfect square. Because 8 is the middle factor, it is the square root of 64: $8 \times 8 = 64$
>
> None of the other factors are the square root of 64 because when they are multiplied by themselves, they do not equal 64:
> $1 \times 1 = 2$, $2 \times 2 = 4$, $4 \times 4 = 16$, etc.

Example

Calculate $\sqrt{50}$.

> *Solution*
> Order the factors of 50 from smallest to largest: 1, 2, 5, 10, 25, 50
>
> Since 50 has six factors, it is not a perfect square. Also, none of the factors when multiplied by themselves equals 50.

Your Turn 1

Write out the factors for each number from lowest to greatest, and explain why each number is a perfect square or not. If the number is a perfect square, give the square root.

a) 81

b) 24

c) 102

d) 144

Method 2

Visualize or draw a square with the given area. The side length of the area is the square root.

Example

Calculate the square root of 121 by drawing a square.

Solution

Draw a square with an area of 121 units.

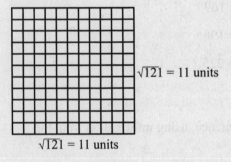

$\sqrt{121} = 11$ units

$\sqrt{121} = 11$ units

The square root of the area is the length of one of its sides. The value of the side length is 11. The square root of 121 is 11. In math symbols the sentence is written as $\sqrt{121} = 11$.

Your Turn 2

Calculate $\sqrt{25}$ by drawing a square using the grid provided.

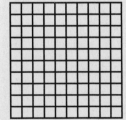

NOTES

Method 3

If the number is small enough, you may be able to think of a number that when multiplied by itself gives the original number. To make calculations quickly, it is a good idea to memorize the first 15 perfect squares.

$\sqrt{1} = 1$	because $1 \times 1 = 1$
$\sqrt{4} = 2$	because $2 \times 2 = 4$
$\sqrt{9} = 3$	because $3 \times 3 = 9$
$\sqrt{16} = 4$	because $4 \times 4 = 16$
$\sqrt{25} = 5$	because $5 \times 5 = 25$
$\sqrt{36} = 6$	because $6 \times 6 = 36$
$\sqrt{49} = 7$	because $7 \times 7 = 49$
$\sqrt{64} = 8$	because $8 \times 8 = 64$
$\sqrt{81} = 9$	because $9 \times 9 = 81$
$\sqrt{100} = 10$	because $10 \times 10 = 100$
$\sqrt{121} = 11$	because $11 \times 11 = 121$
$\sqrt{144} = 12$	because $12 \times 12 = 144$
$\sqrt{169} = 13$	because $13 \times 13 = 169$
$\sqrt{196} = 14$	because $14 \times 14 = 196$
$\sqrt{225} = 15$	because $15 \times 15 = 225$

Example

Fill in the blanks for the given sentence, using information from the previous list.

$\sqrt{36} = $ _____ because _____ $\times$ _____ = _____

Solution

$\sqrt{36} = 6$ because $6 \times 6 = 36$

Your Turn 3

Fill in the blanks for each of the given sentences, using information from the previous list.

a) $\sqrt{121} = $ _____ because _____ $\times$ _____ = _____

b) $\sqrt{25} = $ _____ because _____ $\times$ _____ = _____

c) $\sqrt{81} = $ _____ because _____ $\times$ _____ = _____

Example

Pardeep learned that plants mixed in a garden can help to boost the soil and keep insects from infesting the plants. She designed a square garden with 13 carrot squares alternating with 12 radish squares. Each square has a side length of 2 dm.

a) What is the side length of the garden?

Solution
First, model the square garden.

c	r	c	r	c
r	c	r	c	r
c	r	c	r	c
r	c	r	c	r
c	r	c	r	c

s = squares on side length × unit length
$$= 5 \times 2$$
$$= 10 \text{ dm}$$

The side length is 10 dm.

b) What is the area of the garden?

Solution
Square the length of a side to calculate the area.
$$A_{\text{square}} = s^2$$
$$= 10^2$$
$$= 10 \times 10$$
$$= 100 \text{ dm}^2$$

The area is 100 dm^2.

c) Explain how the square root is used in questions **a)** and **b)**.

Solution
In question **a)** the side length calculated is the square root.
In question **b)** the square root is squared to calculate the area.

Your Turn 4

A square stained glass window has 18 green squares alternating with 18 blue squares. Each square has a side length of 2.5 cm.

a) What is the side length of the stained glass window?

b) What is the area of the window?

c) Explain how the square root is used in questions **a)** and **b)**.

PRACTICE EXERCISES

Complete the following table.

	Square Root	**Perfect Square**
1.	2	
2.		16
3.		9
4.	5	
5.	8	
6.		49

Determine which of the following numbers is a square number based on its factors. If it is a perfect square, highlight or circle the square root.

7. 62

8. 49

State the square root and the perfect square for the following shapes.

9.

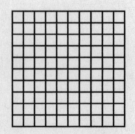

10.

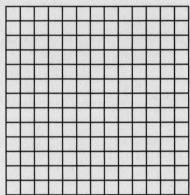

Use the following information to answer the next four questions.

A square has an area of 25 units^2.

11. Draw the square on the grid provided.

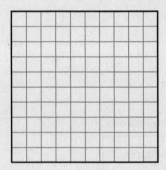

12. What is the side length of the square?

13. What is the square root of 25?

14. For what reason are the answers to questions 12 and 13 the same?

Fill in the blanks for each of the given sentences.

15. $\sqrt{9} =$ ____ because ____ × ____ = ____   16. $\sqrt{196} =$ ____ because ____ × ____ = ____

17. ____ = 25 because ____ × ____ = ____   18. ____ = 7 because ____ × ____ = ____

Find the following square roots using factors.

19. $\sqrt{64}$ 20. $\sqrt{1}$

Match each number in the first column with the number that is equal to it in the second column.

21. 16 ____   A. 4^2

22. $\sqrt{4}$ ____   B. 4

23. 2^2 ____   C. $\sqrt{16}$

24. 4 ____   D. 2

Use the following information to answer the next three questions.

> A square lap quilt has 8 orange squares and 8 purple squares.
> Each quilt square has a side length of 3 dm.

25. What is the side length of the quilt? Draw a model.

26. What is the area of the quilt?

27. Explain how the square root is used in questions **25** and **26**.

Lesson 3   SQUARE ROOTS OF IMPERFECT SQUARES

Imperfect squares are numbers that do not have whole number square roots. The square roots of imperfect squares are often estimated. Knowing what numbers are perfect squares helps to estimate square roots of imperfect squares.

ESTIMATING SQUARE ROOTS USING PENCIL AND PAPER
Method 1
Choose two perfect squares closest to the number, one slightly smaller and one slightly larger than the imperfect square. Model the perfect squares, in which each side length is the square root, to help estimate the square root of the number that is between the perfect squares.

Example
Estimate $\sqrt{52}$ using modelling.

Solution
Begin by using the two perfect squares that are closest to the number in question.

$\sqrt{49} = 7$ because $7 \times 7 = 49$

$\sqrt{64} = 8$ because $8 \times 8 = 64$

On graph paper, draw a square with an area of 49. On the same graph paper, draw an overlapping square with an area of 64.

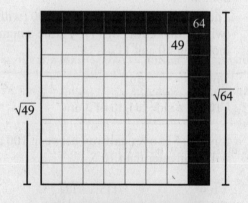

Since 52 is between 49 and 64, its square root is between 7 and 8.

Its side length is $\sqrt{52}$. Since 52 is closer to 49, draw a third overlapping square that is closer to the smaller square.

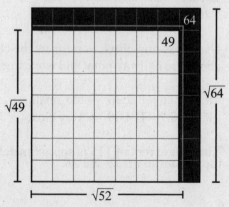

Looking at the model, the square root of 52 is approximately 7.2.

NOTES

Your Turn 1

Use a diagram to estimate $\sqrt{72}$ using modelling.

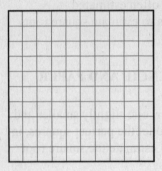

Method 2

Use a number line and the guess-and-check method to estimate the square root of an imperfect square.

Example

Estimate $\sqrt{115}$ using a number line.

Solution

The closest perfect squares are 100 (with a square root of 10) and 121 (with a square root of 11). Create a number line of square roots including 10 and 11.

$$\sqrt{100} \qquad \sqrt{121}$$
$$\begin{array}{c} \leftarrow\!+\!+\!+\!+\!+\!+\!+\!+\!+\!+\!+\!\rightarrow \\ 10 \qquad\qquad 11 \end{array}$$

Since 115 is over halfway between 100 and 121, the square root of 115 will be greater than 10.5.

$$\sqrt{100} \qquad\qquad \sqrt{115} \quad \sqrt{121}$$
$$\begin{array}{c} \leftarrow\!+\!+\!+\!+\!+\!+\!+\!+\!+\!+\!\rightarrow \\ 10 \qquad\qquad 10.7 \quad 11 \end{array}$$

Use guess-and-check to estimate the closest value possible. Start just above the halfway point and work from there.

$10.6 \times 10.6 = 112.36 \rightarrow$ too small
$10.7 \times 10.7 = 114.49 \rightarrow$ very close

The square root of 115 is approximately 10.7.

Your Turn 2

Use the number line provided to complete each statement.

a) $\sqrt{66}$ is between ____ and ____

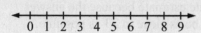

b) $\sqrt{12}$ is between ____ and ____

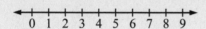

c) Using the number line, estimate $\sqrt{28}$. Indicate this estimate on the number line.

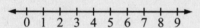

Method 3

Use averages to estimate the square root, and use the most accurate estimate.

Example

Estimate $\sqrt{23}$ using averages.

> *Solution*
> **Step 1**
> Find the closest perfect squares to the number.
> The closest perfect squares are 16 ($\sqrt{16} = 4$) and 25 ($\sqrt{25} = 5$).
>
> **Step 2**
> Divide the number 23 by either of the square roots.
> Divide 23 by 4.
> $23 \div 4 = 5.75$
>
> **Step 3**
> Find the average of the square root used as the divisor and the quotient in step 2.
> $$\frac{\text{square root} + \text{quotient}}{2} = \frac{4 + 5.75}{2} = 4.875$$

NOTES

A divisor is a number that divides into another number ($8 \div 4$, 4 is the divisor). A quotient is the answer from dividing two numbers.

Step 4
Square the answer of step 3.
$$4.875^2 = 4.875 \times 4.875$$
$$= 23.765\ 625$$

This answer is not the most accurate estimate because the answer is almost 24. The estimate should be as close to 23 as possible. Refine the estimate by repeating steps 2, 3 and 4. This time, substitute the answer from step 3 (4.875) for the divisor in step 2 and the square root in step 3. It is fine to round the numbers to make them easier to work with.

Step 2
$$23 \div 4.875 = 4.717\ 948\ 718$$

Step 3
$$\frac{4.875 + 4.72}{2} = 4.7975$$

Step 4
$$4.7975^2 = 4.7975 \times 4.7975$$
$$= 23.016\ 006\ 25$$
This answer is very close to 23.

The approximate square root of 23 is 4.7975.

HINT: Choosing the square root of the perfect square that is closest to the imperfect square will get a more accurate answer faster.
Repeat steps 2–4 using $\sqrt{25} = 5$.

Step 2
$$23 \div 5 = 4.6$$

Step 3
$$\frac{5 + 4.6}{2} = 4.8$$

Step 4
$$4.8^2 = 4.8 \times 4.8$$
$$= 23.04$$
This answer is very close to 23.

Steps 2–4 do not need repeating. You could use 4.8 as an estimate for $\sqrt{23}$.

Your Turn 3

Using averages, estimate $\sqrt{18}$.

CALCULATING SQUARE ROOTS USING TECHNOLOGY

Each calculator uses different methods to calculate square roots. Usually, finding the square root involves one of two methods.

Method 1: Type the number, then press the $\boxed{\sqrt{}}$ sign.

Method 2: Press the $\boxed{\sqrt{}}$ sign, type the number, then press =.

On some calculators, press the second function or the shift key to bring up the $\sqrt{}$.

Example

Using a calculator, find $\sqrt{21}$.

Solution

Method 1: Type $\boxed{2}$, type $\boxed{1}$ then press $\boxed{\sqrt{}}$.

Method 2: Press $\boxed{\sqrt{}}$, type $\boxed{2}$, type $\boxed{1}$, then press $\boxed{=}$.

The answer appears as 4.582 57 5695.

Your Turn 4

Using a calculator, find $\sqrt{98}$, rounded to the tenths place.

A calculator can also be used to find the square root of numbers that contain decimals.

Example

Find $\sqrt{1.9}$ using a calculator. Round the answer to the hundredths place.

Solution

The answer appears as 1.378 404 875.

The hundredths place is two places after the decimal. So, rounded to the hundredths place, $\sqrt{1.9} = 1.38$.

NOTES

Your Turn 5

Find $\sqrt{3.7}$ using a calculator. Round the answer to the hundredths place.

Square roots are often used to find the dimensions of square objects.

Example

The area of a square field is 169 m^2. How long is each side? Use a calculator to determine the answer.

Solution

Because the field is square, each side must be the same length.

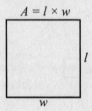

$A = l \times w$

The formula for a square area is $A = s^2$.

Determine what number multiplied by itself results in 169. In other words, find the square root of 169 $\rightarrow \sqrt{169} = 13$.

Each side of the field is 13 m long, since $13 \times 13 = 169$.

Your Turn 6

The area of a square field is 576 m^2. How long is each side?

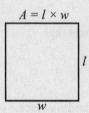

$A = l \times w$

NOTES

Example

A square classroom is 49 m^2. What is its perimeter?

Solution

Just like in the previous example, find $\sqrt{49}$ to determine the side length. $\sqrt{49} = 7$, so each side length is 7 m.

A square has 4 sides. The perimeter of a square is
$4 \times s = 4 \times 7 = 28$ m.

The perimeter of the classroom is 28 m, since $7 + 7 + 7 + 7 = 28$ m.

Your Turn 7

A square classroom is 81 m^2. What is its perimeter?

PRACTICE EXERCISES

1. Draw a diagram to estimate $\sqrt{30}$. Use the grid provided.

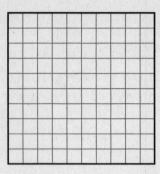

Use the number line of square roots to complete each statement.

2. $\sqrt{40}$ is between _____ and _____

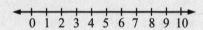

3. $\sqrt{7}$ is between _____ and _____

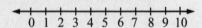

Mark each statement as true or false.

4. $\sqrt{45}$ is between 7 and 8

5. $\sqrt{88}$ is between 81 and 100

6. $\sqrt{23}$ is closer to 4 than 5

7. $\sqrt{55}$ is closer to 7 than 8

Using perfect squares, estimate the following square roots.

8. $\sqrt{20}$

9. $\sqrt{104}$

10. $\sqrt{66}$

11. $\sqrt{171}$

Use the number line of square roots and the guess-and-check strategy to estimate the following square roots. Show all your work.

12. $\sqrt{90}$

13. $\sqrt{33}$

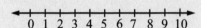

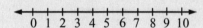

14. $\sqrt{10}$

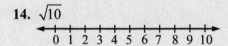

Use the averaging method to find the following square roots. Show all your work. Then, use a calculator to determine the actual square root.

15. $\sqrt{11}$

16. $\sqrt{119}$

17. $\sqrt{54}$

18. $\sqrt{213}$

19. A square wrestling mat is 64 m^2. What is its length?

Use the following information to answer the next two questions.

> A farmer wants to split his square field into 9 identical smaller square sections. The 9 fields have a combined area of 144 km^2.

20. What is the area of each smaller section?

21. What are the dimensions of each smaller section?

Lesson 4   AREA AND LINE SEGMENTS

You have already learned that the area of a triangle can be calculated using the formula $A = \dfrac{bh}{2}$.

Example

Find the area of the given triangle.

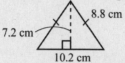

Solution

To find the area of a triangle, multiply the base by the height, then divide the product by 2.

$$A = \frac{bh}{2}$$
$$= \frac{10.2 \times 7.2}{2}$$
$$= \frac{73.44}{2}$$
$$= 36.72 \text{ cm}^2$$

The area of the triangle is 36.72 cm^2.

AREA OF AN ANGLED SQUARE

Side lengths and areas of squares can be calculated using the grids on graph paper. The next example demonstrates how can the area and side length be calculated if the square is angled on the graph paper like the one shown in the following example?

NOTES

Example

Calculate the area and side length of the given square, rounded to the tenths place.

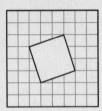

Solution

Step 1 Draw a larger square, following the graph paper lines, that contains the given square.	
Step 2 Calculate the area of the larger square by counting how many grids are along each side of the larger square, then squaring the number.	$A_{\text{square}} = s^2$ $= 4^2$ $= 16 \text{ units}^2$
Step 3 Calculate the area of one of the four triangles created by the larger square. It does not matter which length is used for the base or the height—the answer will be the same. Since the four triangles are identical, multiply the result by 4 to calculate the area of all the triangles.	$A_{\text{triangle}} = \dfrac{bh}{2}$ $= \dfrac{1 \times 3}{2}$ $= \dfrac{3}{2}$ $= 1.5 \text{ units}^2$ $A_{\text{four triangles}} = A_{\text{triangle}} \times 4$ $= 1.5 \times 4$ $= 6 \text{ units}^2$
Step 4 Subtract the area of the four triangles from the area of the large square.	$A_{\text{small square}} = A_{\text{large square}} - A_{\text{four triangles}}$ $= 16 - 6$ $= 10 \text{ units}^2$
Step 5 Take the square root of the area of the small square to calculate the side length. Round the answer to the tenths place.	Estimate or use the calculator to find the square root. $\sqrt{10} = 3.162\ 277\ 66$ $= 3.2$

The area of the given square is 10 units². The side length of the given square, rounded to the tenths place, is 3.2 units.

Your Turn 1

Calculate the area and side length of the given square, rounded to the tenths place.

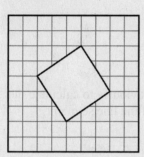

Use a similar strategy when given a line segment on graph paper and asked to determine its length.

Example

Calculate the length of the given line segment, rounded to the hundredths place.

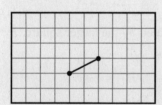

A line segment includes all the points between two given points, as well as the two end points of the line.

Solution

Step 1

Start by creating a square from the given line segment. Rotate the line 90° to the left (counterclockwise).

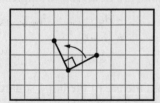

Rotate the original line 90° to the right (clockwise).

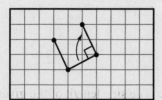

Join the two ends to create a square.

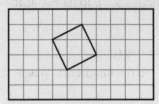

Now, follow the same procedure as outlined previously to calculate the side length of the square, which is the length of the line segment.

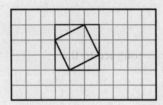

Step 2

Calculate the area of the larger square.

$$A_{\text{square}} = s^2$$
$$= 3^2$$
$$= 9 \text{ units}$$

Step 3

Calculate the area of one of the triangles created by the larger square.

$$A_{\text{triangle}} = \frac{bh}{2}$$
$$= \frac{1 \times 2}{2}$$
$$= \frac{2}{2}$$
$$= 1 \text{ unit}^2$$

Multiply the result by 4 to calculate the total are of all four triangles.

$$A_{\text{triangle}} = A_{\text{triangle}} \times 4$$
$$1 \text{ unit}^2 \times 4 = 4 \text{ units}^2$$

Step 4

Subtract the area of the four triangles from the are of the large square.

$$A_{\text{small square}} = A_{\text{large square}} - A_{\text{four triangles}}$$
$$= 9 - 4$$
$$= 5 \text{ units}^2$$

Step 5

Take the square root of the area of the small square to calculate the side length.

Estimate or use a calculator to find the square root:
$\sqrt{5} = 2.236\ 067\ 977$.   Round the answer to the hundredths place: 2.24 units.

The side length of the small square the length of the given line segment. Therefore the length of the line segments rounded to the nearest hundredth is 2.24 units.

Your Turn 2

Calculate the length of the given line segment, rounded to the hundredths place.

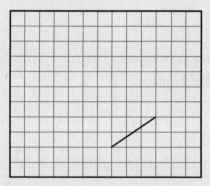

PRACTICE EXERCISES

1. Calculate the length of the given line segment, rounded to the hundredths place.

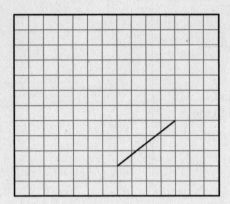

2. Calculate the length of the given line segment, rounded to the hundredths place.

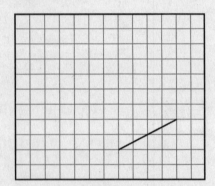

3. Calculate the length of the given line segment, rounded to the tenths place.

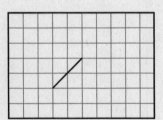

102

4. Calculate the length of the given line segment, rounded to the tenths place.

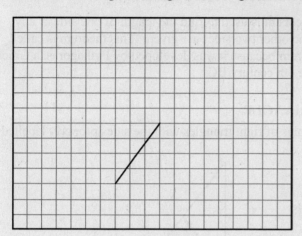

5. Calculate the length of the given line segment, rounded to the tenths place.

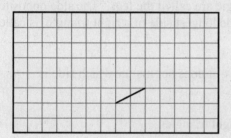

6. Calculate the length of the given line segment, rounded to the tenths place.

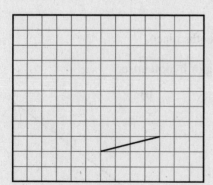

Lesson 5 PYTHAGOREAN THEOREM

The **Pythagorean theorem** is used to find the length of one side of any right triangle when the other two sides are given. This theorem is called the Pythagorean theorem because it was developed by Pythagoras, a Greek mathematician, in the 6th century BC.

LABELLING A TRIANGLE

Here are some examples of right triangles with the sides properly labelled.

A right triangle has a 90° interior (right) angle.

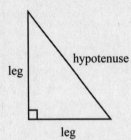 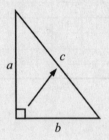

When a leg is adjacent to the right angle, it means it is connected to the right angle.

The theorem states that $a^2 + b^2 = c^2$, in which a and b are the sides adjacent to the right angle and c is the side opposite from the right angle. The sides adjacent to the right angle are called the **legs**. The side opposite the right angle, which is always the longest side of a right triangle, is called the **hypotenuse**.

Sides a and b are interchangeable—it does not matter which side is labelled a and which is labelled b.

Here are two more examples of right triangles.

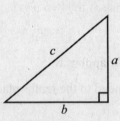 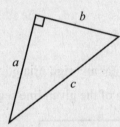

Your Turn 1

Label the sides of the triangle as a leg or hypotenuse.

a)   b)

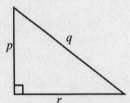   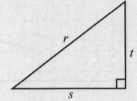

MODELLING THE THEOREM

The Pythagorean theorem states that the area of the square of the hypotenuse is equal to the area of the squares of the legs added together. This can be modelled by drawing a square along each side of a right triangle.

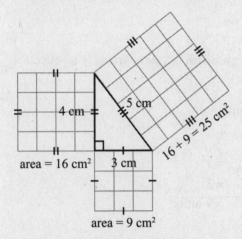

area = 16 cm²   3 cm   5 cm

16 + 9 = 25 cm²

area = 9 cm²

Make a square using the leg that has a length of 4 cm. This square will have an area of $4 \times 4 = 16 \, \text{cm}^2$.

Make a square using the leg that has a length of 3 cm. This square will have an area of $3 \times 3 = 9 \, \text{cm}^2$.

Make a square using the length of the hypotenuse. This square will have an area of $5 \times 5 = 25 \, \text{cm}^2$.

The area of the hypotenuse is equal to the sum of the areas of the two legs, since $16 \, \text{cm}^2 + 9 \text{cm}^2 = 25 \text{cm}^2$.

This relationship is true for any right triangle, and it only applies to right triangles.

Example

In the given triangle, prove the areas of squares formed by the legs are equal to the area of the hypotenuse using modelling.

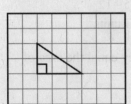

NOTES

Solution

Draw a square on each side of the right triangle.

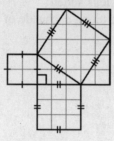

Leg $a = 2$ units and leg $b = 3$ units.

Find the area of each square.

$$A_{\text{leg } a} = s^2 \qquad\qquad A_{\text{leg } b} = s^2$$
$$= 2^2 \qquad\qquad\qquad = 3^2$$
$$= 4 \text{ units}^2 \qquad\qquad = 9 \text{ units}^2$$

$$A_{\text{hypotenuse}} = A_{\text{large square}} - A_{\text{four triangles}}$$

Therefore, square of hypotenuse
$$a^2 + b^2 = c^2$$
$$2^2 + 3^2 = c^2$$
$$4 + 9 = 13$$

is equal to the area of the squares.

$$A_{\text{leg } a} + A_{\text{leg } b} = A_{\text{hypotenuse}}$$
$$4 + 9 = 13$$

$$A_{\text{large square}} = s^2 \qquad\qquad A_{\text{triangle}} = \frac{bh}{2}$$
$$= 5^2 \qquad\qquad\qquad = \frac{3 \times 2}{2}$$
$$= 25 \text{ units}^2 \qquad\qquad = \frac{6}{2} = 3 \text{ units}^2$$

$$A_{\text{four triangles}} = A_{\text{triangle}} \times 4 \qquad A_{\text{hypotenuse}} = A_{\text{large square}} - A_{\text{four triangles}}$$
$$= 3 \times 4 \qquad\qquad\qquad = 25 - 12$$
$$= 12 \text{ units}^2 \qquad\qquad = 13 \text{ units}^2$$

Add the areas created by the two legs to see if they equal the area of the hypotenuse.

$$A_{\text{leg } a} + A_{\text{leg } b} = A_{\text{hypotenuse}}$$
$$4 + 9 = 13$$

The sum of the areas created by the the two legs ($4 + 9 = 13$ units^2) is the same as the area of the hypotenuse (13 units^2). This proves the Pythagorean theorem.

Your Turn 2

For the given triangle, prove the areas of the legs are equal to the area of the hypotenuse using modelling.

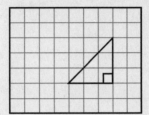

DETERMINING RIGHT TRIANGLES

The Pythagorean theorem can be used to determine whether a triangle is a right triangle, since only for right triangles does the sum of the areas of the legs equal the area of the hypotenuse.

Example

Determine whether or not the following equations are for right triangles. Show your work.

a) $5^2 + 11^2 = 13^2$

Solution

Determine whether the two sides are equal. If they are equal, the triangle is a right triangle. If the sides are not equal ($\neq$), the triangle is not a right triangle.

$$5^2 + 11^2 = 13^2$$
$$25 + 121 = 169$$
$$146 \neq 169$$

The two sides of the equation are not equal. The equation is not for a right triangle.

b) $5^2 + 12^2 = 13^2$

Solution

Determine whether the two sides are equal.

$$5^2 + 12^2 = 13^2$$
$$25 + 144 = 169$$
$$169 = 169$$

The two sides of the equation are equal. This equation is for a right triangle.

NOTES

Your Turn 3

Determine whether or not the following equations are for right triangles. Show your work.

a) $15^2 + 8^2 = 17^2$

b) $15^2 + 9^2 = 17^2$

Example

Using the given values, determine which of the following triangles right triangles are. Show your work.

a)

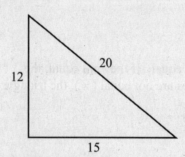

Solution

Label the sides.

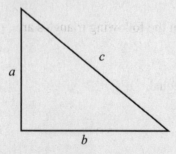

Substitute the given values into the Pythagorean theorem, and simplify.

$$a^2 + b^2 = c^2$$
$$12^2 + 15^2 = 20^2$$

108

NOTES

Complete the calculations to determine whether or not the two sides of the equation are equal. If they are equal, the triangle is a right triangle. If the sides are not equal ($\neq$), the triangle is not a right triangle.

$$12^2 + 15^2 = 20^2$$
$$144 + 225 = 400$$
$$369 \neq 400$$

The two sides of the equation are not equal. This is not a right triangle.

b)

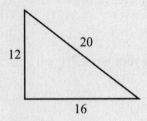

Solution
Label the sides

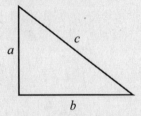

Substitute the values into the Pythagorean theorem and simplify.

$$a^2 + b^2 = c^2$$
$$12^2 + 16^2 = 20^2$$
$$144 + 256 = 400$$
$$400 = 400$$

The two sides of the equation are equal. This is a right triangle.

Your Turn 4

Using the given values, determine which of the following triangles are right triangles. Show your work.

a)

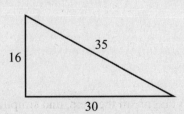

NOTES

b)

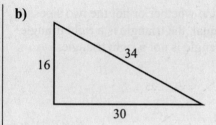

Example

Is the following triangle a right triangle? Show your work.

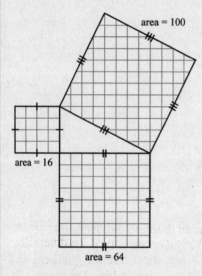

Solution

Add the areas of the squares created by the legs to see if their sum is equal to the area of the hypotenuse. The largest value is always the hypotenuse.

$$16 + 64 = 80$$
$$80 \neq 100$$

The triangle is not a right triangle because the sum of the area of the squares created by the two legs is not equal to the area of the hypotenuse.

Your Turn 5

Is the following triangle a right triangle?

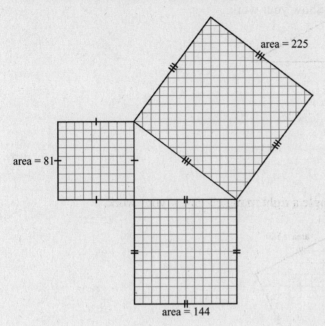

area = 225

area = 81

area = 144

PYTHAGOREAN TRIPLES

When three whole number side lengths satisfy the Pythagorean theorem (meaning $a^2 + b^2 = c^2$), they are called a Pythagorean triple. To determine if a set of three numbers is a Pythagorean triple, substitute the numbers into the Pythagorean theorem to determine if the equation holds. The largest of the three numbers will always be substituted for c in the equation.

Example

Is 35-12-37 a Pythagorean triple?

Solution

Substitute the values into the Pythagorean theorem. The largest value is always c.

$$a^2 + b^2 = c^2$$
$$35^2 + 12^2 = 37^2$$

Calculate the exponents to determine whether both sides of the equation are equal.

$$35^2 + 12^2 = 37^2$$
$$1\ 225 + 144 = 1\ 369$$
$$1\ 369 = 1\ 369$$

The numbers 35-12-37 are a Pythagorean triple because the whole number side lengths satisfy the Pythagorean theorem.

Your Turn 6

Determine which of the following sets of numbers is or is not a Pythagorean triple. Show your work.

a) 5-12-13

b) 33-56-66

c) 12-16-20

PRACTICE EXERCISES

Label the sides a, b, and c on the following right triangles.

1.

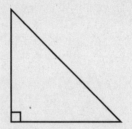

2.

3.

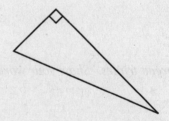

4. For the given triangle, prove the areas of the legs are equal to the area of the hypotenuse using modelling.

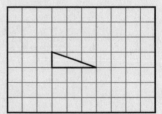

5. For the given triangle, prove the areas of the legs are equal to the area of the hypotenuse using modelling.

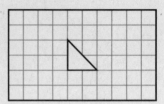

6. For the given triangle, prove the areas of the legs are equal to the area of the hypotenuse using modelling.

Determine whether the side lengths in the following equations are Pythagorean triples. Show your work.

7. $1^2 + 2^2 = 3^2$

8. $6^2 + 8^2 = 10^2$

Determine whether or not the following equations are for right triangles. Show your work.

9. $4.5^2 + 6^2 = 7.5^2$

10. $5^2 + 11.5^2 = 13^2$

Using the given values, determine which of the following triangles are right triangles. Show your work.

11.

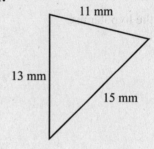

11 mm

13 mm

15 mm

12.

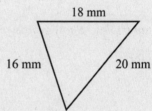

18 mm

16 mm

20 mm

13.

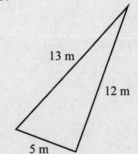

13 m

12 m

5 m

Lesson 6   *USING THE PYTHAGOREAN THEOREM*

CALCULATING MISSING SIDE LENGTHS

To find the missing side of a right triangle, use the Pythagorean theorem, substitute in the given values, and solve for the missing side.

Example

Solve for the missing side of the given triangle.

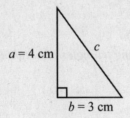

Solution

Use the Pythagorean theorem.
$$a^2 + b^2 = c^2$$

Substitute in the values for a and b.
$$4^2 + 3^2 = c^2$$

Calculate the exponents.
$$4^2 + 3^2 = c^2$$
$$(4 \times 4) + (3 \times 3) = c^2$$
$$16 + 9 = c^2$$
$$25 = c^2$$

A number squared and the square root of a number are opposite operations.

Take the square root of both sides to solve for c.
$$\sqrt{25} = \sqrt{c^2}$$
$$5 \text{ cm} = c$$

Your Turn 1

Solve for the missing side of the given triangle.

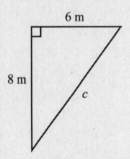

Example

Solve for the missing side of the given triangle. Round the answer to the tenths place.

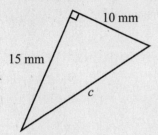

Solution

Use the Pythagorean theorem.

$a^2 + b^2 = c^2$

Label one leg a and the other leg b. Substitute the values into the equation.

$15^2 + 10^2 = c^2$

Calculate the exponents.

$$15^2 + 10^2 = c^2$$
$$(15 \times 15) + (10 \times 10) = c^2$$
$$225 + 100 = c^2$$
$$325 = c^2$$

Take the square root of both sides to solve for c.

$$\sqrt{325} = \sqrt{c^2}$$
$$18.027\ 756\ 38 = c$$
$$c \doteq 18.0 \text{ mm}$$

The missing side measures 18.0 mm.

It is not necessary to insert the units while calculating, but remember to insert the units in the final answer.

Your Turn 2

Find the missing side of the following right triangle. Round the answer to the tenths place.

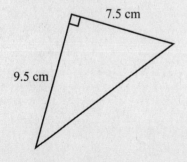

Because most square roots are irrational numbers (the decimal never ends), answers are usually left rounded to the nearest tenth.

In order to be the most precise, do not round any numbers until the final answer.

NOTES

Example

Solve for the missing side of the given triangle.

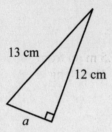

In this figure, the missing side is one of the legs (side a), not the hypotenuse (side c) as in the previous examples.

Solution

Use the Pythagorean theorem

$$a^2 + b^2 = c^2$$

Substitute the values in for b and c. Remember that the larger number will always be substituted for c in the equation.

$$a^2 + 12^2 = 13^2$$

Calculate the exponents.

$$a^2 + 144 = 169$$

Solve for a.
Subtract 144 from both sides of the equation to isolate a^2.

$$a^2 + 144 - 144 = 169 - 144$$
$$a^2 = 25$$

Take the square root of both sides to solve for a.

$$\sqrt{a^2} = \sqrt{25}$$
$$a = 5$$

Side a is 5 cm.

Your Turn 3

Find the missing side of the given triangle.

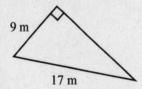

You can use the Pythagorean theorem to solve problems that involve a right triangle.

APPLICATIONS IN REAL LIFE

Example

The top of a ladder is leaning against the side of a wall 1.5 m up from the ground. The base of the ladder is 2 m from the wall. How long is the ladder?

Solution

Draw and label a figure that illustrates the problem.

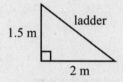

This figure lets you see the right triangle, so it is easy to label the sides. Label the wall a and the ground b (or vice versa); the ladder will be side c because it is opposite the right angle.

Substitute the values into the Pythagorean theorem and solve for c, the length of the ladder.

$$a^2 + b^2 = c^2$$
$$1.5^2 + 2^2 = c^2$$
$$2.25 + 4 = c^2$$
$$6.25 = c^2$$
$$\sqrt{6.25} = \sqrt{c^2}$$
$$2.5 = c$$
$$c = 2.5 \text{ m}$$

The ladder is 2.5 m long.

Your Turn 4

Joel is flying a kite. If the string of his kite is 7 m long and the kite is a horizontal distance of 4 m away from him, how high is the kite, rounded to the tenths place?

NOTES

Example

A square field has a path running diagonally across it. If the sides of the field measure 4.2 m long, how long is the path, rounded to the tenths place?

Solution

Draw a diagram. Label the sides *a* and *b*; label the diagonal path *c*.

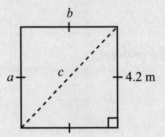

Solve for the length of the path using the Pythagorean theorem.

$$a^2 + b^2 = c^2$$
$$4.2^2 + 4.2^2 = c^2$$
$$17.64 + 17.64 = c^2$$
$$35.28 = c^2$$
$$\sqrt{35.28} = \sqrt{c^2}$$
$$5.939\ 696\ 96... = c$$
$$c \doteq 5.9 \text{ m}$$

The path across the field is 5.9 m long.

Your Turn 5

A square piece of paper has a line running diagonally across it. If the sides of the page measure 11 cm long, how long is the line, rounded to the tenths place?

PRACTICE EXERCISES

Find the missing side in each of the following right triangles, rounded to the tenths place.

1.

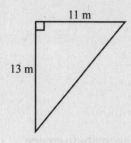

2.

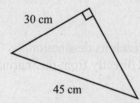

Use the following information to answer the next question.

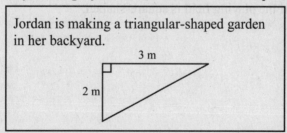

Jordan is making a triangular-shaped garden in her backyard.

3. If the left corner of the garden is made from sides that are 2 m and 3 m long, how long is the other side? Rounded to the tenths place.

Solve each of the following problems as directed. Round your answers to the tenth place.

4. A 9-metre ladder is leaning against a wall. If the base of the ladder is 4.5 m from the bottom of the wall, how far up the wall does the ladder reach?

5. A square park has sides that are 30 m long. How long is the path that runs diagonally from one corner of the park across to the other?

6. A boat leaves a marina and travels east for 75 km, then south for 25 km to reach its destination. How much shorter would the trip have been if the boat could have travelled directly from the marina to its destination?

7. The bases of a ball diamond are 14 m apart. What is the distance between second base and home plate? Assume that the playing field is square-shaped.

REVIEW SUMMARY

- A number written in exponential form shows how many times a number (base) is multiplied by itself (exponent).
- A number squared is a number multiplied by itself, shown by an exponent of 2.
- A whole number squared results in a perfect square.
- Perfect squares have an odd number of factors.
- The square root of a number is the number that, when multiplied by itself, results in the original number. Finding the square root of a number can be shown with a radical sign ($\sqrt{}$).
- A perfect square has a whole number as its square root.
- An imperfect square does not have a whole number as its square root. These square roots can be estimated using two perfect squares that are close to the imperfect square.
- Calculators can be used to find all perfect and imperfect squares and square roots.
- The Pythagorean theorem is used to determine side lengths of right triangles only.
- The formula for the Pythagorean theorem is $a^2 + b^2 = c^2$.
- The Pythagorean theorem can be proved by modelling, using squares to represent the side lengths of a right triangle.
- Three whole numbers that satisfy the Pythagorean theorem equation $a^2 + b^2 = c^2$ are called Pythagorean triples.
- The Pythagorean theorem is used to find the length of an unknown side of a right triangle, given the lengths of the other two sides.

PRACTICE TEST

1. Complete the following table.

	Read As	**Base**	**Exponent**	**Factored**	**Perfect Square**
13^2					
6^2					

Explain why the following areas are or are not perfect squares.

2. $43 \times 34 = 1\ 462\ \text{cm}^2$

3. $32 \times 32 = 1\ 024\ \text{cm}^2$

4.

5.

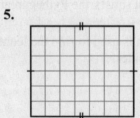

Determine whether the following numbers are perfect squares based on a list of their factors. If the number is a perfect square, circle or highlight the square root.

6. 16

7. 32

8. Determine the square root of 100 using a model of the area. Use the grid provided.

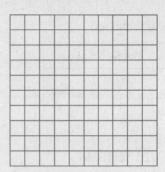

Fill in the blanks for each of the given sentences.

9. $\sqrt{64}$ = ___ because ___ × ___ = ___   **10.** $\sqrt{225}$ = ___ because ___ × ___ = ___

State the square root and the perfect square of the following shape.

11.

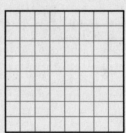

Match each number in the first column with the number that is equal to it in the second column.

12. $\sqrt{9}$ ___   **A.** 9

13. 81 ___   **B.** $\sqrt{81}$

14. 3^2 ___   **C.** 3

15. 9 ___   **D.** 9^2

Mark each statement as true or false.

16. $\sqrt{32}$ is closer to 5 than 6

17. $\sqrt{32}$ is between $\sqrt{5}$ and $\sqrt{6}$

18. $\sqrt{32}$ is between 25 and 36

19. $\sqrt{32}$ is between $\sqrt{25}$ and $\sqrt{36}$

Use the number line of square roots and the guess-and-check strategy to estimate the following square roots. Show all your work.

20. $\sqrt{76}$

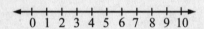

21. $\sqrt{129}$

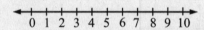

22. Label the sides of the following triangle as a leg or the hypotenuse.

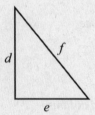

Use the following information to answer the next question.

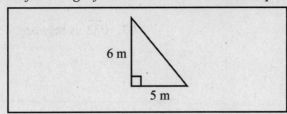

6 m

5 m

23. Determine the length of the unknown side. Highlight or circle the correct answer.

A. $\sqrt{11}$ **B.** $\sqrt{61}$

C. 11   **D.** 61

24. For the given triangle, prove the areas of the legs are equal to the area of the hypotenuse using modelling.

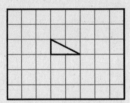

Find the missing side in each of the following right triangles, rounded to the tenths place.

25.

10 mm

13 mm

26.

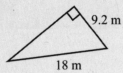

9.2 m

18 m

27. A computer screen is 30 cm by 20 cm. What is the length of its diagonal?

28. A flagpole is 4 m high. There is a wire attached from the tip of the pole to the ground. If the wire is 8.2 m long, at what distance from the bottom of the pole is the wire attached to the ground? Round to the nearest tenth.

29. Is 80-18-82 a Pythagorean triple? Show your work.

PERCENT

When you are finished this unit, you will be able to…

• represent percent in different forms
• understand and represent situations where percent may be more than 100%, less than 1%, or factional
• use grids to represent percents
• convert between percents, decimals, and fractions
• find the percent of a number
• calculate discounts, taxes, and commissions
• solve problems involving percents

PREREQUISITE SKILLS AND KNOWLEDGE

Prior to starting this unit, you should be able to…

• read and write numbers using a place value table
• estimate and calculate percent
• convert between fractions and decimal numbers
• convert between mixed numbers and improper fractions

Lesson 1 REPRESENTING PERCENT

YOU ALREADY KNOW...

Percent means "out of 100" and is a ratio which compares a number to 100. The percent symbol (%) means a number is being compared to 100.

There are different forms for writing percents.

• Percent form → $x\%$

• Fraction form → $\dfrac{x}{100}$. The percent is the numerator.

• Decimal form → $0.xx$. The percent is the two digits after the decimal.

PICTURING PERCENT

A 10×10 grid shows a percent by comparing the number of shaded squares to the total number of squares (100).

Example

Write the ratio of shaded squares to all squares as a percent, fraction, and decimal.

Solution

• Percent form
  Count the number of shaded squares, and write the number in front of the % symbol.
  $= 34\%$

• Fraction form
  The percent is the number of shaded squares written over the denominator of 100.
  $= \dfrac{34}{100}$

• Decimal form
  The percent is written after the decimal.
  $34 \div 100 = 0.34$

Your Turn 1

Consider the three grids given. Write the ratio of shaded squares to all squares as a percent, fraction, and decimal.

Grid 1   Grid 2   Grid 3

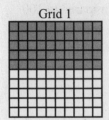 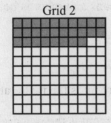 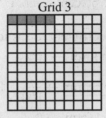

Grid	Percent	Fraction	Decimal
1			
2			
3			

FRACTIONAL PERCENTS

Until this point, only complete squares have been shaded on the 10×10 grid when representing percents. It is possible to have partially shaded squares. When only a part of a square is shaded, it is called a **fractional percent** because a fraction or part of a square is shaded.

Example

Write the ratio of shaded squares to all squares as a percent, decimal, and fraction.

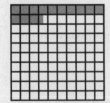

Solution

- Percent form
  Count how many complete and partial squares are shaded.

  13 complete squares and $\dfrac{1}{2}$ a square

  $= 13.5\%$

- Decimal form
  The percent is written after the decimal.
  $13.5 \div 100 = 0.135$

- Fraction form
  The numerator is the percent (13.5) over the denominator of 100.

  $= \dfrac{13.5}{100}$

Since fractions in this case are representing ratios, it is permitted to have decimal numbers in the fractions

Your Turn 2

Write the ratio of shaded squares to all squares as a percent, decimal and fraction.

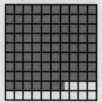

When written with a fraction instead of a decimal, fractional percents can be expressed by writing the entire percentage as a fraction over 100, converting to an equivalent fraction without any fractions in the numerator, and writing the resulting fraction in lowest terms.

Example

Express $35\frac{1}{2}\%$ as a fraction.

Solution

$\dfrac{35\frac{1}{2}}{100}$	Place the value of the percent $\left(35\frac{1}{2}\right)$ over a denominator of 100.
$\dfrac{35\frac{1}{2} \times 2}{100 \times 2} = \dfrac{71}{200}$	Write an equivalent fraction where the numerator is a whole number.

The fraction cannot be reduced. It is in lowest terms.

Written as a fraction, $35\frac{1}{2}\%$ is $\dfrac{71}{200}$.

Your Turn 3

Express $17\frac{1}{4}\%$ as a fraction.

Fractional percents can be expressed as a decimal by converting the fractional portion of the percent to a decimal, and then converting the entire percentage to a decimal using one of two strategies.

Example

Express $47\frac{1}{4}\%$ as a decimal.

Solution

$47\frac{1}{4}\% = 47.25\%$	Change the fractional percent to a decimal percent.
$47.25\% = 47.25 \div 100$ $= 0.4725$	**Method 1** Divide the percentage by 100.
47.25	**Method 2** Move the decimal two places to the left.

Written as a decimal, $47\frac{1}{4}\%$ is 0.4725.

Your Turn 4

Use two methods to convert $94\frac{1}{2}\%$ to a decimal.

PERCENTS GREATER THAN 100

It is possible to have a percent that is greater than 100. For example, both 101% or 320% are greater than 100. This means the part is greater than the whole, much like an improper fraction.

Percents which are greater than 100 indicate an increase from the original value. For example, if the price of a coat was $30 and the price increased to $33, the new price of the coat is 110% of the original price because the price increased by $3, or 10%. 100% is the initial value ($30), and 10% is the increase ($3).

Example

The new price of a chocolate bar is 125% of the original price.

a) Represent this percent on a grid.

Solution

125% means $\dfrac{125}{100}$. Shade the first grid completely. This indicates 100%. Next, shade 25 squares in the second grid. The total shaded area is 125. Since the denominator is 100, the total area is 125 out of 100, or 125%.

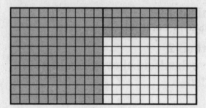

b) Explain what the percent means.

Solution

The initial value is 100%. 125% means the price of the chocolate bar increased by 25%.

Your Turn 5

A car salesperson is required to sell 10 cars every month. One salesperson sold 110% in the month of July.

a) Represent this percent on a grid.

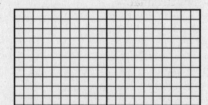

b) Explain what the percent means.

PERCENTS LESS THAN 1

It is possible to have a percent that is less than 1, for example 0.1% or 0.025% are less than 1. This means that the number being compared to 100 is less than 1. Percentages can be written as decimals, but there cannot be decimals in fractions. If the percentage is converted to a fraction, it must be written with no decimals in the fraction.

Since the value is so small, percents less than 1 are very difficult to represent on a grid. Calculations involving percents less than 1 are done the same way as any other percent calculation.

Example

Use two methods to convert 0.0125% as a decimal.

Solution

Method 1
Divide the percentage by 100.

$$0.0125\% = 0.0125 \div 100$$
$$= 0.000\,125$$

Method 2
Move decimal two places to the left.

0.0125

Written as a decimal, 0.0125% is 0.000 125.

Your Turn 6

Use two strategies to convert 0.085% as a decimal.

PRACTICE EXERCISES

1. Write the ratio of shaded squares to all squares as a percent, fraction, and decimal.

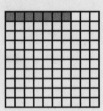

2. Each grid is made from 100 squares. Write the ratio of shaded squares to all squares as a percent, fraction, and decimal.

GRID 1	GRID 2	GRID 3
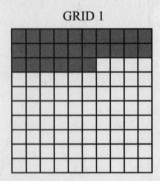	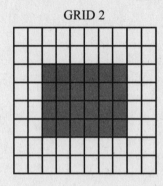	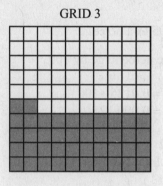

Grid	Percent	Fraction	Decimal
1			
2			
3			

3. Express $46\frac{1}{3}\%$ as a fraction.

4. Using two strategies, convert $27\frac{1}{4}\%$ to a decimal.

5. Using two strategies, convert 0.61% to a decimal.

Lesson 2   DECIMALS IN PERCENT OR FRACTION FORM

Fractions, decimals, and percents are all related to one another. In mathematics, conversions between fractions, decimals, and percents are frequently done as a first step in solving problems.

CONVERTING A DECIMAL TO A PERCENT

There are two methods to convert a decimal to percent.

Method 1: Multiplication

• Multiply the decimal number by 100.
• Place a % sign behind the answer.

Example

Change 0.195 to a percent.

Solution

$0.195 \times 100 = 19.5$	Multiply the decimal number by 100.
19.5%	Place a % sign behind the answer.

Written as a percent, 0.195 is 19.5%

Your Turn 1

Change 0.245 to a percent.

Method 2: Move the decimal

• Move the decimal two places to the *right*.
• Drop any zeros in front of the number.
• Place a % sign behind the answer.

Example

Change 0.425 to a percent.

Solution

0.425	Move the decimal point two places to the right.
$042.5 \rightarrow 42.5$	Drop the zero in front of the number.
42.5%	Place a % sign behind the answer.

Written as a percent, 0.425 is 42.5%.

Your Turn 2

Change 0.86 to a percent.

Example

Using both methods, represent 0.7225 as a percent.

Solution

$0.7225 \times 100 = 72.25\%$	**Method 1** Multiply the decimal by 100. Add the percent sign behind the number.
0.7225 $0.7225 \rightarrow 72.25$ $\rightarrow 72.25\%$	**Method 2** Move the decimal two places to the right. Add the percent sign behind the number.

Written as a percent, 0.7225 is 72.25%.

Your Turn 3

Using both methods, represent 0.935 as a percent.

CONVERTING A DECIMAL TO A FRACTION

Use the following steps to convert a decimal into a fraction.

- Use the place value of the last digit in the decimal number as the denominator of the fraction.
- Remove the decimal point, and use the number as the numerator of the fraction. Drop any zeros in front of the number.
- Reduce the fraction to lowest terms.

Example

Change 0.45 to a fraction in lowest terms.

Solution

0.45	5 is in the hundredths place. The denominator is 100.
$0.45 \rightarrow 45$	Remove the decimal. The numerator is 45. The fraction is $\dfrac{45}{100}$.
$\dfrac{45}{100} \xrightarrow[\div 5]{\div 5} \dfrac{9}{20}$	Reduce the fraction to lowest terms.

Written as a fraction, 0.45 is $\dfrac{9}{20}$.

Your Turn 4

Change 0.124 to a fraction in lowest terms.

If the resulting fraction is improper, it can be converted into a mixed number.

Example

Change 2.6 to a fraction in lowest terms.

Solution

2.6	6 is in the tenths place. The denominator is 10.
26	Remove the decimal. The numerator is 26. The fraction is $\dfrac{26}{10}$. This is an improper fraction.
$\dfrac{26}{10} \xrightarrow[\div 2]{\div 2} \dfrac{13}{5}$	Reduce the improper fraction to lowest terms.
$\dfrac{13}{5} \to 2\dfrac{3}{5}$	Convert the improper fraction to a mixed number.

Written as a fraction, 2.6 is $2\dfrac{3}{5}$.

Your Turn 5

Change 3.82 to a fraction in lowest terms.

PRACTICE EXERCISES

Use multiplication to write each of the following decimals as a percentage. Show your work.

1. 0.68

2. 0.92

3. 0.7

4. 4.6

5. 0.08

6. 0.025

Move the decimal to write each of the following decimals as a percentage.

7. 0.73

8. 0.4

9. 2.7

10. 0.09

11. 0.64

12. 0.085

Write each of the following decimals as a fraction or mixed number in lowest terms.

13. 0.2

14. 0.24

15. 0.85

16. 0.56

17. 1.25

18. 2.04

*In each of the following six questions, write the decimals as a percent. Insert a >, < or = sign to make each of the following statements **true**.*

19. 3.5 ☐ 35%

20. 0.06 ☐ 60%

21. 0.5 ☐ 5%

22. 0.7 ☐ 70%

23. 0.062 ☐ 62%

24. 9.5 ☐ 9.5%

*In each of the following three questions, write the decimals as a fraction. Insert a >, < or = sign to make each of the following statements **true**.*

25. 0.4 ☐ $\frac{2}{5}$

26. 0.88 ☐ $\frac{8}{10}$

27. 2.6 ☐ $2\frac{2}{5}$

Lesson 3   FRACTIONS AS PERCENT OR DECIMALS

CONVERTING A FRACTION TO A DECIMAL

To convert any fraction, including an improper fraction, into a decimal number, divide the numerator by the denominator.

Example

Change $\dfrac{4}{5}$ to a decimal.

Solution

$4 \div 5 = 0.8$	Divide the numerator (4) by the denominator (5).

As a decimal, $\dfrac{4}{5}$ is 0.8.

Your Turn 1

Change $\dfrac{3}{12}$ to a decimal.

There are two methods for changing a mixed number into a decimal number.

Method 1

• Convert the mixed number into an improper fraction.
• Divide the numerator by the denominator.

Example

Change $2\dfrac{1}{8}$ to a decimal.

Solution

$2\dfrac{1}{8} \rightarrow \dfrac{17}{8}$	Convert the mixed number into an improper fraction
$17 \div 8 = 2.125$	Divide the numerator (17) by the denominator (8).

As a decimal, $2\dfrac{1}{8}$ is 2.125.

Your Turn 2

Change $3\frac{1}{5}$ to a decimal.

Method 2

- Divide the numerator by the denominator.
- Add the whole number to the resulting decimal number.

Example

Change $3\frac{2}{5}$ to a decimal.

Solution

| $2 \div 5 = 0.4$ | Divide the numerator (2) by the denominator (5). |
| $3 + 0.4 = 3.4$ | Add the whole number (3) to the resulting decimal number (0.4). |

Your Turn 3

Using both methods, change $4\frac{13}{20}$ to a decimal.

Example

Using both methods, change $5\frac{2}{3}$ to a decimal.

Solution

Method 1

$5\frac{2}{3} \rightarrow \frac{17}{3}$	Convert the mixed number to an improper fraction.
$17 \div 3 = 5.666\ 666\ 666\ldots$	Divide the numerator (17) by the denominator (3).
$5.\overline{6}$	Bar notation is used to represent the repeating decimal.

Calculators may round the last number of a repeating decimal (3.666 666 667). This does not mean that the decimal ends.

NOTES

Method 2

$2 \div 3 = 0.666\ 666\ 666\ldots = 0.\overline{6}$	Divide the numerator (2) by the denominator (3).
$5 + 0.\overline{6} = 5.\overline{6}$	Add the whole number (5) to the resulting decimal number. Use bar notation to show the repeating decimal.

As a decimal, $5\dfrac{2}{3}$ is $5.\overline{6}$.

Your Turn 4

Using both methods, change $5\dfrac{7}{9}$ to a decimal.

CONVERTING A FRACTION TO A PERCENT

There are two methods for converting a fraction to a percentage.

Method 1: Division and Multiplication

• Divide the numerator by the denominator.
• Multiply the result by 100.
• Place a % sign behind the answer.

Example

Write $\dfrac{3}{8}$ as a percentage using division and multiplication.

Solution

$3 \div 8 = 0.375$	Divide the numerator (3) by the denominator (8).
$0.375 \times 100 = 37.5$	Multiply the result by 100.
37.5%	Place the % sign behind the answer.

When using the calculator, the first two steps can be combined into one.

$$\text{numerator} \div \text{denominator} \times 100 = \text{percentage}$$
$$3 \div 8 \times 100 = 37.5$$

As a percent, $\dfrac{3}{8}$ is 37.5%.

Your Turn 5

Write $\dfrac{24}{50}$ as a percentage.

Method 2: Cross Products

- Set up a proportion with the second fraction having a denominator of 100. The numerator is the unknown value x.
- Multiply the numerator of the *first* fraction by the denominator of the *second* fraction.
- Multiply the numerator of the *second* fraction by the denominator of the *first* fraction.
- Solve for the unknown by isolating the variable.

Example

Write $\dfrac{5}{12}$ as a percentage using cross products.

Solution

$\dfrac{5}{12} = \dfrac{x}{100}$	Set up a proportion. The second fraction is the percentage. The numerator is x. The denominator is 100.
$\dfrac{5}{12} = \dfrac{x}{\mathbf{100}}$ $5 \times 100 = 500$	Multiply the numerator of the first fraction by the denominator of the second fraction.
$\dfrac{5}{\mathbf{12}} = \dfrac{x}{100}$ $x \times 12 = 12x$	Multiply the numerator of the second fraction by the denominator of the first fraction.
$500 = 12x$ $\dfrac{500}{12} = \dfrac{12x}{12}$ $41.\overline{6} = x$	Solve for the missing number by dividing both sides by 12 and isolating the variable.

As a percent, $\dfrac{5}{12}$ is $41.\overline{6}\%$

Your Turn 6

Write $\dfrac{4}{7}$ as a percentage.

Mixed numbers are converted into percentages greater than 100. First, convert the mixed number into an improper fraction. Next, convert the improper fraction into a percent. Either method can be used.

Example

Write $1\frac{2}{10}$ as a percentage. Show both methods.

Solution

Method 1

$1\frac{2}{10} \rightarrow \frac{12}{10}$	Convert the mixed number to an improper fraction.
$12 \div 10 \times 100 = 120$	Divide the numerator (12) by the denominator (10), and multiply the result by 100.
120%	Place the % sign behind the answer.

Method 2:

$1\frac{2}{10} \rightarrow \frac{12}{10}$	Convert the mixed number to an improper fraction.
$\frac{12}{10} = \frac{x}{100}$	Set up a proportion.
$12 \times 100 = x \times 10$ $1200 = 10x$	Multiply each numerator by the denominator across from it.
$1200 = 10x$ $\frac{1200}{10} = \frac{10x}{10}$ $120 = x$	Solve for x by isolating the variable. Divide both sides by 10 to isolate the variable x.
120%	Place the % sign behind the answer.

As a percent, $1\frac{2}{10}$ is 120%.

Your Turn 7

Write $2\frac{1}{4}$ as a percentage. Show both methods.

PRACTICE EXERCISES

Write each of the following fractions as a decimal.

1. $\dfrac{5}{8}$

2. $\dfrac{3}{5}$

3. $\dfrac{4}{25}$

4. $\dfrac{50}{250}$

5. $\dfrac{9}{96}$

6. $2\dfrac{3}{8}$

Using both methods, write each of the following fractions as a percent. Show your work.

7. $\dfrac{3}{4}$

8. $\dfrac{2}{5}$

9. $\dfrac{3}{8}$

10. $\dfrac{5}{25}$

11. $2\dfrac{1}{2}$

12. $10\dfrac{1}{10}$

*In each of the following six questions, write the fractions as a decimal. Insert a $>$, $<$ or $=$ sign to make each of the following statements **true**.*

13. $\dfrac{8}{20}$ ☐ 0.35

14. $\dfrac{6}{25}$ ☐ 0.27

15. $\dfrac{2}{5}$ ☐ 0.4

16. $3\dfrac{2}{5}$ ☐ 3.2

17. $\dfrac{3}{50}$ ☐ 0.06

18. $\dfrac{41}{500}$ ☐ 0.078

*In each of the following three questions, write the fractions as a percent. Insert a >, < or = sign to make each of the following statements **true**.*

19. $\dfrac{1}{3}$ ☐ $33.\overline{3}\%$

20. $\dfrac{2}{5}$ ☐ 20%

21. $\dfrac{15}{50}$ ☐ $33.\overline{3}\%$

Use the following information to answer the next two questions.

A student correctly answered 7 out of 20 questions on a pop quiz.

22. What percent did the student receive?

23. Represent the percent on a 10 × 10 grid.

Lesson 4   PERCENT OF A NUMBER

The percent of a number is calculating a *part* of the number. If the percent is greater than 100, the resulting answer will be larger than the original number.

There two ways to find the percent of a number.

Method 1: Division and multiplication
• Convert the percentage into a decimal.
• Multiply the decimal number by the given number.

Method 2: Cross products
• Set up a proportion with the first fraction having the unknown value, x, as the numerator and the given number as the denominator.
• The second fraction is the percent expressed as a fraction over 100.
• Multiply the numerator of the *first* fraction by the denominator of the *second* fraction.
• Multiply the numerator of the *second* fraction by the denominator of the *first* fraction.
• Solve for the unknown by isolating the variable.

Example
What is 124% of 488? Show using both methods.

Solution
Method 1
Convert the percent into a decimal, and multiply the decimal by the given number.

Like converting a fraction to a percent, you can use a calculator to combine both steps.

$$\text{percentage} \div 100 \times \text{given number} = \text{percent of a number}$$
$$124 \div 100 \times 488 = 605.12$$

124% of 488 is 605.12.

Method 2
Set up a proportion, and solve for the unknown value, x.
$$\frac{x}{488} = \frac{124}{100}$$
$$100x = 60\ 512$$
$$\frac{100x}{100} = \frac{60\ 512}{100}$$
$$x = 605.12$$

124% of 488 is 605.12.

Your Turn 1

What is 230% of 28? Use both methods. Show your work.

Example

What is 0.3% of 250? Show using both methods.

Solution

Method 1

Convert the percent into a decimal, and multiply the decimal by the given number.

$0.3 \div 100 \times 250 = 0.75$

0.3% of 250 is 0.75

Method 2

Set up a proportion, and solve for the unknown value, x.

$$\frac{x}{250} = \frac{0.3}{100}$$
$$100x = 75$$
$$\frac{100x}{100} = \frac{75}{100}$$
$$x = 0.75$$

0.3% of 250 is 0.75

Your Turn 2

What is 0.25% of 325? Use both methods. Show your work.

Look back at the two examples in this lesson, and notice the results of the percent of a number.
- If the $\% < 100$, the result is less than the given number.
- If the $\% > 100$, the result is greater than the given number.
- If the $\% < 1$, the result is very small compared to the given number.

Watching for these results is a quick way to check the reasonableness of the answer calculated.

You can solve problems involving finding the percent of a number.

Example

A school's population is 650. 94% of the students attended the track meet. What number of students attended the track meet? Use both methods. Show your work.

Solution

Method 1

Convert the percent into a decimal, and multiply the decimal by the given number.
$$94 \div 100 \times 650 = 611$$

611 students attended the track meet.

Method 2

Set up a proportion, and solve for the unknown value, x.
$$\frac{x}{650} = \frac{94}{100}$$
$$100x = 61\,100$$
$$\frac{100x}{100} = \frac{61\,100}{100}$$
$$x = 611$$

611 students attended the track meet.

Your Turn 3

Stan answered 60% of questions on a test correctly. There were 60 questions on the test. How many questions did Stan answer correctly? Use both methods. Show your work.

NOTES

Example

The population of Prince Edward Island increased 0.4% over one year. If the population was 137 300 the previous year, what is the current population?

Solution

Method 1

$0.4 \div 100 = 0.004$	Convert the percent into a decimal.
$0.004 \times 137\ 300 = 549.2$	Multiply the decimal number (0.004) by the given number (137 300).
$137\ 300 + 549.2 = 137\ 849.2$	Add the increase in population to the previous year's population.

Method 2

Merge steps 1 and 2 in the previous method by multiplying the population by 100.4%.

100% represents the population in the previous year. 0.4% represents the increase in population. When the current population is multiplied by 100.4%, the addition is done in the calculation.

Set up a proportion, and solve for the unknown by isolating the variable.

$$\frac{x}{137\ 300} = \frac{100.4}{100}$$
$$100x = 13\ 784\ 920$$
$$\frac{100x}{100} = \frac{13\ 784\ 920}{100}$$
$$x = 137\ 849.2$$

The current population is 137 849. (The decimal is left off because a partial person is not possible)

Your Turn 4

The average Canadian household spent $141.20 on bakery products in October. If the amount of Canadians spent on bakery products in November increased 0.5%, how much did they spend?

Example

The average Canadian household spends 0.34% of the household income on reading materials and other print matter. If the household income is $64 944.00, how much is spent?

Solution

$0.34 \div 100 = 0.0034$	Convert the percent to a decimal number.
$0.0034 \times 64\ 944 = 220.8096$	Multiply the decimal number (0.0034) by the given number (64 944).

The number is rounded to the hundredths place because it is money.

The average Canadian household spends $220.81 on reading materials and other print matter.

Your Turn 5

When a company pays all its expenses, the money left over is profit. The total revenue, or money coming in, for a company in one year is $2 303 200 and the profit is 0.9%. What were the profit earnings for the year?

Example

A movie theatre holds 150 people. After it is renovated, its seating capacity increases 150%. How many seats does the renovated theatre have?

Solution

$150 \div 100 = 1.5$	Convert the percent to a decimal number.
$1.5 \times 150 = 225$	Multiply the decimal number by the given number.

The renovated theatre holds 225 seats.

Your Turn 6

When Kevin was 4 years old, he was 110 cm tall. His height had increased 168.2% by the time he was 20 years old. What was Kevin's height when he was 20?

PRACTICE EXERCISES

Calculate the percent of the number.

1. 30% of 45

2. 110% of 600

3. 0.5% of 22

4. 7.5% of 20

5. $9\frac{1}{2}$% of 38

6. 140% of 77

*For each of the next six questions, insert a >, < or = sign to make each of the following statements **true**. Show your work to justify your answer.*

7. 12% of 504 ☐ 48% of 93

8. 3% of 130 ☐ 6% of 60

9. 225% of 330 ☐ 148% of 505

10. 0.67% of 80 ☐ 0.28% of 230

11. 0.06% of 200 ☐ 0.03% of 400

12. $1\frac{1}{3}$% of 100 ☐ $2\frac{1}{5}$% of 75

Complete the following statements.

13. If the percentage is less than one hundred, the percent of the number will be _____ than the given number.

14. If the percentage is less than one, the percentage of the number will be _____ than the given number.

15. If the percentage is greater than one hundred, the percent of the number will be _____ than the given number.

16. A Grade 8 class collected money for a charity. They collected $133.\overline{3}\%$ of their goal. Their goal was $60. Rounded to the nearest whole number, how much money did the class collect?

17. During the autumn, 330 people visit the movie theatre a day. During the holiday season, the attendance increases 148%. How many people attend the theatre daily during the holiday season?

18. In April, 950 000 people were unemployed. In May, the number of people unemployed dropped by 0.12%. How many people were unemployed in May?

19. A hotel has 60 rooms. From Sunday to Thursday, it is 60% full. On Friday and Saturday, it is 95% full. How many rooms are rented each week?

Lesson 5 DISCOUNTS

Questions that involve discounts and sale prices involve percentages.

DISCOUNTS

Discount is the amount the price is reduced.
Sale price is the discount subtracted from the original price.

To calculate the *discount,* calculate the percentage of the original price.
To calculate the *sale price,* subtract the discount from the original price.

original price – discount = sale price

Example

A CD is regularly priced $20.00.

a) Calculate a 10% discount on the CD.

Solution
Use either of the two methods for calculating the percent of a number.

Method 1	**Method 2**
Division and Multiplication	Cross Products
10% of $20.00	$\dfrac{x}{20} = \dfrac{10}{100}$
$10 \div 100 \times 20 = 2$	$100x = 200$
	$\dfrac{100x}{100} = \dfrac{200}{100}$
	$x = 2$

A 10% discount on a $20.00 item is a savings of $2.00.

b) What is the discounted price of the CD?

Solution
Subtract the discount from the original price.
$20 – $2 = $18

The discounted price of the CD is $18.00.

Your Turn 1

A DVD is regularly priced at $29.00.

a) Calculate a 25% discount on the DVD.

b) What is the discounted price of the DVD?

Sometimes the price of an item is adjusted more than once. In these situations, the operations must be completed separately, and *in the order* they are presented in the question.

Example

A $90.00 pair of shoes is on sale for 15% off. The shoes are later discounted another 20%. What is the final sale price before taxes?

Solution

Calculate the first discount on the original price.

Method 1	**Method 2**
Division and Multiplication	Cross Products
15% of $90.00	$\dfrac{x}{90} = \dfrac{15}{100}$
$15 \div 100 \times 90 = 13.50$	$100x = 1\,350$
	$\dfrac{100x}{100} = \dfrac{1\,350}{100}$
	$x = 13.50$

The reduced price is $90 - \$13.50 = \$76.50$.

Calculate the second discount on the reduced price.

Method 1	**Method 2**
Division and Multiplication	Cross Products
20% of $76.50	$\dfrac{x}{76.50} = \dfrac{20}{100}$
$20 \div 100 \times 76.5 = 15.30$	$100x = 1530$
	$\dfrac{100x}{100} = \dfrac{1530}{100}$
	$x = 15.30$

The reduced price is $76.50 - \$15.30 = \$61.20$.

The final sale price after two discounts is $61.20, before taxes.

NOTES

If the discounts were added together and then applied to the original price, the result would be different.

Method 1	Method 2
Division and Multiplication	Cross Products
35% of $90.00	$\dfrac{x}{90} = \dfrac{35}{100}$
$35 \div 100 \times 90 = 31.50$	$100x = 315$
	$\dfrac{100x}{100} = \dfrac{315}{100}$
	$x = 31.50$

$90 - \$31.50 = \$58.50$.

$58.50 is not the same as $61.20. Therefore, this method of calculation is incorrect.

Your Turn 2

A $60.00 shirt is on sale for 20% off. The shirt is later discounted another 10% for a special event. What is the new sale price before taxes?

PRACTICE EXERCISES

Use the following information to answer the next two questions.

A pair of shoes originally cost $49.95.

1. If the price is increased by 20% and then reduced by 15%, what is the final selling price, before taxes?

2. Jill buys a high definition television set that originally sells for $2100.00. The price is reduced by 20%, and then by a further 15%. How much does Jill pay for the television set, before taxes?

3. Caitlin wants to buy a camcorder. The original price is marked as $390.00. The price of the camcorder has been reduced by 30%, and then by a further 10%. How much would Caitlin pay for the camcorder, before taxes?

4. David buys a blue-ray disc player. The original price was $140.00. The price was increased by 20% and then deceased by 30%. How much did Dalbir pay for the disc player, before taxes?

5. A hot tub is originally priced at $5 000.00. It is discounted by 10%, then another 20%, and finally another 30%. What is the final price of the hot tub, before taxes?

Lesson 6   TAXES

Taxes, such as PST and GST, are added to the price of purchased goods. Provincial tax (PST) varies in each province and territory. Alberta does not have PST. GST is currently 5%.

To calculate the *tax,* calculate the percentage of the original price.

To calculate the *total cost,* add the amount of the tax to the original price.
original price + tax = total cost

Example

A pair of runners cost $95.00.

a) Calculate the GST.

Solution

Method 1	Method 2
Division and Multiplication	Cross Products
5% of $95.00	$\dfrac{x}{95} = \dfrac{5}{100}$
$5 \div 100 \times 95 = 4.75$	$100x = 475$
	$\dfrac{100x}{100} = \dfrac{475}{100}$
	$x = 4.75$

The GST on a $95.00 item is $4.75.

b) Calculate the total cost after tax.

Solution
Add the tax to the original price.
$4.75 + 95 = 99.75$

The runners, including tax, are $99.75.

Your Turn 1

A shirt costs $75.00. The provincial sales tax is 8%.

a) Calculate the tax.

b) Calculate the total cost after tax.

Sometimes an item has a discount applied to it first, before any tax is added. Calculate the amount after the discount, then calculate the amount of the tax on the discounted amount, not the original amount. The total purchase price will then be the discounted amount added to the amount of tax.

Example

A $120.00 MP3 player is on sale for 25% off the regular price. What is the total purchase price of the MP3 player after the 5% GST is included?

Solution

Calculate the discount on the original price.

Method 1	**Method 2**
Division and Multiplication	Cross Products
25% of $120.00	$\dfrac{x}{120} = \dfrac{25}{100}$
$25 \div 100 \times 120 = 30$	$100x = 3000$
	$\dfrac{100x}{100} = \dfrac{3000}{100}$
	$x = 30$

The discounted price is $120 - 30 = 90$.

Calculate the GST on the reduced price.

Method 1	**Method 2**
Division and Multiplication	Cross Products
5% of $90.00	$\dfrac{x}{90} = \dfrac{5}{100}$
$5 \div 100 \times 90 = 4.5$	$100x = 450$
	$\dfrac{100x}{100} = \dfrac{450}{100}$
	$x = 4.5$

The total purchase price is the sales price plus the amount of the GST.
$90 + 4.50 = 94.50$

The $120 MP3 on sale for 25% off will cost $94.50 with the taxes included.

You can calculate the total cost without the addition step by multiplying the reduced price by 105%.

Your Turn 2

A $200.00 jacket is on sale for 30% off the regular price. What is the total purchase price after the 5% GST is included?

PRACTICE EXERCISES

Use the following information to answer the next two questions.

Jon bought a coat for $125.00. The sales tax was 5%.

1. Calculate the amount of the tax.

2. What is the total cost of the coat, including sales tax?

3. Jill buys a pair of jeans that is 30% off the original price of $30. What is the total purchase price after the 5% GST is included?

4. A lawn mower is on sale for 25% off its original price of $400.00. What is the price of the lawn mower, after the discount is deducted and the GST of 5% is added?

5. A $300.00 vacuum is marked down 40%. What is the discounted price of the vacuum, including 5% GST?

6. A $1 500.00 snow blower is marked down by 15%. What is the sales price including 5% GST?

7. While travelling in British Columbia, Marie purchased a piece of native Indian art for $500. In British Columbia the PST is 7%, and the GST is 5%. How much did Marie pay for the piece of art including the PST and GST?

8. Lewis was in a golf store in Saskatchewan. He purchased a set of clubs originally priced at $1 100.00. The golf clubs were marked down 20%. In Saskatchewan the PST is 5% and the GST is 5%. Including taxes, how much did Lewis pay for the golf clubs?

Lesson 7 COMMISSIONS

Commissions are a percentage of money earned by sales people based on their total amount of sales.

To calculate commission, take the percent of a number. This is the amount of money the sales person will earn.

Example

Gary, a car salesman, receives 7.5% commission on all his sales. If Gary sells a truck for $45 000, how much does he earn in commission?

Solution

Method 1 Division and Multiplication 7.5% of $45 000 $7.5 \div 100 \times 45\ 000 = 3\ 375$	Method 2 Cross Products $\dfrac{7.5}{100} = \dfrac{x}{45\ 000}$ $337\ 500 = 100x$ $\dfrac{337\ 500}{100} = \dfrac{100x}{100}$ $3\ 375 = x$

Gary earns $3 375.00 for selling the truck.

Your Turn 1

A salesperson's commission is 4.5%. How much does he earn if he sells a home theatre system worth $12 000?

PRACTICE EXERCISES

1. A salesperson sells $190.00 worth of greeting cards for which he receives 30% commission. How much does he earn in commission?

2. A clerk sells $20 000 worth of goods. The clerk's commission rate is 5.5% of all sales. What is the clerk's commission?

3. A real estate salesman earns 3.5% of all sales. In March he sold $280 000 of real estate. How much commission did he earn?

4. A car salesman earns 25% of the front end gross product (selling price minus the purchase price). He sells a car for $37 500, that cost the dealer $32 000 to buy. What is his commission?

5. A financial advisor earns 1.2% of the money he invests for his clients. During February he invested $375 000. How much commission did the financial advisor earn?

REVIEW SUMMARY

- There are different forms you can use to write percentages. These are percent form, with a percent sign, fraction form, where the denominator is 100 and the numerator shows the percentage, and decimal form, where the percentage is the two digits after the decimal.

- A 10×10 grid shows a percent by comparing the number of shaded squares to the total number of squares (100).

- Fractional percents can be shown on a grid by shading part of a square.

- Percents greater than 100 mean that the part is greater than the whole. This can be shown on grids by having more than one 10×10 grid.

- Percents less than 1 are very difficult to represent on grid because the value is so small.

- There are two methods to change a decimal to a percent. One is the multiplication method, where the decimal number is multiplied by 100 and a % sign placed behind the answer. The other is moving the decimal two places to the right, dropping any zeros in front of the number, and placing a % sign behind the answer.

- To change a decimal into a fraction, use the place value of the last digit in the decimal number as the denominator of the fraction, remove the decimal point, use the given number as the numerator of the fraction, and reduce the fraction to lowest terms.

- If the resulting fraction is improper, it can be converted into a mixed number.

- To change a fraction or improper fraction into a decimal number, divide the numerator by the denominator.

- There are two methods for changing a fraction to a percentage. One method is division and multiplication, where the numerator is divided by the denominator, the result is multiplied by 100 and a % sign is placed behind the answer. The other is cross products, where an equivalent fraction with an unknown value over 100 is written as part of an equation, and the unknown value is the percentage.

- There two ways to find the percent of a number. One method is using division and multiplication, where the percentage is converted into a decimal and multiplied by the given number. The other is using cross products.

- When finding the percent of a number, if the $\% < 100$, the result is less than the given number. If the $\% > 100$, the result is greater than the given number. If the $\% < 1$, the result is very small compared to the given number.

- To calculate a discount, calculate the percentage of the original price; to calculate a sale price subtract the discount from the original price.

- To calculate a tax, such as the GST, calculate the percentage of the original price; the total cost will be the amount of tax added to the original price.

- To calculate commission, take the percent of the sales. This will be the amount of money the salesperson will earn.

PRACTICE TEST

Write the ratio of shaded squares to all squares in the given image as a percent, fraction, and decimal.

1.

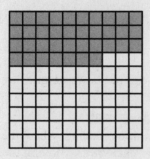

2.

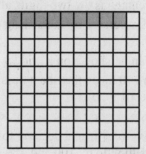

3.

4. Express $75\frac{1}{2}\%$ as a fraction.

5. Express $22\frac{3}{4}\%$ as a decimal.

6. Represent 120% on a grid.

7. Change 0.825 to a percent.

8. Change 0.910 to a percent.

9. Change 0.65 to a fraction in lowest terms.

10. Change 0.945 to a fraction in lowest terms.

11. Change 5.62 to a mixed number.

12. Change 4.12 to a mixed number.

*For each of the next two questions, write the decimals as a percent. Insert a >, < or = sign to make each of the following statements **true**.*

13. 9.0 ☐ 90%　　　　　　　　　　**14.** 0.55 ☐ 55%

*For the next two questions, write each of the following decimals as a fraction. Insert a >, < or = sign to make each of the following statements **true**.*

15. 0.5 ☐ $\frac{1}{2}$　　　　　　　　**16.** 1.6 ☐ $1\frac{2}{5}$

17. Change $\frac{3}{5}$ to a decimal.

18. Change $2\frac{1}{4}$ to a decimal.

19. Change $7\frac{2}{3}$ to a decimal.

20. Write $\dfrac{5}{8}$ as a percent.

21. Write $\dfrac{7}{25}$ as a percent.

22. Write $\dfrac{7}{8}$ as a percent.

23. Write $2\dfrac{5}{10}$ as a percent.

*For each of the next two questions, write the fractions as a decimal. Insert a >, < or = sign to make each of the following statements **true**.*

24. $\dfrac{4}{20}$ ☐ 0.5

25. $2\dfrac{2}{5}$ ☐ 2.4

26. What is 112% of 350?

27. What is 0.5% of 150?

28. A test has 10 questions. If Isabella answers 70% of the questions correctly, how many questions did she answer incorrectly?

29. Insert a >, < or = sign to make the following statement **true**. Show your work to justify your answer.

11% of 400 ☐ 67% of 80

30. In a class of 30 students, 40% are girls. Calculate the number of boys in the class.

31. An auditorium has 112 seats. After it is renovated, its seating capacity increases 175%. How many seats does the renovated theatre have?

Use the following information to answer the next two questions.

> A shirt is regularly priced at $30.00.

32. Calculate a 15% discount the shirt.

33. What is the discounted price of the shirt?

34. A pair of jeans originally cost $50.00. If it is increased by 30% and then reduced by 25%, what is the final selling price, before taxes?

35. A $300.00 television is on sale for 25% off the regular price. What is the total purchase price of the television after the 5% GST is included?

36. Ms. Williams is a real estate agent. She receives a 4.5% commission on each property she sells. She sells a plot of land for $75 000. How much money does she earn?

SURFACE AREA

When you are finished this unit, you will be able to…
• understand and identify prisms and cylinders
• recognize nets for three-dimensional objects such as prisms and cylinders
• calculate the surface area of prisms and cylinders
• solve problems involving the surface area of prisms and cylinders

PREREQUISITE SKILLS AND KNOWLEDGE

Prior to starting this unit, you should be able to…
• perform calculations involving exponents
• solve algebraic equations
• substitute into an expression and solve
• calculate the area of various two-dimensional shapes
• identify π as a number with a rounded value of 3.14
• understand the difference between two-dimensional shapes and three-dimensional objects

Lesson 1 *THREE-DIMENSIONAL OBJECTS*

Three-dimensional objects can be classified into three main groups: prisms, pyramids, and circular objects.

Prisms are objects that are made up of rectangular sides (faces) and various end pieces. The end pieces are always two identical copies of the same shape. The names for the objects come from the end pieces, called bases. The number of faces is determined by the number of sides each base has.

For example, a rectangular prism has a rectangle base on each end and four rectangular faces that join the ends together.

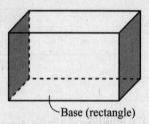

Base (rectangle)

A special type of rectangular prism is one in which the two bases and the four faces are all identical squares. This rectangular prism is called a cube.

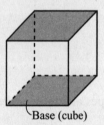

Base (cube)

A triangular prism has a triangle base on each end and three rectangular faces.

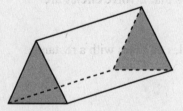

A pentagonal prism has a pentagon base on each end and five rectangular faces.

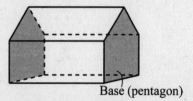

Base (pentagon)

All prisms follow this pattern: the shape of the base and the number of sides the base has determines the name of the three-dimensional object.

Pyramids are objects made up of a single base and triangular faces that meet at a single point at the top called the vertex. The name for the pyramid comes from the shape of the base. The number of faces is determined by the number of sides the base has.

For example, a square pyramid has a square base and four equal triangles for faces.

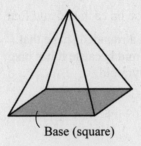

Base (square)

A pentagonal pyramid has a pentagon base and five triangles for faces.

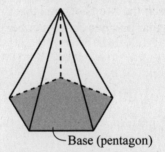

Base (pentagon)

All pyramids follow this pattern: the shape of the base and the number of sides the base has determines the name of the three-dimensional object.

The most common three-dimensional objects that involve circles are cylinders, spheres, and cones.

A **cylinder** is an object made up of two circles as bases with a rectangle wrapped around the middle.

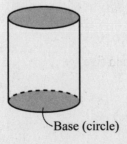

Base (circle)

NOTES

A **sphere** is a round, ball-shaped object. It does not have any bases, faces, or vertices.

A **cone** is an object that has one circle as a base and a rounded shape that meets at a single vertex. A cone is similar to a pyramid because it has one base and a vertex, but it does not have faces like a pyramid.

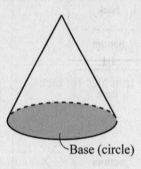

Base (circle)

Three-dimensional (3-D) objects can be shown in different ways. If you flatten three-dimensional objects according to their faces, the two-dimensional drawing you see is called a **net**. A net is a two-dimensional representation of a three-dimensional object. Nets are used to build three-dimensional objects. The following diagram shows three-dimensional objects and their corresponding nets.

Name	Three-Dimensional Object	Net
Rectangular prism		
Triangular Prism		
Cylinder		

When constructing a 3-D object from a net, imagine cutting out the net and gluing the edges together. This will help visualize the construction.

NOTES

Example

Draw the net that represents the given rectangular prism.

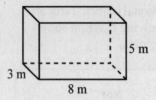

3 m
5 m
8 m

Solution

A rectangular prism is made up of four rectangles that join the two rectangular bases. Draw the net showing the front, back, top, bottom, and sides of the given rectangular prism, as shown.

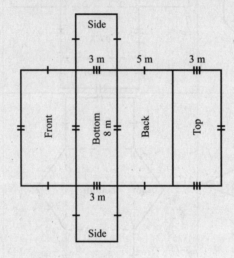

Your Turn 1

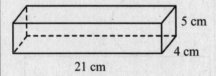

5 cm
4 cm
21 cm

Draw the net that represents the given rectangular prism.

Example

Draw the net that represents the given triangular prism.

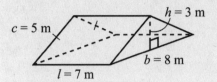

Solution

A triangular prism is made up of three rectangles that join the two triangular bases. Draw the net showing the front, back, bottom, and bases of the triangular prism.

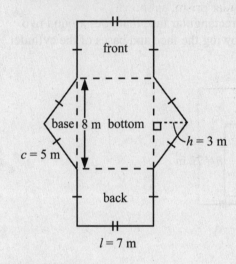

Your Turn 2

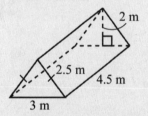

Draw the net that represents the given triangular prism.

NOTES

Example

Draw the net that represents the given cylinder.

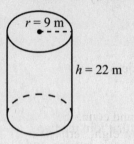

Solution

A cylinder is made up of one rectangular face that goes around two circle bases. Draw the net showing the face and bases of the cylinder.

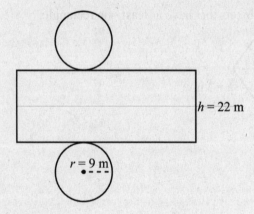

Your Turn 3

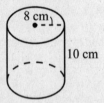

Draw the net that represents the given cylinder.

The specific characteristics of various objects allow you to group the objects according to their similar features. For example, you could group objects by the number of faces, by the shapes of the bases, by the number of edges, or by the number of vertices.

Example

List the three-dimensional objects that have eight vertices.

Solution

Look at the objects you have already considered, and count the vertices. A rectangular prism and a cube both have eight vertices. In addition, a heptagonal pyramid has eight vertices. It has seven vertices around the bottom of the heptagon and one at the point where all the triangles meet.

Your Turn 4

Name the three-dimensional objects that have at least one rectangle.

PRACTICE EXERCISES

For each of the first three questions, list the two-dimensional shapes that make up the given three-dimensional objects.

1. A pentagonal pyramid

2. An octagonal prism

3. A cylinder

4. What three-dimensional object studied in this section has no parallel sides?

5. Name all the three-dimensional objects that contain exactly one rectangle.

6. Name the three-dimensional objects with exactly six vertices.

For each of the following objects, draw its net, and state the number of edges and vertices it has.

7. A rectangular prism

8. A square pyramid

9. A cube

10. A triangular pyramid

Lesson 2 CALCULATING THE SURFACE AREA OF PRISMS

The surface area of a three-dimensional object is the sum of the areas of the faces that make up the object. Units for surface area are always squared because area is two-dimensional. To calculate the surface area, find the area of each part, and add the areas together.

Example

Calculate the surface area of this rectangular prism.

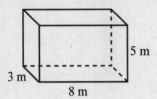

Solution

Draw the net for the rectangular prism.

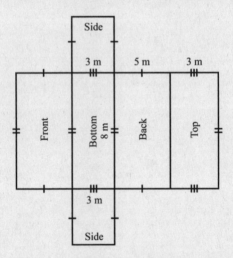

Some of the faces of the prism are the same size. The front and the back are the same, the top and the bottom are the same, and the sides are the same. Consequently, to calculate the surface area of the two equal sides, find the area for one side and multiply it by 2

Front and Back	Top and Bottom	Sides
(2 equal rectangles)	(2 equal rectangles)	(2 equal rectangles)
$A = lw$	$A = lw$	$A = lw$
$= 5 \times 8$	$= 3 \times 8$	$= 5 \times 3$
$= 40$	$= 24$	$= 15$
$40 \times 2 = 80$	$24 \times 2 = 48$	$15 \times 2 = 30$

Add the areas together to get the surface area.

$SA = 80 + 48 + 30 = 158 \text{ m}^2$

The surface area of the given rectangular prism is 158 m².

Your Turn 1

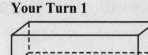

Calculate the surface area of the given rectangular prism.

Example

Calculate the surface area of this triangular prism.

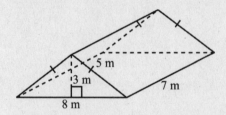

Solution

Draw the net for the given triangular prism.

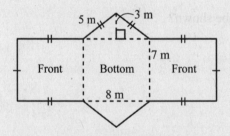

In this net, the bases are the same size and are isosceles triangles. Thus, the front sides joining these two bases are the same.

Calculate the area of one front side, and multiply by 2. Then, calculate the area of the remaining bottom face. Finally, find the area of one triangle base, and multiply by 2.

An isosceles triangle has two sides that are equal in length.

Front and Back	Bottom	Sides
(2 equal rectangles)	(rectangle)	(2 equal triangles)
$A = lw$ $= 7 \times 5$ $= 35$ $35 \times 2 = 70$	$A = lw$ $= 7 \times 8$ $= 56$	$A = \dfrac{bh}{2}$ $= \dfrac{8 \times 3}{2}$ $= 12$ $12 \times 2 = 24$

NOTES

Add the areas together to get the surface area.
$$SA = 70 + 56 + 24 = 150 \text{ m}^2$$

The surface area of the given triangular prism is 150 m².

Your Turn 2

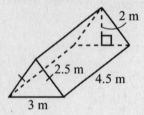

Calculate the surface area of the given triangular prism.

Example

What is the surface area of the cube shown?

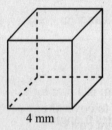

4 mm

Solution

Draw the net for the given cube.

4 mm

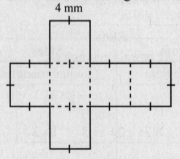

A cube has six equal sides. To find the total surface area, find the area of one side (a square), and multiply by 6.

$$A = lw$$
$$= 4 \times 4$$
$$= 16$$
$$16 \times 6 = 96$$

The surface area of the cube is 96 mm^2.

Your Turn 3

Calculate the surface area of the given cube.

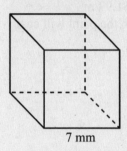

7 mm

Calculating the surface area of three-dimensional objects can help you solve real world, everyday problems.

Example

Anne wants to paint the walls of her bedroom. If the room is 3.5 m long, 3 m wide, and 2.5 m high, how much paint will she need to cover the walls? If the paint costs $1.49/m^2, how much will the paint cost?

Solution

Since Anne is painting the walls, consider only the front, back, and sides of the rectangular prism, not the top and bottom.

Front and Back (2 equal rectangles)	Sides (2 equal rectangles)
$A = lw$ $= 3 \times 2.5$ $= 7.5$ $7.5 \times 2 = 15$	$A = lw$ $= 3.5 \times 2.5$ $= 8.75$ $8.75 \times 2 = 17.5$

NOTES

Add the areas together to get the surface area.
$SA = 15 + 17.5 = 32.5 \text{ m}^2$

Anne will need 32.5 m^2 of paint to cover the walls. Since the paint costs \$1.49/m^2, multiply the cost of paint by the surface area.
$32.5 \times 1.49 = 48.43$

It will cost Anne \$48.43 to paint her room.

Your Turn 4

Len wants to paint the sides and top of a cube shaped shipping container. Each edge of the cube is 4 m long, and the paint costs \$1.99/m². Calculate how much paint Len will need and how much the paint will cost.

PRACTICE EXERCISES

For each of the first four questions, use the information given to find the surface area of the given three-dimensional objects.

1.

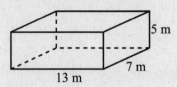

2.

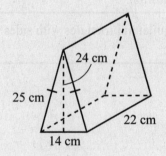

3.

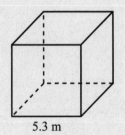

4.

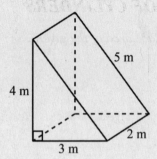

Use the following information to answer the next question.

A box of chocolates is in the shape of a triangular prism. The bases are equilateral triangles with sides of 25 mm and a height of 18 mm, and the length of the box is 80 mm.

5. Calculate the surface area of the box.

190

Lesson 3   CALCULATING THE SURFACE AREA OF CYLINDERS

The surface area of a cylinder is calculated with the same method used to calculate the surface area of a prism. Find the surface area of the bases and side, and add these values together. With a cylinder, two of the surfaces are circles that have identical areas; they form the bases. The side of the cylinder is a rectangle that wraps around the two circular bases.

To calculate the surface area, calculate the area of each part, and add the areas together.

Example

Find the surface area of the following cylinder.

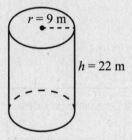

Solution

Draw the net of the cylinder.

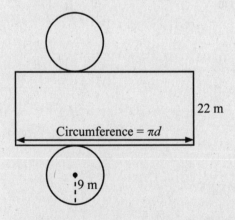

Find the area of the two bases (2 identical circles).

$$A = \pi r^2$$
$$= 3.14 \times 9^2$$
$$= 3.14 \times 81$$
$$= 254.34$$
$$254.34 \times 2 = 508.68$$

NOTES

Recall that the formula for the area of a rectangle is $A = lw$. In the rectangular part of the cylinder, the length l is equal to the height h. When you unroll the middle, the width w is the same as the circumference of the circle. The circumference of the circle is found using the formula $C = \pi d$. Therefore, the area formula for the rectangular part is as follows:

$A = lw$
$A = h \times \pi d$
$A = \pi d \times h$

In this question, $h = 22$ and $d = 9 \times 2 = 18$.

Find the area of the rectangle.
$A = \pi d \times h$
$\quad = 3.14 \times 18 \times 22$
$\quad = 1\ 243.44$

Add the areas together to get the surface area.
$SA = 508.66 + 1\ 243.44$
$\quad = 1\ 752.12 \text{ m}^2$

Your Turn 1

Calculate the surface area of the given cylinder.

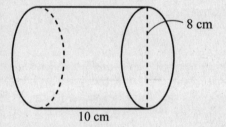

8 cm

10 cm

PRACTICE EXERCISES

For each of the first two questions, find the surface area of the given cylinder.

1.

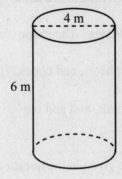

4 m

6 m

2.

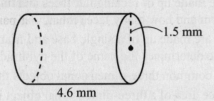

1.5 mm

4.6 mm

Use the following information to answer the next question.

A cylinder has a base with a diameter of 15 cm, and a height of 35 cm. A rectangular prism has bases with dimensions of 10 cm by 8 cm, and a length of 25 cm.

3. Which three-dimensional object has a greater surface area, and by how much is it greater?

4. A soup can with a label that goes all the way around it has a radius of 3.5 cm and the height of 11 cm. Find the area of the label.

REVIEW SUMMARY

- Three-dimensional objects can be classified into three main groups: prisms, pyramids, and circular objects.
- Prisms are made up of rectangular faces and two bases. The shape of the base determines the name of the prism and how many faces it has.
- Pyramids are made up of a single base and triangular faces that meet at a single vertex. The shape of the base determines the name of the pyramid and how many faces it has.
- The most common three-dimensional objects that involve circles are cylinders, spheres, and cones.
- The surface area of a three-dimensional object is the sum of the areas of the faces.
- To calculate the surface area of a three-dimensional object, find the area of each part, and add the areas together.
- Units for surface area are always squared because area is two dimensional.
- Solve problems involving prisms and cylinders by taking the dimensions you are given in the question and substituting them into the area formulas.

PRACTICE TEST

For the first four questions, find the surface area of the given three-dimensional objects.

1.

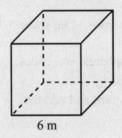

6 m

2.

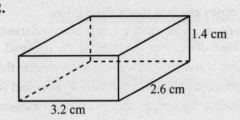

1.4 cm

2.6 cm

3.2 cm

3.

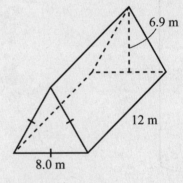

6.9 m

12 m

8.0 m

4.

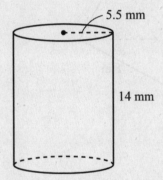

5.5 mm

14 mm

5. A textbook has the dimensions 20 cm by 23 cm by 3 cm. Find the surface area of the given textbook.

Use the following information to answer the next question.

A cylindrical tank has a base with a diameter of 1.5 m, and a height of 7.5 m. The tank is sitting on the ground, so the bottom is not included in the calculation of the area.

6. Find the surface area of the given tank.

Calculate the surface area of the following three-dimensional objects.

7.

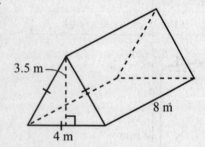

3.5 m

8 m

4 m

8.

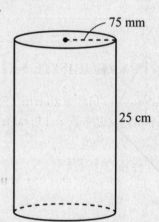

75 mm

25 cm

9.

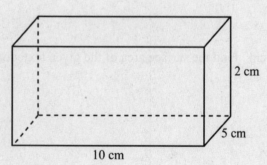

2 cm

5 cm

10 cm

FRACTION OPERATIONS

When you are finished this unit, you will be able to…

- multiply fractions by whole or mixed numbers
- divide fractions by whole or mixed numbers
- use order of operations to solve problems

PREREQUISITE SKILLS AND KNOWLEDGE

Prior to starting this unit, you should be able to…

- read and write numbers using a place value table
- solve problems involving fractions
- reduce fractions to their lowest terms
- convert between improper fractions and mixed numbers
- apply the order of operations

Lesson 1 MULTIPLYING A FRACTION BY A WHOLE NUMBER

NOTES

Multiplication of a fraction by a whole number can be shown using a model, using a diagram of a number line, or showing the multiplication.

Method 1: Using a model

Example

Determine the value of $\dfrac{2}{5} \times 4$ by using a model.

Solution

The multiplication can be expressed by using repeated addition.

$$\frac{2}{5} \times 4 = \frac{2}{5} + \frac{2}{5} + \frac{2}{5} + \frac{2}{5}$$

Model the fractions using fraction strips.

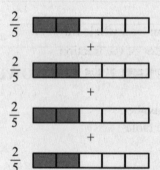

Total the shaded number of fraction strips.

$$\frac{2}{5} + \frac{2}{5} + \frac{2}{5} + \frac{2}{5} = \frac{8}{5}$$

Model the answer, and ensure the final answer is in lowest terms.

$$\frac{8}{5}$$

The answer is already in lowest terms.

$$\frac{2}{5} \times 4 = \frac{8}{5}$$
$$= 1\frac{3}{5}$$

Method 2: Using a diagram of a number line

Example

Determine the value of $\frac{3}{4} \times 3$ by using a diagram of a number line.

Solution

Model the fractions using a number line.

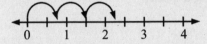

$$\frac{3}{4} + \frac{3}{4} + \frac{3}{4} = \frac{9}{4}$$
$$= 2\frac{1}{4}$$

Method 3: Showing the multiplication

Use the following steps to multiply a **fraction** by a **whole number**.

• Multiply the whole number by the numerator of the fraction.
• Write the resulting number over the denominator of the fraction.
• Reduce the fraction to lowest terms.
• Rewrite an improper fraction as a mixed number.

Example

Evaluate $\frac{2}{3} \times 5$.

Solution

Multiply the whole number by the numerator, and write the resulting number over the denominator. Ensure the fraction is in lowest terms.

$$\frac{2 \times 5}{3} = \frac{10}{3}$$
$$= 3\frac{1}{3}$$

Example

Evaluate $3 \times \frac{4}{5}$.

Solution

Multiply the whole number by the numerator, and write the resulting number over the denominator. Ensure the fraction is in lowest terms.

$$\frac{3 \times 4}{5} = \frac{12}{5}$$
$$= 2\frac{2}{5}$$

NOTES

Your Turn 1

Evaluate each of the following expressions using all three methods.

a) $4 \times \dfrac{3}{7}$

b) $\dfrac{1}{2} \times 5$

c) $7 \times \dfrac{2}{9}$

d) $\dfrac{4}{9} \times 5$

PRACTICE EXERCISES

Evaluate.

1. $4 \times \dfrac{3}{8}$

2. $\dfrac{7}{9} \times 5$

3. $\dfrac{4}{11} \times 3$

4. $7 \times \dfrac{6}{7}$

Lesson 2 *MULTIPLYING A FRACTION BY A MIXED NUMBER*

NOTES

Use the following steps to multiply a *fraction* by a *mixed number*.
- Change the mixed number to an improper fraction.
- Multiply the improper fraction by the fraction.
- Reduce the fraction to lowest terms.
- Rewrite the improper fraction as a mixed number.

Example

Evaluate $\dfrac{2}{3} \times 3\dfrac{1}{4}$.

Solution

Change the mixed number to an improper fraction, and multiply by the given fraction. Ensure the fraction is in lowest terms.

$$3\dfrac{1}{4} \rightarrow \dfrac{13}{4}$$

$$\dfrac{2}{3} \times \dfrac{13}{4} = \dfrac{26}{12}$$

Reduce the fraction to lowest terms.

$$\dfrac{26 \div 2}{12 \div 2} = \dfrac{13}{6}$$

Rewrite $\dfrac{13}{6}$ as a mixed umber.

$$\dfrac{13}{6} \rightarrow 2\dfrac{1}{6}$$

$$\dfrac{2}{3} \times 3\dfrac{1}{4} = 2\dfrac{1}{6}$$

Your Turn 1

Evaluate each of the following expressions.

a) $\dfrac{4}{5} \times 3\dfrac{3}{7}$

b) $\dfrac{2}{7} \times 4\dfrac{1}{2}$

Example

Evaluate $4\dfrac{2}{5} \times \dfrac{3}{4}$.

Solution

Change the mixed number to an improper fraction, and multiply by the given fraction.

$$4\dfrac{2}{5} \rightarrow \dfrac{22}{5}$$

$$\dfrac{22}{5} \times \dfrac{3}{4} = \dfrac{66}{20}$$

Reduce the fraction to lowest terms.

$$\dfrac{66 \div 2}{20 \div 2} = \dfrac{33}{10}$$

Rewrite $\dfrac{33}{10}$ as a mixed number.

$$\dfrac{33}{10} \rightarrow 3\dfrac{3}{10}$$

$$4\dfrac{2}{5} \times \dfrac{3}{4} = 3\dfrac{3}{10}$$

Your Turn 2

Evaluate each of the following expressions.

a) $5\dfrac{1}{4} \times \dfrac{5}{8}$

b) $6\dfrac{1}{4} \times \dfrac{7}{9}$

PRACTICE EXERCISES

Evaluate.

1. $\dfrac{2}{3} \times 2\dfrac{2}{7}$

2. $\dfrac{5}{9} \times 4\dfrac{1}{2}$

3. $7\dfrac{3}{4} \times \dfrac{3}{8}$

4. $2\dfrac{2}{3} \times \dfrac{7}{8}$

Lesson 3   *DIVIDING A FRACTION BY A WHOLE NUMBER*

To divide a fraction by a whole number, it is necessary to change the question into a multiplication question first.

Use the following steps to divide a *fraction* by a *whole number:*
- Write the whole number as a fraction over 1.
- Take the reciprocal of this fraction by switching the numerator and the denominator. This will result in a numerator of 1.
- Multiply the fraction by the whole number.
- Ensure the resulting fraction is in lowest terms.

NOTES

The reciprocal of a fraction is when the numerator and the denominator switch places.

Example

Evaluate $\dfrac{1}{2} \div 3$.

> *Solution*
>
> First, change the whole number to a fraction over 1, and take its reciprocal. Next, multiply the fractions together.
>
> $$3 \rightarrow \frac{3}{1} \rightarrow \frac{1}{3}$$
>
> $$\frac{1}{2} \div 3 = \frac{1}{2} \times \frac{1}{3}$$
> $$= \frac{1}{6}$$

Your Turn 1

Evaluate each of the following expressions.

a) $\dfrac{3}{4} \div 5$ **b)** $\dfrac{2}{3} \div 6$

c) $\dfrac{1}{5} \div 7$ **d)** $\dfrac{4}{7} \div 12$

PRACTICE EXERCISES

Evaluate

1. $\dfrac{1}{3} \div 5$

2. $\dfrac{3}{7} \div 15$

3. $\dfrac{4}{5} \div 4$

4. $\dfrac{8}{11} \div 6$

Lesson 4   DIVIDING BY A FRACTION

To divide a *fraction* by a *fraction*, change the question into a multiplication question.

Use the following steps to divide a fraction by a fraction.
• Take the reciprocal of the fraction after the division sign.
• Multiply the resulting fractions together.

Example

Evaluate $\dfrac{1}{3} \div \dfrac{2}{5}$.

Solution

Take the reciprocal of the fraction after the division sign.

$$\dfrac{2}{5} \to \dfrac{5}{2}$$

Multiply the resulting fractions together.

$$\dfrac{1}{3} \div \dfrac{2}{5} = \dfrac{1}{3} \times \dfrac{5}{2}$$
$$= \dfrac{5}{6}$$

Your Turn 1

Evaluate $\dfrac{7}{10} \div \dfrac{2}{9}$.

To divide a *whole number* by a *fraction*, it is not necessary to change the whole number into a fraction.

Use the following steps to divide a whole number by a fraction.
• Take the reciprocal of the fraction after the division sign.
• Multiply the whole number by the numerator of the reciprocal fraction, leaving the denominator as written.

NOTES

Example

Evaluate $4 \div \dfrac{2}{3}$.

Solution

Take the reciprocal of the fraction after the division sign.

$$\dfrac{2}{3} \rightarrow \dfrac{3}{2}$$

Change the question into a multiplication question by multiplying the whole number by the numerator of the fraction, leaving the denominator as written.

$$4 \div \dfrac{2}{3} = 4 \times \dfrac{3}{2}$$
$$= \dfrac{4 \times 3}{2}$$
$$= \dfrac{12}{2}$$
$$= 6$$

Your Turn 2

Evaluate $3 \div \dfrac{3}{4}$.

When dividing a *mixed number* by a *fraction*, use the following steps.
• Convert the mixed number to an improper fraction.
• Take the reciprocal of the fraction after the division sign.
• Multiply the resulting fractions together.

Example

Evaluate $4\frac{1}{2} \div \frac{2}{3}$.

Solution

Convert the mixed number to an improper fraction.

$$4\frac{1}{2} \to \frac{9}{2}$$

Take the reciprocal of the fraction after the division sign.

$$\frac{2}{3} \to \frac{3}{2}$$

Multiply the resulting fractions together.

$$\begin{aligned}\frac{9}{2} \div \frac{2}{3} &= \frac{9}{2} \times \frac{3}{2} \\ &= \frac{27}{4} \\ &= 6\frac{3}{4}\end{aligned}$$

Your Turn 3

Evaluate $3\frac{2}{5} \div \frac{1}{4}$.

PRACTICE EXERCISES

Evaluate.

1. $\dfrac{1}{7} \div \dfrac{4}{5}$

2. $5 \div \dfrac{4}{9}$

3. $2\dfrac{2}{5} \div \dfrac{1}{7}$

4. $5\dfrac{1}{3} \div \dfrac{5}{12}$

Lesson 5   *USING ORDER OF OPERATIONS TO SOLVE PROBLEMS*

The order of operations is used to help evaluate expressions involving whole numbers. It is also used to evaluate expressions involving combinations of whole numbers, fractions, and mixed numbers.

Recall the order of operations:
- Evaluate any expressions in *brackets* first.
- Next, evaluate terms that are *divided* or *multiplied* together.
- Finally, evaluate terms that are *added* or *subtracted* together.

Using the order of operations in the proper manner will ensure that the solutions will be correct. As always, make sure the final answer is in lowest terms.

Example

Evaluate $\dfrac{1}{2} + \dfrac{2}{3} \times \dfrac{1}{4}$.

Solution

The order of operations states that the multiplication part of the expression must be done first. Then, the addition part of the expression can be done. Writing fractions in lowest terms as you evaluate the expression can make the next steps easier.

$$\frac{2}{3} \times \frac{1}{4} = \frac{2 \times 1}{3 \times 4}$$
$$= \frac{2}{12}$$
$$= \frac{1}{6}$$

$$\frac{1}{2} + \frac{1}{6} = \frac{3}{6} + \frac{1}{6}$$
$$= \frac{4}{6}$$
$$= \frac{2}{3}$$

Remember that to add and subtract fractions, the fractions must first be written with a common denominator.

No matter how many terms are in the expression, always use the order of operations to evaluate the expression.

NOTES

Your Turn 1

Evaluate $6 \times \dfrac{1}{2} - 2 \div \dfrac{5}{3}$.

Example

Evaluate $3\dfrac{1}{4} + \left(\dfrac{1}{2} \times 1\dfrac{2}{3} \right)$.

Solution
Follow the order of operations.

Evaluate the expression in the brackets first.

$$\left(\dfrac{1}{2} \times 1\dfrac{2}{3} \right) = \dfrac{1}{2} \times \dfrac{5}{3}$$
$$= \dfrac{1 \times 5}{2 \times 3}$$
$$= \dfrac{5}{6}$$

Add.

$$3\dfrac{1}{4} + \dfrac{5}{6} = \dfrac{13}{4} + \dfrac{5}{6}$$
$$= \dfrac{39}{12} + \dfrac{10}{12}$$
$$= \dfrac{49}{12}$$

Change $\dfrac{49}{12}$ into a mixed fraction.

$$\dfrac{49}{12} \rightarrow 4\dfrac{1}{12}$$

Your Turn 2

Evaluate $2\dfrac{1}{5} \div \left(\dfrac{3}{5} - \dfrac{1}{3} \right)$.

Example

Evaluate $2\dfrac{1}{2} - \dfrac{1}{4} \times \left(\dfrac{3}{4} + \dfrac{1}{8}\right)$.

Solution

Follow the order of operations.

Evaluate the expression in the brackets first.

$$\left(\dfrac{3}{4} + \dfrac{1}{8}\right) = \dfrac{6}{8} + \dfrac{1}{8}$$

$$= \dfrac{7}{8}$$

Multiply.

$$\dfrac{1}{4} \times \dfrac{7}{8} = \dfrac{1 \times 7}{4 \times 8}$$

$$= \dfrac{7}{32}$$

Subtract.

$$2\dfrac{1}{2} - \dfrac{7}{32} = \dfrac{5}{2} - \dfrac{7}{32}$$

$$= \dfrac{80}{32} - \dfrac{7}{32}$$

$$= \dfrac{73}{32}$$

$$= 2\dfrac{9}{32}$$

Change $\dfrac{73}{32}$ into a mixed fraction.

$$\dfrac{73}{32} \rightarrow 2\dfrac{9}{32}$$

Your Turn 3

Evaluate $2\dfrac{2}{5} \times 1\dfrac{1}{2} \div \left(1\dfrac{1}{8} - \dfrac{2}{3}\right)$.

NOTES

APPLYING FRACTION OPERATIONS TO PROBLEMS

You can use the order of operations to solve problems expressed using combinations of fractions, whole numbers, and mixed numbers.

Example

Raj earns $30 an hour working in an automotive repair shop. His normal work week is 40 hours. Anytime he works more than 40 hours in a week, he earns pay at time-and-a-half. If Raj works 46 h in a week, how much money does he earn?

Solution

If Raj works 46 hours in a week, he earns his regular pay for 40 h, and he earns $1\frac{1}{2}$ times his regular pay for 6 h. His regular pay is $30 an hour.

Write an expression to represent Raj's total earnings for the week.

$$30 \times \left(40 + 1\frac{1}{2} \times 6 \right)$$

Evaluate this expression using order of operations. Evaluate the expression in the brackets first, also following order of operations.

$$
\begin{aligned}
30 \times \left(40 + 1\frac{1}{2} \times 6 \right) &= 30 \times \left(40 + \frac{3}{2} \times 6 \right) \\
&= 30 \times \left(40 + \frac{3 \times 6}{2} \right) \\
&= 30 \times \left(40 + \frac{18}{2} \right) \\
&= 30 \times (40 + 9) \\
&= 30 \times 49 \\
&= 1\ 470
\end{aligned}
$$

Raj earns $1 470 for working 46 hours in a week.

Your Turn 4

Three-quarters of the land on a farm is used as grazing land for cattle. The rest is used to grow crops. Two-thirds of the land for crops is used to grow grain. What fraction of the total land is used to grow grain?

PRACTICE EXERCISES

Evaluate.

1. $12 \times \dfrac{1}{3} - \dfrac{1}{3} \div \dfrac{11}{8}$

2. $5\dfrac{1}{6} \div \left(2\dfrac{3}{5} + \dfrac{1}{3}\right)$

3. $5\dfrac{3}{4} \times 1\dfrac{1}{3} \div \left(2\dfrac{1}{8} - \dfrac{4}{5}\right) + \dfrac{1}{2}$

4. $1\dfrac{1}{2} \times \left(5\dfrac{1}{4} \div \dfrac{1}{8}\right) - \dfrac{1}{8}$

5. $1\dfrac{1}{5} \times 2\dfrac{3}{5} \div \dfrac{1}{5} + \dfrac{1}{5}$

Use the following information to answer the next question.

Jackson's monthly cell phone bill is $40 plus an additional charge per minute. Each minute costs half of a dollar. He has talked for 50 minutes.

6. What is the total cost of the cell phone bill?

REVIEW SUMMARY

- When multiplying fractions together, it is not necessary for the fractions to have a common denominator.
- To multiply a fraction by a fraction, multiply the numerators together. Next, multiply the denominators together.
- To multiply a fraction and a whole number together, multiply the whole number by the numerator of the fraction, and keep the denominator the same.
- To multiply a fraction by a mixed number, first change the mixed number into an improper fraction.
- Change division questions involving fractions into multiplication questions by taking the *reciprocal* of the term after the division sign.
- To divide a whole number by a fraction, it is *not* necessary to change the whole number into a fraction.
- To divide a fraction by a whole number, *it is* necessary to change the whole number into a fraction.
- Change mixed numbers into improper fractions in division questions involving mixed numbers
- Use the order of operations to solve complex expressions and word problems involving complex expressions.

PRACTICE TEST

Using all three methods, evaluate.

1. $2 \times \dfrac{5}{7}$

2. $5 \times \dfrac{1}{6}$

3. $\dfrac{5}{9} \times 3$

4. $\dfrac{1}{3} \times 4$

Evaluate.

5. $\dfrac{4}{5} \times 3\dfrac{2}{7}$

6. $\dfrac{4}{9} \times 5\dfrac{1}{2}$

7. $\dfrac{5}{8} \times 8\dfrac{3}{4}$

8. $3\dfrac{2}{3} \times \dfrac{5}{8}$

9. $7\dfrac{1}{4} \times \dfrac{2}{3}$

10. $8\dfrac{1}{4} \times \dfrac{7}{11}$

11. $\dfrac{1}{4} \div 7$

12. $\dfrac{4}{5} \div 10$

13. $\dfrac{7}{11} \div 9$

14. $\dfrac{4}{5} \div 24$

15. $\dfrac{9}{13} \div 5$

16. $\dfrac{8}{9} \div 40$

17. $11 \div \dfrac{3}{8}$

18. $5 \div \dfrac{4}{7}$

19. $\dfrac{2}{5} \div \dfrac{1}{2}$

20. $\dfrac{12}{13} \div \dfrac{3}{5}$

21. $2\dfrac{2}{7} \div \dfrac{1}{7}$

22. $9\dfrac{2}{3} \div \dfrac{7}{9}$

23. $9\dfrac{1}{4} \div \dfrac{13}{16}$

24. $4\dfrac{1}{2} \div 1\dfrac{2}{3} \times \left(5\dfrac{1}{8} - \dfrac{1}{4}\right)$

25. $3\dfrac{1}{2} \times \left(2\dfrac{1}{4} \div \dfrac{1}{2}\right) - \dfrac{1}{4}$

26. $3\dfrac{1}{5} \times 5\dfrac{4}{10} \div \dfrac{1}{5} + \dfrac{3}{4}$

27. Jake buys three shirts, four pairs of jeans, and two pairs of shoes. The cost of a pair of jeans is $15. The cost of a shirt is one-third of the cost of a pair of jeans, and the cost of a pair of shoes is two-thirds of the cost of a pair of jeans. How much did Jake spend?

VOLUME

When you are finished this unit, you will be able to…
- calculate the volume of right prisms
- calculate the volume of cylinders
- solve problems involving volume

PREREQUISITE SKILLS AND KNOWLEDGE

Prior to starting this unit, you should be able to…
- perform calculations involving exponents
- substitute a number into an expression and solve
- calculate the area of various shapes
- identify π as a number with a rounded value of 3.14
- understand the difference between two-dimensional and three-dimensional objects

Lesson 1 CALCULATING THE VOLUME OF PRISMS

The volume of a prism is the amount of space the prism takes up. To calculate the volume of any three-dimensional shape, use the following formula: $V = A_{base} \times h$, where A_{base} is the area of the base, and h is the height of the prism. Ensure that all values are in the same units before calculating.

Example

Calculate the volume of the given rectangular prism.

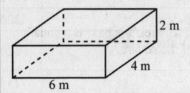

Solution

For a rectangular prism, the base is a rectangle, and the height is how high the prism rises.

$$V = A_{base}h$$
$$= (l \times w) \times h$$
$$= 6 \times 4 \times 2$$
$$= 48 \text{ m}^3$$

The units for volume are always *cubed* because volume is three dimensional. When finding volume, three lengths with the same unit are multiplied together. This results in an answer with cubed units.

Your Turn 1

Calculate the volume of the given rectangular prism.

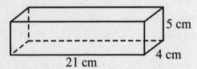

Example

Find the volume of the given cube.

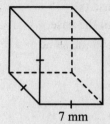

7 mm

Solution

Since all six faces of a cube are identical squares, the base is a square, and the height is the length of one side of the square.

$$V = A_{base} \times h$$
$$= (lw)h$$
$$= 7 \times 7 \times 7$$
$$= 343 \text{ mm}^3$$

Your Turn 2

Find the volume of the given cube.

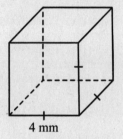

4 mm

Example

Find the volume of the given triangular prism.

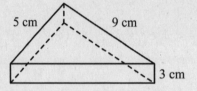

Solution

For a triangular prism, the base is a triangle, and the height is how much the prism rises.

$V = A_{base} \times h$

$= \left(\dfrac{9 \times 5}{2} \right) \times 3$

$= \dfrac{135}{2}$

$= 67.5 \text{ cm}^3$

Your Turn 3

Find the volume of the given triangular prism.

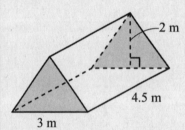

PRACTICE EXERCISES

Find the volume of the given objects.

1.

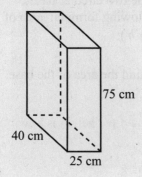

75 cm

40 cm

25 cm

2.

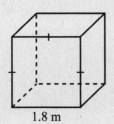

1.8 m

3.

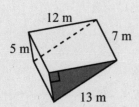

12 m

5 m

7 m

13 m

Lesson 2 CALCULATING THE VOLUME OF CYLINDERS

The volume of a cylinder is calculated the same way as the volume of a prism. The one difference is that the base of a cylinder is always a circle. The height will always be the distance between the two circular bases. To calculate the volume of a cylinder, use the following formula: area of the base times the height of the object ($V = A_{base} \times h$).

Use the formula for the area of a circle (πr^2) to find the area of the base.

Example

Find the volume of the given cylinder.

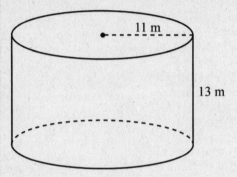

Solution

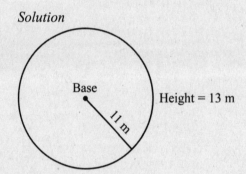

$$V = \pi r^2 h$$
$$= 3.14 \times (11)^2 \times 13$$
$$= 3.14 \times 121 \times 13$$
$$= 4\ 939.22 \text{ m}^3$$

Your Turn 1

Find the volume of the given cylinder.

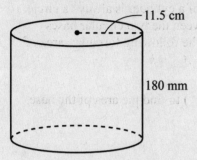

11.5 cm

180 mm

PRACTICE EXERCISES

Find the volume of the given objects.

1.

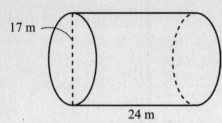

17 m

24 m

2.

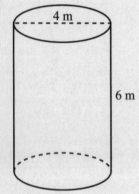

4 m

6 m

3.

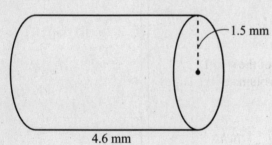

1.5 mm

4.6 mm

Lesson 3 *PROBLEM SOLVING INVOLVING THE VOLUMES OF PRISMS AND CYLINDERS*

There are many real world problem solving situations where the formulas for the volume of a prism or a cylinder can be used.

Example

The dimensions of a juice box are 3 cm × 2 cm × 7 cm. How much juice can it hold?

Solution

A juice box is a rectangular prism. Find the volume to see how much juice it can hold.

$$V = lwh$$
$$= 3 \times 2 \times 7$$
$$= 42 \text{ cm}^3$$

The juice box can hold 42 cm³ of juice.

Your Turn 1

The dimensions of a milk carton are 10 cm × 10 cm × 25 cm. How much milk can it hold?

Example

Find the volume of the given composite figure.

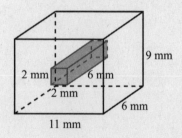

Solution

To find the volume of this figure, find the volume of the small rectangular prism. Subtract this volume from the volume of the large rectangular prism. $(V = V_{\text{large prism}} - V_{\text{small prism}})$

$$V_{\text{large prism}} = lwh$$
$$= 11 \times 6 \times 9$$
$$= 594 \text{ mm}^3$$

$$V_{\text{small prism}} = lwh$$
$$= 2 \times 6 \times 2$$
$$= 24 \text{ mm}^3$$

$$V = V_{\text{large prism}} - V_{\text{small prism}}$$
$$= 594 - 24$$
$$= 570 \text{ mm}^3$$

Your Turn 2

The given diagram shows a solid cylinder with a smaller cylinder cut out of the inside. Find the volume of the remaining portion.

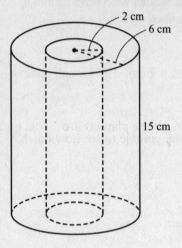

2 cm
6 cm
15 cm

Example

A paint can has a diameter of 25 cm and is 40 cm tall. If the can is half-full, how much paint is in it?

Solution

A paint can is a cylinder. Calculate the volume of the cylinder. Then, divide by two because the can is only half-full.

Find the length of the radius of the circular base first.
$$r = \frac{25 \text{ cm}}{2}$$
$$= 12.5 \text{ cm}$$

$$
\begin{aligned}
V &= \pi r^2 h \\
&= 3.14 \times (12.5)^2 \times 40 \\
&= 3.14 \times 156.25 \times 40 \\
&= 19\ 625 \text{ cm}^3
\end{aligned}
$$

$$19\ 625 \div 2 = 9\ 812.5 \text{ cm}^3$$

There are 9 812.5 cm³ of paint in the half-full can.

Your Turn 3

A pop can has a diameter of 6 cm and is 25 cm tall. If the can is half-full, how much pop is in it?

PRACTICE EXERCISES

1. If the dimensions of a fish tank are 90 cm by 75 cm by 60 cm, how much water can it hold?

2. Charles is making 3 planters for his garden. If the planters are 54 cm by 30 cm by 25 cm, how much soil does he need to fill them all?

3. Mark is filling a cube with packing peanuts. If he measured one side of the box to be 55 cm, how many cubic centimetres of peanuts does he need to fill the cube?

Use the following diagram to answer the next question.

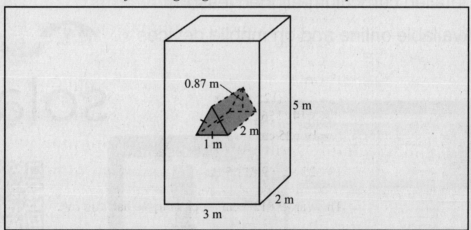

4. Find the volume of the given composite figure.

REVIEW SUMMARY

- The volume of a prism is the amount of space that the object takes up; to calculate the volume of any three-dimensional shape, use the formula $V = A_{base} \times h$.

- The volume of a cylinder is calculated the same way as the volume of a prism, using the formula $V = A_{base} \times h$, where the base is a circle.

- Units for volume are always cubed because volume is three dimensional.

- Problem solving involving prisms and cylinders involves determining the size and dimensions of the shapes given in the problem and then using the formulas to solve for the unknown value.

Looking for extra practice?

- Extra practice questions

- Detailed curriculum-aligned lessons

- Available online and on mobile devices

solaro

www.solaro.com

PRACTICE TEST

Determine the volume of the given objects.

1.

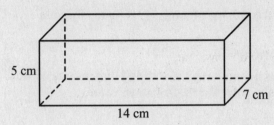

2.

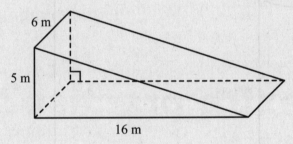

3.

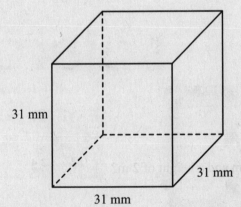

4. If the side length of a cube is 9.3 cm, what is its volume?

Use the following diagram to answer the next question.

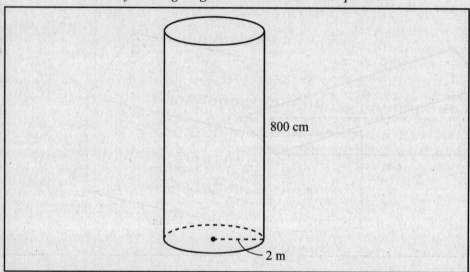

5. Determine the volume of the given cylinder.

6. What is the volume of a cylinder with a diameter of 13.4 m and a height of 2 m?

7. If the radius of a cylindrical vessel is 15.8 cm and height is 0.125 m, how much liquid it can hold?

Use the following diagram to answer the next question.

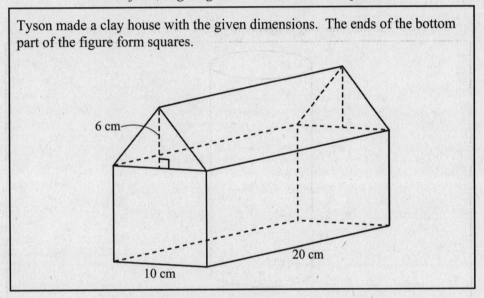

Tyson made a clay house with the given dimensions. The ends of the bottom part of the figure form squares.

6 cm

10 cm

20 cm

8. Determine the volume of the house shown in the figure.

Use the following diagram to answer the next question.

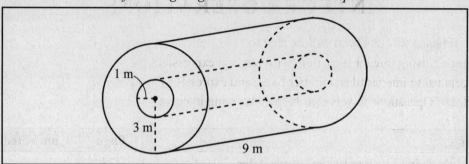

9. The given diagram shows a solid cylinder with a smaller cylinder cut out of the inside. Find the volume of the remaining portion.

INTEGER OPERATIONS

When you are finished this unit, you will be able to…
- multiply integers using integer tiles, number lines, and expressions
- divide integers using integer tiles, number lines, and expressions
- use the Order of Operations to solve problems involving integers

PREREQUISITE SKILLS AND KNOWLEDGE

Prior to starting this unit, you should be able to…
- read and write numbers using a place value table
- understand, compare, and order integers
- add and subtract integers

Lesson 1 MULTIPLYING INTEGERS USING INTEGER TILES

NOTES

YOU ALREADY KNOW...

Integers are the set of positive and negative whole numbers and zero, and can be represented by the following set of numbers:

$$\{...-2, -1, 0, +1, +2, ...\},$$

or on a number line, as illustrated below.

–5 –4 –3 –2 –1 0 1 2 3 4 5

Manipulatives such as integer tiles can be used to demonstrate the multiplication process of integers. Shaded squares represent positive integers, and unshaded squares represent negative integers.

The *quantity* of integer tiles remaining represents the answer, while the *shade* represents their value

MULTIPLYING USING A POSITIVE MULTIPLYER

Follow these steps when multiplying integers using a positive multiplier:
Step 1
Determine how many integers are in each set. This is represented by the second number in the expression.

Step 2
Determine how many sets to draw. This is represented by the first number in the expression.

Step 3
Calculate the product.

Example

Use integer tiles to evaluate the expression (+2) × (+3).

Solution
Step 1
Determine how many integers are in the set. The second integer, (+3), indicates there will be 3 positive (shaded) tiles in each set.

Step 2
Determine how many sets to draw. The first integer, (+2), indicates there will be two sets of three positive (shaded) tiles.

Step 3
Calculate the product.

The shade and the number of the tiles represent the product.
Six positive tiles are shown. The product is (+6).
$(+2) \times (+3) = (+6)$

Your Turn 1

Evaluate $(+4) \times (+2)$.

Example

Use integer tiles to evaluate the expression $(+2) \times (-3)$.

Solution
Step 1
Determine how many integers are in the set.

The second integer, (–3), indicates there will be three negative
(unshaded) tiles in each set.

Step 2
Determine how many sets to draw.

The first integer, (+2), indicates there will be two sets of three negative
(unshaded) tiles.

Step 3
Calculate the product.

The shade and the number of the tiles represent the product.
Six negative tiles are shown. The product is (–6).

$(+2) \times (-3) = (-6)$

Your Turn 2

Evaluate $(+3) \times (-5)$.

NOTES

MULTIPLYING USING A NEGATIVE MULTIPLYER

The **associative property** says that the sum or product of a set of numbers is the same no matter how the numbers are arranged. For example, $2 \times 3 = 6$ and $3 \times 2 = 6$.

When given an expression with a negative multiplier, use the associative property to make it a positive multiplier. Then, evaluate the expression.

Example

Use integer tiles to evaluate the expression $(-2) \times (+3)$.

Solution

Step 1

Use the associative property to create a positive multiplier.

$(-2) \times (+3)$ is the same as $(+3) \times (-2)$.

Step 2

Determine how many integers are in the set.

The second integer, (-2), indicates there will be 2 negative (unshaded) tiles will be in each set.

▯▯

Step 3

Determine how many sets to draw.

The first integer, $(+3)$, indicates there will be three sets of two negative (unshaded) tiles.

▯▯
▯▯
▯▯

Step 4

Calculate the product.

The shade and the number of the tiles represent the product.
Six negative tiles are shown. The product is (-6).
$(-2) \times (+3) = (-6)$

Your Turn 3

Evaluate $(-5) \times (+2)$.

MULTIPLYING TWO NEGATIVE INTEGERS

Follow these steps when multiplying two negative integers using integer tiles:

Step 1

Determine how many zero pairs are in the set. This is represented by the second integer.

Step 2

Determine how many sets of zero pairs to draw. This is represented by the first integer.

Step 3

Calculate the product. The first integer indicates the number of sets to take away while the second integer indicates which sets to take away.

Example

Use integer tiles to evaluate the expression $(-2) \times (-3)$.

Solution

Step 1

Determine how many zero pairs are in the set.

The second integer, (-3), indicates there will be three zero pairs in each set.

Step 2

Determine how many sets of zero pairs to draw.

The first integer, (-2), indicates there will be two sets of 3 zero pairs.

A zero pair is a pair of tiles with one representing $(+1)$ and the other representing (-1). It is called a zero pair because it represents zero, since $(+1) + (-1) = 0$.

Step 3

Calculate the product.

The first integer, (–2), indicates the number of sets to take away.
The second integer, (–3), indicates which sets to take away.
Take away 2 sets of (–3) tiles.

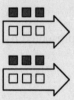

The shade and the number of the remaining tiles represent the sum.

Six positive tiles remain. The product is (+6).
$(-2) \times (-3) = (+6)$

Your Turn 4

Evaluate $(-3) \times (-3)$.

PRACTICE EXERCISES

Use integer tiles to evaluate the following expressions.

1. $(+5) \times (+2)$

2. $(+4) \times (-5)$

3. $(-2) \times (+6)$

4. $(-5) \times (-3)$

5. $(-4) \times (-4)$

Lesson 2 *MULTIPLYING INTEGERS USING NUMBER LINES*

A number line can be used to show the multiplication of integers. The size of the line segments shown above the number line indicates the multiplier, and the number of line segments drawn shows what number is being multiplied. The direction of the line segments show if the multiplier is positive or negative. The series of line segments always starts from zero on the number line.

Example

Use a number line to model the solution to (+3) × (+3).

Solution

The expression (+3) × (+3) can be modeled on a number line like this:

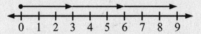

The first integer shows how many lines to draw above the number line.

The second integer shows the size of each of the lines, and the direction of the lines. A positive integer indicates that the lines will be drawn to the right of zero, while a negative integer indicates the lines will be drawn to the left.

Follow the three lines above the number line from beginning to end to see the product, which in this case is (+9).

Your Turn 1

Use a number line to model the solution to (+4) × (+2).

Example

Use a number line to model the solution to (+2) × (–4).

Solution

The first integer shows how many lines to draw above the number line. Two lines will be drawn.

The second integer shows the size of each line, and their direction. Lines with size (–4) will be drawn to the left of zero.

The correct modelling is shown below.

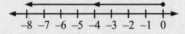

Follow the lines from beginning to end to see the product, which is (–8).

244

Your Turn 2

Use a number line to model the solution to $(+3) \times (-5)$.

Example

Use a number line to model the solution to $(-3) \times (+4)$.

Solution

Use the associative property to create a positive first integer.
$(-3) \times (+4) = (+4) \times (-3)$

The first integer shows how many lines to draw above the number line. Four lines will be drawn. The second integer shows the size of each line, and their direction. Lines with size (-3) will be drawn to the left of zero.

The correct modelling is shown below.

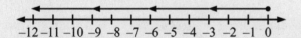

Follow the lines from beginning to end to see the product, which is (-12).

Your Turn 3

Use a number line to model the solution to $(-2) \times (+5)$.

NOTES

Example

Use a number line to model the solution to $(-3) \times (-5)$.

Solution

Since both integers are negative, they can be changed to positive and the answer will still be correct.
$(-3) \times (-5) = (+3) \times (+5)$

Then, the expression can be modeled just like any other expression with two positive integers.

The first integer shows how many lines to draw above the number line. Three lines will be drawn.

The second integer shows the size of each line, and their direction. Lines with size 5 will be drawn.

The correct modelling is shown below.

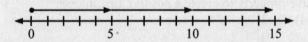

Follow the lines from beginning to end to see the product, which is $(+15)$.

Your Turn 4

Use a number line to model the solution to $(-3) \times (-3)$.

PRACTICE EXERCISES

Use a number line to multiply the following expressions.

1. $(+4) \times (+5)$

2. $(+2) \times (-2)$

3. $(-5) \times (+2)$

4. $(-7) \times (-2)$

5. $(-2) \times (-8)$

Lesson 3 *MULTIPLYING INTEGERS USING EXPRESSIONS*

There are four rules to follow when multiplying integers.

Rule 1: When multiplying two integers with the *same signs* (two positives or two negatives), multiply the values and insert a positive integer sign in front of the product.

Example

Calculate the product of (+4) and (+6).

Solution
Step 1
Multiply the values.

The values are 4 and 6.
$4 \times 6 = 24$

Step 2
Insert a positive (+) integer sign in front of the product.
$(+4) \times (+6) = (+24)$

Your Turn 1

Evaluate $(+5) \times (+8)$.

Example

Calculate the product of (−3) and (−5).

Solution
Step 1
Multiply the values.

The values are 3 and 5.
$3 \times 5 = 15$

Step 2
Insert a positive (+) integer sign in front of the product.
$(-3) \times (-5) = (+15)$

Your Turn 2

Evaluate $(-4) \times (-9)$.

Rule 2: When multiplying two integers with *different signs* (one positive and one negative), multiply the values and insert a negative integer sign in front of the product.

Example

Calculate the product of $(+5)$ and (-6).

Solution
Step 1
Multiply the values.

The values are 5 and 6.
$5 \times 6 = 30$

Step 2
Insert a negative (–) integer sign in front of the product.
$(+5) \times (-6) = (-30)$

Your Turn 3

Evaluate $(+4) \times (-11)$.

Example

Calculate the product of (-7) and $(+4)$.

Solution
Step 1
Multiply the values.

The values are 7 and 4.
$7 \times 4 = 28$

Step 2
Insert a negative (–) integer sign in front of the product.
$(-7) \times (+4) = (-28)$

Your Turn 4

Evaluate $(-3) \times (+10)$.

The Sign Rule for multiplying integers states that the product of two integers with the same signs will always be positive, while the product of two integers with different signs will always be negative.

Rules 3 and 4 apply to expressions with more than two integers.

Rule 3: If there is an even number of negative signs, multiply the values and insert a positive integer sign in front of the product.

Example

Simplify the following expression: $(-4)(+3)(-8)$.

Solution
Step 1
Multiply the values.

The values are 4, 3, and 8.
$4 \times 3 \times 8 = 96$

Step 2
Count the number of negative integer signs.

There is an even number of negative signs (2) in this expression. Although the number of integers in total is odd (3), the even number of negatives determines the sign of the solution. The solution will be positive.
$(-4)(+3)(-8) = (+96)$

Your Turn 5

Simplify $(+2)(-6)(-3)(+3)$.

Rule 4: If there is an odd number of negative signs, multiply the values and insert a negative integer sign in front of the product.

Example

Simplify the following expression: $(-2)(+3)(-4)(-5)$.

Remember that values in brackets written without an operation sign will always be multiplied.

Solution

Step 1

Multiply the values.

The values are 2, 3, 4, and 5.
$2 \times 3 \times 4 \times 5 = 120$

Step 2

Count the number of negative integer signs.

There is an odd number of negative signs (3) in this expression. Although the number of integers in total is even (4), the odd number of negatives determines the sign of the solution. The solution will be negative.
$(-2)(+3)(-4)(-5) = (-120)$

Your Turn 6

Simplify $(-3)(+5)(+4)$.

PRACTICE EXERCISES

Evaluate the product of each of the following expressions.

1. $(+3) \times (+7)$

2. $(-5) \times (-7)$

3. $(+3) \times (-6)$

4. $(-8) \times (+5)$

5. $(+8) \times (-7)$

6. $(-9) \times (+5)$

7. $(-5)(+4)(-9)$

8. $(+3)(-6)(-7)$

9. $(-3)(+4)(-5)(-6)$

10. $(-7)(+6)(-4)(-2)$

Lesson 4   DIVIDING INTEGERS USING INTEGER TILES

Division is the opposite operation of multiplication. For example, $12 \div 3 = 4$ and $4 \times 3 = 12$.

Manipulatives such as integer tiles can be used to demonstrate the division process of integers. Shaded squares represent positive integers, while unshaded squares represent negative integers.

Follow these steps when dividing integers using integer tiles:
Step 1
Rewrite the division expression as a multiplication equation.

Step 2
Draw the integer tiles to represent the multiplication equation.

Step 3
Calculate the quotient.

DIVIDING TWO INTEGERS WITH THE SAME SIGNS

When dividing two integers with the *same signs*, the sets of integer tiles are added to determine the quotient.

Example

Use integer tiles to evaluate the expression $(+6) \div (+3)$.

> *Solution*
> **Step 1**
> Rewrite the division expression as a multiplication equation.
> $(\_) \times (+3) = (+6)$
>
> **Step 2**
> Draw the integer tiles to represent the multiplication equation.
>
> $(+3)$ indicates sets of 3 positive (shaded) tiles. The product is 6 positive (shaded) tiles.
>
> Draw 2 sets of 3 positive tiles to make 6 positive tiles.
>
>
>
> **Step 3**
> Calculate the quotient.
>
> The number of sets indicates the missing number. Adding (+) indicates the integer sign.
>
> Two sets of tiles were added. The quotient is $(+2)$.
> $(+6) \div (+3) = (+2)$

NOTES

Your Turn 1

Use integer tiles to evaluate the expression $(+8) \div (+4)$

Example

Use integer tiles to evaluate the expression $(-6) \div (-3)$.

Solution

Step 1

Rewrite the division expression as a multiplication equation.

$(\_) \times (-3) = (-6)$

Step 2

Draw the integer tiles to represent the multiplication equation.

(-3) indicates sets of 3 negative (unshaded) tiles to equal 6 negative (unshaded) tiles.

Draw 2 sets of 3 negative tiles to make 6 negative tiles.

Step 3

Calculate the quotient.

The number of sets indicates the missing number. Adding $(+)$ indicates the integer sign.

Two sets of tiles were added. The quotient is $(+2)$.

$(-6) \div (-3) = (+2)$

Your Turn 2

Use integer tiles to evaluate the expression $(-8) \div (-4)$.

DIVIDING TWO INTEGERS WITH DIFFERENT SIGNS

When dividing two integers with *different signs*, sets of integer tiles are subtracted from zero pairs to determine the quotient.

Example

Use integer tiles to evaluate the expression $(+6) \div (-3)$.

Solution

Step 1

Rewrite the division expression as a multiplication equation.

$(\_) \times (-3) = (+6)$

Step 2

Draw the integer tiles to represent the multiplication equation.

(-3) indicates sets of 3 negative (unshaded) tiles. The product is 6 positive (shaded) tiles.

Draw 6 zero pairs.

Step 3

Calculate the quotient.

Subtract the number of sets to equal the product of the multiplication equation.

Two sets of three negative tiles were subtracted to equal $(+6)$.

The quotient is (-2).

$(+6) \div (-3) = (-2)$

Your Turn 3

Use integer tiles to evaluate the expression $(+8) \div (-4)$.

Example

Use integer tiles to evaluate the expression $(-6) \div (+3)$.

Solution

Step 1

Rewrite the division expression as a multiplication expression.
$(\_) \times (+3) = (-6)$

Step 2

Draw the integer tiles to represent the multiplication equation.

(+3) indicates sets of 3 positive (shaded) tiles. The product is 6 negative (unshaded) tiles.

Draw 6 zero pairs.

Step 3

Calculate the quotient.

Subtract the number of sets to equal the product of the multiplication equation.

Two sets of positive tiles were subtracted to equal (-6). This leaves two sets of negative tiles.

The quotient is (-2).
$(-6) \div (+3) = (-2)$

Your Turn 4

Use integer tiles to evaluate the expression $(-8) \div (+4)$.

PRACTICE EXERCISES

Determine the quotient using integer tiles.

1. $(+12) \div (+3)$

2. $(-18) \div (-3)$

3. $(+15) \div (-3)$

4. $(-16) \div (+8)$

5. $(+10) \div (-5)$

Lesson 5 DIVIDING INTEGERS USING NUMBER LINES

A number line can be used to show division of integers. The size and direction of the line segment shown above the number line indicates the dividend (the number before the division sign). The line is divided into segments. The divisor (the number after the division sign) determines the size of the segments. The number of segments the line is divided into indicates the quotient. The direction of the line segment shows whether the dividend is positive or negative. The line segment always starts from zero on the number line.

The Sign Law can be used to determine if the answer will be positive or negative. An expression with two integers with the *same signs* will always have a positive answer, while an expression with *different signs* will always have a negative answer.

Example

Use a number line to model the solution to $(+12) \div (+4)$.

Solution

The expression $(+12) \div (+4)$ can be modeled on a number line like this:

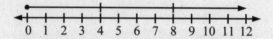

The first integer shows the size of the line to draw above the number line. A positive integer indicates that the lines will be drawn to the right of zero, while a negative integer indicates that the lines will be drawn to the left.

The second integer shows the size of each of the segments the line is divided into. The total number of segments the line is divided into shows the quotient, which in this case is $(+3)$.

Your Turn 1

Use a number line to model the solution to $(+18) \div (+6)$.

Example

Use a number line to model the solution to $(-10) \div (-5)$.

Solution

The first integer shows the size of the line to draw above the number line. The second integer shows the size of the segments the line will be divided into. The correct modelling is shown below.

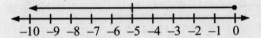

The total number of segments the line is divided into gives the quotient, which is $(+2)$.

Your Turn 2

Use a number line to model the solution to $(-15) \div (-5)$.

Example

Use a number line to model the solution to $(-14) \div (+7)$.

Solution

The first integer shows the size of the line to draw above the number line. The second integer shows the size of the segments the line will be divided into. The correct modelling is shown below.

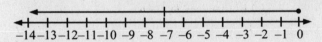

Using the Sign Law, since the integers in the expression are not the same, the quotient will be negative. Total the number of segments the line is divided into and insert a negative sign in front. This gives a quotient of (-2).

Your Turn 3

Use a number line to model the solution to $(-9) \div (+3)$.

NOTES

Example

Use a number line to model the solution to $(+15) \div (-3)$.

Solution

The first integer shows the size of the line to draw above the number line. The second integer shows the size of the segments the line will be divided into. The correct modelling is shown below.

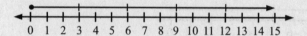

Using the Sign Law, since the integers in the expression are not the same, the quotient will be negative. Total the number of segments the line is divided into and insert a negative sign in front. This gives a quotient of (-5).

Your Turn 4

Use a number line to model the solution to $(+16) \div (-4)$.

PRACTICE EXERCISES

Determine the quotient using number lines.

1. $(+15) \div (+5)$

2. $(-12) \div (-6)$

3. $(+16) \div (+4)$

4. $(-27) \div (+3)$

5. $(+24) \div (+4)$

Lesson 6 DIVIDING INTEGERS USING EXPRESSIONS

There are two rules to follow when dividing integers.

Rule 1: When dividing two integers with the *same signs* (two positives or two negatives), divide the values and insert a positive integer sign in front of the quotient.

Example

Calculate the quotient of (+24) and (+6).

Solution
Step 1
Divide the values of the integers.

The values are 24 and 6.
$24 \div 6 = 4$

Step 2
Insert a positive (+) integer sign in front of the quotient.
$(+24) \div (+6) = (+4)$

Your Turn 1
Evaluate $(+54) \div (+9)$.

Example

Calculate the quotient of (−25) and (−5).

Solution
Step 1
Divide the values of the integers.

The values are 25 and 5.
$25 \div 5 = 5$

Step 2
Insert a positive (+) integer sign in front of the quotient.
$(−25) \div (−5) = (+5)$

Your Turn 2
Evaluate $(−49) \div (−7)$.

Rule 2: When dividing two integers with *different signs* (one positive and one negative), divide the values and insert a negative integer sign in front of the quotient.

Example

Calculate the quotient of (+28) and (−7).

> *Solution*
> **Step 1**
> Divide the values of the integers.
>
> The values are 28 and 7.
> $28 \div 7 = 4$
>
> **Step 2**
> Insert a negative (−) integer sign in front of the quotient.
> $(+28) \div (−7) = (−4)$

Your Turn 3

Evaluate $(+36) \div (−12)$.

Example

Calculate the quotient of (−35) and (+5).

> *Solution*
> **Step 1**
> Divide the values of the integers.
>
> The values are 35 and 5.
> $35 \div 5 = 7$
>
> **Step 2**
> Insert a negative (−) integer sign in front of the quotient.
> $(−35) \div (+5) = (−7)$

Your Turn 4

Evaluate $(−48) \div (+3)$.

The Sign Rule for dividing integers states that the quotient of two integers with the same signs will always be positive, while the quotient of two integers with different signs will always be negative.

NOTES

PRACTICE EXERCISES

Evaluate the quotient of each of the following expressions.

1. $(-21) \div (-7)$

2. $(-42) \div (+6)$

3. $(+32) \div (+4)$

4. $(-42) \div (-7)$

5. $(+21) \div (-3)$

6. $(-48) \div (+8)$

7. $(+16) \div (+2)$

8. $(-63) \div (-9)$

9. $(+64) \div (-8)$

10. $(-56) \div (+7)$

264

Lesson 7   INTEGER OPERATIONS

Integer expressions involving combinations of addition, subtraction, multiplication, and division can be solved using the order of operations. Apply the order of operations in the correct order to calculate the answer to integer expressions.

Example

Calculate $(-20) \div (+5) + (+2) \times (-3)$.

Solution

The order of operations states that any division and multiplication must be done before any addition or subtraction. First, multiply and divide the integers above from left to right. Then, add the two resulting integers.

$$(-20) \div (+5) + (+2) \times (-3)$$
$$= (-4) + (-6)$$
$$= (-10)$$

It is very important to apply the order of operations correctly from left to right, or else wrong answers may be obtained.

NOTES

Your Turn 1

Calculate $(+30) \div (-5) + (-20) \div (-1)$.

Example

Calculate $(-7) - (-9) + (-10) \div (+2)$.

Solution

To follow the order of operations correctly, division must be done first. Then, the addition and subtraction can be done in order from left to right.

$$(-7) - (-9) + (-10) \div (+2)$$
$$= (-7) - (-9) + (-5)$$
$$= (+2) + (-5)$$
$$= (-3)$$

265

NOTES

Your Turn 2

Calculate $(-2) + (-18) \div (+2) \times (-4)$.

When solving problems involving integers, translate the key words in the problem into a mathematical expression. Look for keywords indicating the value of the integers.

A few examples of positive (+) keywords include above, increased, gain, higher, rise, up, over, more, charge, profit.

A few examples of negative (–) keywords include below, lower, decreased, diminished, down, under, less, loss, discount, owed.

A few examples of multiplication keywords include product, of, times, multiply, double, triple.

A few examples of division keywords include quotient, split, divided, half, third, quarter, cut, distributed.

Follow these steps when solving a problem involving integers:

Step 1

Identify integer and operation keywords.

Step 2

Write an expression representing the problem.

Step 3

Solve.

Example

Ming charges $10.00 an hour for mowing the lawn. She owed her neighbour $11.00. It took her two hours to cut her neighbour's lawn. How much money did she end up with in total?

Solution

Step 1

Identify integer and operation keywords.

Integer keyword(s): charge indicates positive
received $20.00 → (+$20.00)
owed $11.00 → (−$11.00)

Operation keyword: *in total* indicates addition

Step 2

Write an expression representing the problem.
(+$20.00) + (−$11.00)

Step 3

Solve.
(+$20.00) + (−$11.00) = (+$9.00)

Ming ended up with $9.00.

Your Turn 3

Gary bought some beverages for the hockey tournament with an agreement that he could return unused full cases. He purchased 25 cases for $7.00 per case. On Tuesday, he returned 9 cases. How many cases of beverage did they drink?

Ming earned
$2 \times 10.00 = \$20.00$

NOTES

Example

A submarine was at a depth of 65 m when it was brought up 21 m. What is the new depth of the submarine?

Solution

Step 1

Identify integer and operation keywords.

Integer keyword: *depth* indicates negative
   depth of 65 m $\rightarrow (-65)$
brought up 21 m $\rightarrow (+21)$

Operation keyword: *up* indicates addition

Step 2

Write an expression representing the problem.
$(-65) + (+21)$

Step 3

Solve.
$(-65) + (+21) = (-44)$

The submarine is now at a depth of –44 m, which means 44 m below the surface of the water.

Your Turn 4

The temperature one winter morning was –15°C. By noon, the temperature increased by 9°C. What is the temperature at noon?

PRACTICE EXERCISES

Simplify the following expressions.

1. $(-40) \div (+2) + (+4) \times (+2)$

2. $(+50) \div (-5) - (+6) \times (+2)$

3. $(-9) + (-7) + (-50) \div (+2)$

4. $(+50) \div (+10) + (-18) \div (+3)$

5. $(+21) \div (+3) \times (+6) + (-64) \div (-8)$

6. $(-18) + (+9) - (+55) \div (+11) \times (-3)$

7. Kelly has $17 in her purse. She earns $12 by selling candy. How many dollars does she have now?

8. The level of water in a tank is at 6 metres on Monday. On Friday, the water level decreased to a depth of 1 metre. What was the change in depth of the water level in the tank?

9. Hillary bought 6 pens for $10 each. How much money did she pay in total for the pens?

10. Isabella took 60 balloons and split them into bunches to decorate for a party. She put 20 balloons in each bunch. How many bunches did Isabella make?

REVIEW SUMMARY

- To multiply integers together with a positive multiplier using integer tiles, determine how many integers are in each set, then determine how many sets to draw and calculate the product. The quantity of integer tiles remaining represents the answer, while the shade represents their value.
- To multiply integers together with a negative multiplier using integer tiles, use the associative property to change the question into one where the multiplier is positive; then, the above process can be used.
- To multiply integers together with a negative multiplier, determine how many zero pairs are in the set, then determine how many sets of zero pairs to draw before calculating the product.
- To multiply integers together using a number line, draw a line above the number line to show the multiplier, then divide this line into segments to show what number is being multiplied.
- If the first integer is negative, use the associative property to change it to where the first integer is positive. If both integers are negative, the answer will be positive.
- When multiplying two integers with the *same signs* (two positives or two negatives), divide the values and insert a positive integer sign in front of the quotient.
- When multiplying two integers with *different signs* (one positive and one negative), multiply the absolute values and insert a negative integer sign in front of the product.
- The Sign Rule for multiplying integers states that the product of two integers with the same signs will always be positive, while the product of two integers with different signs will always be negative.
- If an expression has more than two integers with an even number of negative signs, multiply the values and insert a positive integer sign in front of the product.
- If an expression has more than two integers with an odd number of negative signs, multiply the absolute values and insert a negative integer sign in front of the product.
- To divide integers using integer tiles, rewrite the expression as a multiplication expression, then draw the integer tiles to represent the parts of the multiplication equation before calculating the quotient.
- When dividing two integers with the *same signs*, sets of integer tiles are added to determine the quotient.
- When dividing two integers with the *different signs*, sets of integer tiles are subtracted from zero pairs to determine the quotient.
- To divide integers using a number line, the size and direction of the line segment shown above the number line indicates the dividend, the line is divided into segments the size of which is indicated by the divisor, and the number of segments the line is divided into indicates the quotient.
- Use the Sign Law to determine if the answer will be positive or negative; an expression with two integers with the same signs will always have a positive answer, while an expression with different signs will always have a negative answer.
- When dividing two integers with the *same signs*, divide the values and insert a positive integer sign in front of the quotient.
- When dividing two integers with *different signs*, divide the absolute values and insert a positive integer sign in front of the quotient.
- To solve a problem involving integers, identify integer and operation keywords, then write an expression representing the problem before solving.

PRACTICE TEST

Use integer tiles to evaluate the next two expressions.

1. $(+4) \times (-3)$

2. $(-3) \times (-2)$

Use a number line to model the solution to the next two expressions.

3. $(+2) \times (-3)$

4. $(+3) \times (+3)$

Use expressions to determine the product of the following.

5. $(+5) \times (+2)$

6. $(-6) \times (-4)$

7. $(-9) \times (+6)$

8. $(+4) \times (-8)$

9. $(-2)(+4)(-6)$

10. $(-7)(+5)(-3)(-2)$

Use integer tiles to evaluate the next two expressions.

11. $(+16) \div (+4)$

12. $(+12) \div (-3)$

Use a number line to model the solution to the next two expressions.

13. $(-16) \div (-2)$

14. $(-9) \div (+3)$

Use expressions to determine the quotient of the following.

15. $(+45) \div (+9)$

16. $(-225) \div (-5)$

17. $(-48) \div (-4)$

18. $(+81) \div (-3)$

19. $(-60) \div (+6)$

20. $(+72) \div (-8)$

Simplify the following expressions.

21. $(-180) \div (+3) + (+5) \times (+5)$

22. $(+100) \div (+5) - (+9) \times (+7)$

23. $(-19) + (-17) + (-560) \div (+7)$

24. $(+70) \div (-7) + (-78) \div (+3)$

25. $66 \div 3 \times 6 + (-120) \div 10 \times 2$

26. $(-88)+(-9)-(+56)\div(-2)\times(-5)$

27. A Kite was at a height of 50 m, when it was brought down to a height of 25 m. What was the change in height of the kite?

28. Edie bought some snack packets for a birthday party with an agreement that she could return any unused snack packets. She purchased 20 packets. On Monday, she returned 6 packets. How many packets of snacks were used?

PATTERNS WITH LINEAR RELATIONS

When you are finished this unit, you will be able to…

- use a linear relation to create a table of values
- recognize patterns in tables of values and graphs
- analyse data from tables of values and graphs
- use Order of Operations to solve problems involving linear relations

PREREQUISITE SKILLS AND KNOWLEDGE

Prior to starting this unit, you should be able to…

- understand how to perform operations with integers
- create a table of values
- explain and understand tables of values and ordered pairs
- understand the difference between expressions and equations
- understand how to plot ordered pairs and draw simple graphs
- understand what it means to solve and verify an equation

Lesson 1   GRAPHS OF LINEAR RELATIONS

NOTES

YOU ALREADY KNOW...

Numbers and **variables** (letters or symbols that represent a number) are used to make up algebraic expressions and equations.

Equations and expressions are similar, but there is one main difference. **Equations** have an equal sign and can be solved; **expressions** do not have an equal sign.

Algebraic equations containing two variables can be shown visually on a graph. Before you can graph an algebraic equation, it is important to understand how the variables in the equation are related, or the *relation* between the variables.

A **relation** is another term for the algebraic equation. A graph of a relation will always be a straight line, which means the equation can also be called a **linear relation**. The easiest way to construct a graph for a linear relation is to first write the variables from the equation in a table of values.

A linear relation will always be written in the form $y = \ldots$ or $\ldots = y$.

For the relation $x + 1 = y$, the table of values is shown. This table of values is correct because each y-value is one more than the x-value.

x	y
1	2
2	3
3	4
4	5
5	6

Follow these steps to make a table of values for a relation:
Step 1
Draw a T-chart.

Step 2
Pick any values for x (usually 4 or 5 values).

Step 3
Substitute each value of x into the equation and use the Order of Operations to solve for y.

Step 4
Complete the table.

Example

Make a table of values for the relation $2x - 3 = y$.

Solution

Step 1

Draw a T-chart.

x	y

Step 2

Pick any values for x (usually 4 or 5 values).

x	y
1	
2	
3	
4	
5	

Step 3

Substitute each value of x into the equation and use the Order of Operations to solve for y.

$$2x - 3 = y$$
$$\rightarrow 2(1) - 3 = -1$$
$$\rightarrow 2(2) - 3 = 1$$
$$\rightarrow 2(3) - 3 = 3$$
$$\rightarrow 2(4) - 3 = 5$$
$$\rightarrow 2(5) - 3 = 7$$

Step 4

Complete the table.

x	y
1	−1
2	1
3	3
4	5
5	7

NOTES

Your Turn 1

Make a table of values for the relation $3x + 4 = y$. Use the values 1 through 5 for x.

The graph of a linear relation will always be a straight line. This is because there is an infinite number of points that will make the relation true, not just the few that are included in a table of values.

To graph a linear relation:
Step 1
Make a table of values.

Step 2
Write the ordered pairs for each point from the table of values.

Step 3
Plot the ordered pairs on the Cartesian plane.

Example

Draw the graph of the linear relation $x + 2 = y$.

Solution
Step 1
Make a table of values.

x	y
0	2
1	3
2	4
3	5

Step 2
Write the ordered pairs for each point from the table of values.

Remember that an ordered pair is always written with brackets and a comma between the two numbers. The x-value is always written first, then the y-value.
(0, 2)
(1, 3)
(2, 4)
(3, 5)

Step 3
Plot the ordered pairs on the Cartesian plane.

When plotting points, make sure you start at the origin (0, 0) and go horizontally first to the value of the *x*-coordinate, and then vertically second to the value of the *y*-coordinate.

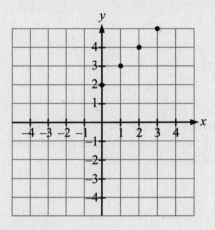

Your Turn 2

Draw a graph of the linear relation $x + y = 3$. Use the values 1 through 5 for *x*.

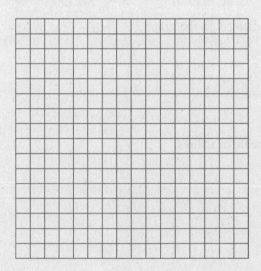

Knowing this process, it is now possible to create a table of values based on a graph of a linear relation, and to describe the pattern that is made by the graph.

Example

Make a table of values for the ordered pairs on the graph. Describe the pattern on the graph.

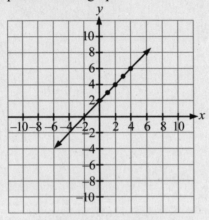

Solution

It is possible to make a table of values using the points indicated on the graph.

These are the main points indicated on the graph:
(0, 2)
(1, 3)
(2, 4)
(3, 5)
(4, 6)

Using these points, create a table of values.

x	y
0	2
1	3
2	4
3	5
4	6

The pattern indicated is that for every value of x, the corresponding y-value is 2 more.

Your Turn 3

Make a table of values for the ordered pairs on the graph below.
Describe the pattern on the graph.

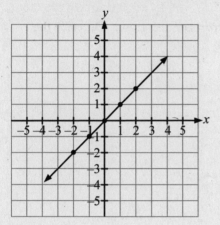

PRACTICE EXERCISES

Make a table of values for the ordered pairs on the graphs below. Describe the pattern on the graphs.

1.

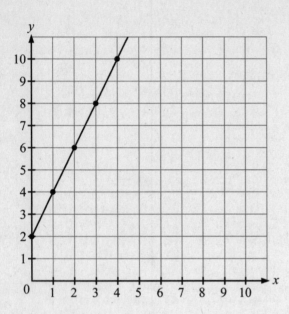

2.

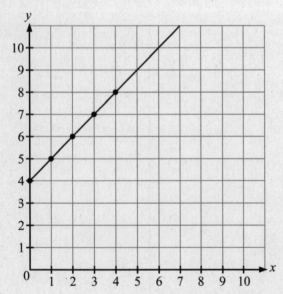

3.

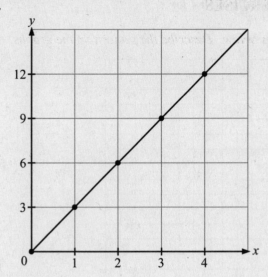

4.

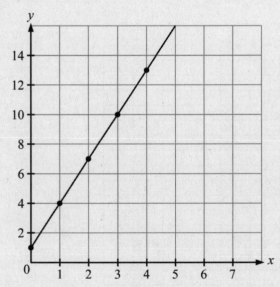

Draw the graph of each of the linear relation, using values 0 through 4 for x.

5. $y = 4x + 2$

x	y

6. $y = x + 3$

x	y

Lesson 2   PATTERNS WITH LINEAR RELATIONS

Learning about creating tables of values from a graph of a linear relation shows how patterns can be seen from both graphs and tables of values. It is now possible to identify the relationship in a table of values and use this information to graph the linear relation. The linear relation can then be described in words and then in an equation.

FINDING THE RELATIONSHIP IN A TABLE OF VALUES

Example

Using the given table of values, graph the ordered pairs and determine the relationship in words and in an equation.

x	y
−2	−4
−1	−2
0	0
1	2
2	4

Solution

List the ordered pairs from the table of values.

(−2, −4)
(−1, −2)
(0, 0)
(1, 2)
(2, 4)

Graph the ordered pairs.

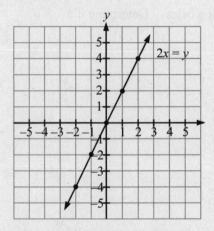

Describe the pattern in words, and then in an equation.

For every x-value, the corresponding y-value is twice as large.
This gives an equation of $2x = y$.

NOTES

Your Turn 1

Using the table of values below, graph the ordered pairs and determine the relationship in words and in an equation.

x	y
4	6
5	5
6	4
7	3
8	2

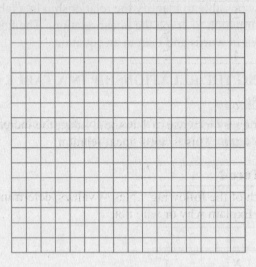

USING A TABLE OF VALUES TO DETERMINE IF A LINEAR RELATION EXISTS

It is also possible that the table of values gives a relation that is not linear. You can determine whether or not a linear relation exists by determining whether or not there is a pattern.

Example

Look at the each tables of values given below. Determine if a pattern exists.

a)

x	y
2	5
4	7
6	9
8	11
10	13

Solution

For every x-value, the corresponding y-value is greater by 3.
This would give an equation of $x + 3 = y$. This is a linear relation.

b)

x	y
1	2
2	3
3	5
4	7
5	8

Solution

For every increase of 1 in the *x*-value, the increase in the *y*-value is not the same. This is not a linear relation.

Your Turn 2

For each of the following tables of values, determine if the relationship is linear. Explain why or why not.

a)

x	y
1	3
2	7
3	10
4	12
5	15

b)

x	y
1	2
2	4
3	6
4	8
5	10

USING A TABLE OF VALUES TO SOLVE PROBLEMS
Example
The boys' basketball team wants to purchase new jerseys. The cost to purchase them is $75 for the shipment and $25 for each jersey.

a) Make a table of values showing the cost of the jerseys in relation to the number of jerseys ordered.

Solution
Make a table of values.

Number of Jerseys	Cost of Each Jersey ($)
1	100
2	125
3	150
4	175
5	200

b) Is this a linear relation? Why?

Solution
The price of one jersey, including the cost of shipping, is $100.
For each additional jersey purchased, the cost increases by $25.
The number of jerseys and the cost of each jersey increase in a regular pattern. This is a linear relation.

c) What is the linear relation?

Solution
To determine the linear relation, let x be the number of jerseys and y be the cost. The linear relation for this table of values would be
$y = 25x + 75$.

d) How much will 5 jerseys cost?

Solution
From the table of values, 5 jerseys would cost $200.

This result could also be obtained from the linear relation by substituting $x = 5$ and solving for y using the Order of Operations.
$$y = 25x + 75$$
$$= 25(5) + 75$$
$$= 200$$

e) How many jerseys can be ordered with $300?

Solution

To determine how many jerseys can be ordered, substitute $y = 300$ into the linear relation and solve for x using the Order of Operations.

$$y = 25x + 75$$
$$300 = 25x + 75$$
$$300 - 75 = 25x + 75 - 75$$
$$225 = 25x$$
$$\frac{225}{25} = \frac{25x}{25}$$
$$9 = x$$

For $300, 9 jerseys can be ordered.

Your Turn 3

Oliver, a plumber, earns $90 for every hour he works, and $10 as an allowance pay.

a) Make a table of values showing the amount of earning in relation to the number of working hours for the first five hours.

x	y

b) Is this a linear relation? Why?

c) What is the linear relation?

d) How much will he earn for working 7 hours?

e) How many hours must he work to earn $550?

PRACTICE EXERCISES

Using the tables of values, graph the ordered pairs and determine the relationship in words and in an equation.

1.

x	y
1	2
2	5
3	8
4	11
5	14

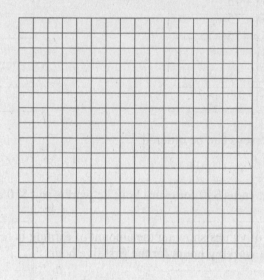

2.

x	y
1	0
2	2
3	4
4	6
5	8

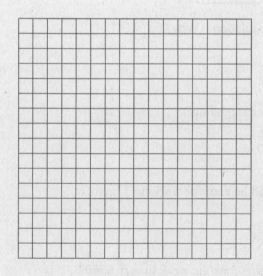

Look at each table of values and determine if a pattern exists.

3.

x	y
1	1
2	6
3	8
4	9
5	12

4.

x	y
2	7
4	9
6	11
8	13
10	15

5.

x	y
1	1
2	0
3	3
4	2
5	4

6.

x	y
2	0
4	2
6	4
8	6
10	8

Use the following information to answer the next five questions.

Max wants to buy new hats for his class. The cost to purchase them is $5 for the delivery charge and $2 for each hat.

7. Make a table of values showing the cost of the hats in relation to the number of hats ordered.

x	y

8. Is this a linear relation? Why?

9. What is the linear relation?

10. How much will 4 hats cost?

11. How many hats can be ordered for $45?

Use the following information to answer the next five questions.

Aaron, a mechanic, earns $1.00 for every minute he works, and $15.00 as an allowance pay.

12. Make a table of values showing what Aaron earns in relation to the number of minutes he works.

x	y

13. Is this a linear relation? Why?

14. What is the linear relation?

15. How much will he earn for working 5 minutes?

16. How many minutes must Aaron work to earn $60?

REVIEW SUMMARY

- Linear relations can be shown on a graph, which can be drawn using a table of values.
- A table of values can be used to draw a graph of a linear relation.
- The graph of a linear relation will always be a straight line.
- Patterns that describe a linear relation can be shown in a table of values and on a graph.
- If there is no pattern in a table of values, or if the corresponding graph is not a straight line, the relation is not linear.
- Real world problems can be solved by constructing a table of values and then determining what, if any, patterns exist.

PRACTICE TEST

Make a table of values for the ordered pairs on the following graphs. Describe the pattern on each graph.

1.

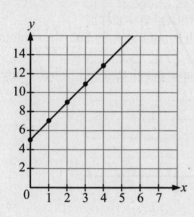

2.

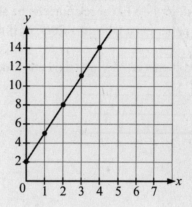

3.

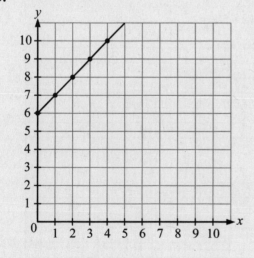

4.

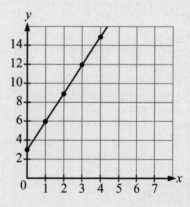

5.

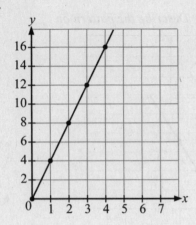

6.

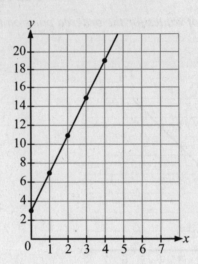

Draw a graph for the given relations. Use the values 1 through 5 for x in the table of values.

7. $y = -x + 7$

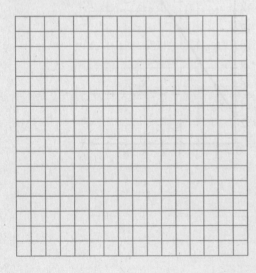

8. $4x + 5 = y$

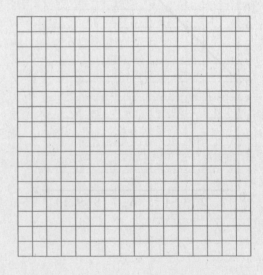

Look at the following tables of values and determine if a pattern exists.

9.

x	y
2	12
4	14
6	16
8	18
10	20

10.

x	y
1	1
2	10
3	18
4	20
5	23

11.

x	y
2	5
4	7
6	8
8	10
10	13

12.

x	y
1	10
2	11
3	12
4	13
5	14

13.

x	y
2	17
4	19
6	21
8	23
10	25

14.

x	y
1	1
2	3
3	4
4	7
5	10

Use the following information to answer the next five questions.

Sahara saves $50 each month from her salary.

15. Make a table of values showing the amount of savings for each month, for the first five months.

x	y

16. Is this a linear relation? Why?

17. What is the linear relation?

18. Calculate the amount Sahara saves after 8 months.

19. After how many months will she have saved $1 000?

Use the following information to answer the next four questions.

> Samuel wants to buy some new shirts. The cost of a shirt in a store is $15 and the store offers a $1 discount at the till.

20. Make a table of values showing the cost of the shirts in relation to the number of shirts purchased, for the first five shirts.

x	y

21. Is this a linear relation? Why?

22. What is the linear relation?

23. What is the total cost if Samuel purchases 6 shirts?

Use the following information to answer the next five questions

> Wayne earns a monthly salary of $2 300 and a commission of $150 for each car he sells.

24. Make a table of values showing how much he earns in relation to the number of cars he sells, for the first five cars.

x	y

25. Is this a linear relation? Why?

26. What is the linear relation?

27. How much will he earn if he sells 7 cars in a month?

28. How many cars does he need to sell to earn $3 800?

Use the following information to answer the next five questions.

> Wilfred is renting a car for spring break. A rental car costs $40 for the week and $0.25 per kilometre.

29. Make a table of values showing the relation between the rental fee and number of kilometres Wilfred drives, if he drives 10, 20, 30, 40 and 50 kilometres.

x	y

30. Is this a linear relation? Why?

31. What is the linear relation?

32. What will be the rental cost if Wilfred drives for 100 kilometres?

33. How many kilometres does he drive if his rental fee is $80?

NOTES

LINEAR RELATIONS

When you are finished this unit, you will be able to…
• solve one-step linear relations
• solve two-step linear relations

Lesson	Page	Completed on
1. Equations in the Form $ax = b$	304	
2. Equations in the Form $\dfrac{x}{a} = b$	309	
3. Equations in the Form $ax + b = c$	314	
4. Equations in the Form $\dfrac{x}{a} + b = c$	320	
Review Summary	324	
Practice Test	325	
Answers and Solutions	at the back of the book	

PREREQUISITE SKILLS AND KNOWLEDGE

Prior to starting this unit, you should be able to…
• distinguish between expressions and equations
• understand how to perform operations with integers

Lesson 1   EQUATIONS IN THE FORM ax = b

One-step algebra equations can be solved by performing one operation to both sides of the equation to isolate the variable. The phrase "isolate the variable" means to get the variable on one side of the equation by itself and the numbers on the other side. The sides in the equation are separated by an equal sign.

Addition and subtraction are opposite operations, and multiplication and division are opposite operations.

To isolate a variable, always perform the opposite operation of what is given. Whatever operation is done on one side of the equation must also be done to the other side in order to keep the equation balanced.

Equations in the form $ax = b$ are one-step equations, and they involve multiplying a variable by a number. To solve for the unknown number, apply the opposite operation to both sides of the equation, which in this case will always be division.

Example

Solve $4m = 20$.

Solution

To isolate the variable m, divide both sides of the equation by 4.

$$4m = 20$$
$$\frac{4m}{4} = \frac{20}{4}$$
$$m = 5$$

Your Turn 1

Solve $3x = 21$.

Example

Solve $-8h = 56$.

Solution

To isolate the variable h, divide both sides of the equation by -8.

$$-8h = 56$$
$$\frac{-8h}{-8} = \frac{56}{-8}$$
$$h = -7$$

304

Your Turn 2

Solve $-4d = 44$.

Example

Solve $6x = -36$.

Solution

To isolate the variable x, divide both sides of the equation by 6.
$$6x = -36$$
$$\frac{6x}{6} = \frac{-36}{6}$$
$$x = -6$$

Your Turn 3

Solve $5y = -60$.

Example

Solve $-5b = -45$.

Solution

To isolate the variable b, divide both sides of the equation by -5.
$$-5b = -45$$
$$\frac{-5b}{-5} = \frac{-45}{-5}$$
$$b = 9$$

Your Turn 4

Solve $-3n = -33$.

Knowing how to set up and solve one-step equations can help to solve problems.

Example

The product of negative ten and a number is seventy. What is the number?

Solution

Set up the one-step equation based on the information given in the problem. Let x stand for the unknown number.

$-10x = 70$

$\dfrac{-10x}{-10} = \dfrac{70}{-10}$

$x = -7$

The number is -7.

Your Turn 5

The product of six and a number is negative fifty-four. What is the number?

PRACTICE EXERCISES

Solve.

1. $2q = 6$

2. $-9g = 126$

3. $7f = -77$

4. $-12s = -96$

5. $6y = 18$

6. $7t = 63$

7. $-9j = 90$

8. $-10l = 130$

9. $5v = -80$

10. $11z = -132$

11. $-9d = -81$ **12.** $-3h = -15$

13. The product of three and a number is negative eighteen. What is the number?

14. The product of negative five and a number is twenty-five. What is the number?

Lesson 2   EQUATIONS IN THE FORM $\frac{x}{a} = b$

Equations in the form $\frac{x}{a} = b$ are one-step equations, and they involve dividing a variable by a number. To solve for the unknown number, apply the opposite operation to both sides of the equation, which in this case will always be multiplication.

Example

Solve $\frac{t}{5} = 7$.

Solution

To isolate the variable t, multiply both sides of the equation by 5.

$$\frac{t}{5} = 7$$
$$\frac{t}{5} \times 5 = 7 \times 5$$
$$t = 35$$

Your Turn 1

Solve $\frac{a}{4} = 9$.

Example

Solve $\frac{r}{-3} = -5$.

Solution

To isolate the variable r, multiply both sides of the equation by –3.

$$\frac{r}{-3} = -5$$
$$\frac{r}{-3} \times -3 = (-5) \times (-3)$$
$$r = 15$$

NOTES

Your Turn 2

Solve $\dfrac{f}{-5} = -6$.

Example

Solve $\dfrac{q}{-4} = 7$.

Solution

To isolate the variable q, multiply both sides of the equation by –4.

$$\frac{q}{-4} = 7$$

$$\frac{r}{-4} \times -4 = 7 \times (-4)$$

$$r = -28$$

Your Turn 3

Solve $\dfrac{z}{-6} = 8$.

Example

Solve $\dfrac{k}{2} = -16$.

Solution

To isolate the variable k, multiply both sides of the equation by 2.

$$\frac{k}{2} = -16$$

$$\frac{k}{2} \times 2 = (-16) \times 2$$

$$k = 32$$

Your Turn 4

Solve $\frac{w}{3}=-9$.

Knowing how to set up and solve one-step equations can help to solve problems.

Example

A number divided by nine is seven. What is the number?

Solution

Set up the one-step equation based on the information given in the problem. Let y stand for the unknown number.

$$\frac{y}{9}=7$$

$$\frac{y}{9}\times 9=7\times 9$$

$$y=63$$

The number is 63.

Your Turn 5

A number divided by negative four is negative eight. What is the number?

PRACTICE EXERCISES

Solve.

1. $\dfrac{x}{5} = 8$

2. $\dfrac{y}{-7} = -3$

3. $\dfrac{c}{2} = -5$

4. $\dfrac{n}{-8} = 3$

5. $\dfrac{a}{7} = 8$

6. $\dfrac{b}{6} = 4$

7. $\dfrac{f}{-3} = -12$

8. $\dfrac{t}{-6} = -10$

9. $\dfrac{w}{3} = -81$

10. $\dfrac{e}{9} = -5$

11. $\dfrac{m}{-12} = 4$

12. $\dfrac{y}{-11} = 3$

13. A number divided by two is negative ten. What is the number?

14. A number divided by negative seven is four. What is the number?

Lesson 3 *EQUATIONS IN THE FORM* $ax + b = c$

Think about solving two-step equations as performing the order of operations in reverse order.

Two-step algebra equations require two operations to be performed in order to isolate the variable. Just as with one-step equations, the goal is to isolate the variable on one side of the equal sign and the numbers on the other.

Follow these steps to solve two-step equations:
• Do the opposite operation of the addition or subtraction first.
• Do the opposite operation of the multiplication or division second.
• In order to keep the equation balanced, whatever operation is done to one side must be done to the other side.

By performing the first operation to isolate the term that contains the variable, the equation will change into a one-step equation, which can be solved just like any other one-step equation.

Equations in the form $ax + b = c$ are two-step equations, and they involve multiplying a variable by a number, and then adding or subtracting a number. To solve for the unknown number, first apply the opposite operation to the number being added or subtracted. Then, the resulting one-step equation can be solved by division.

Example

Solve $2x + 4 = 10$.

Solution

To isolate the variable x, isolate the term that contains the variable. This requires that 4 be subtracted from both sides of the equation.
$$2x + 4 = 10$$
$$2x + 4 - 4 = 10 - 4$$
$$2x = 6$$

Now, this is a one-step equation. The variable can be isolated by dividing both sides by 2.
$$\frac{2x}{2} = \frac{6}{2}$$
$$x = 3$$

Your Turn 1

Solve $3a + 7 = 22$.

Example

Solve $-5w + 7 = -18$.

Solution

To isolate the variable w, first subtract 7 from both sides of the equation.

$$-5w + 7 = -18$$
$$-5w + 7 - 7 = -18 - 7$$
$$-5w = -25$$
$$\frac{-5w}{-5} = \frac{-25}{-5}$$
$$w = 5$$

Your Turn 2

Solve $-2c + 4 = 14$.

Example

Solve $4g - 9 = 15$.

Solution

To isolate the variable g, first add 9 to both sides of the equation.

$$4g - 9 = 15$$
$$4g - 9 + 9 = 15 + 9$$
$$4g = 24$$
$$\frac{4g}{4} = \frac{24}{4}$$
$$g = 6$$

Your Turn 3

Solve $6j - 6 = 48$.

Example

Solve $-6z - 7 = -55$.

Solution

To isolate the variable z, first add 7 to both sides of the equation.

$$-6z - 7 = -55$$
$$-6z - 7 + 7 = -55 + 7$$
$$-6z = -48$$
$$\frac{-6z}{-6} = \frac{-48}{-6}$$
$$z = 8$$

Your Turn 4

Solve $-4r - 4 = -40$.

Knowing how to set up and solve two-step equations can help to solve real-world problems.

Example

Three more than four times a number is twenty-three. What is the number?

Solution

Set up the two-step equation based on the information given in the problem. Let x stand for the unknown number.

$$4x + 3 = 23$$
$$4x + 3 - 3 = 23 - 3$$
$$4x = 20$$
$$\frac{4x}{4} = \frac{20}{4}$$
$$x = 5$$

The number is 5.

Your Turn 5

Four less than six times a number is forty-four. What is the number?

Example

If Shereen has 8 more DVDs than Chad and together they have 30 DVDs, how many DVDs does each person have?

Solution

Write the equation, then solve. Let x stand for the number of DVDs that Chad has, since he owns the smaller amount.
Chad $\rightarrow x$
Shereen $\rightarrow x + 8$

Together they have 30 DVDs.
Chad's DVDs + Shereen's DVDs = 30 DVDs
$$x + (x + 8) = 30$$
$$2x + 8 = 30$$

Solve the equation for x.
$$2x + 8 = 30$$
$$2x + 8 - 8 = 30 - 8$$
$$2x = 22$$
$$\frac{2x}{2} = \frac{22}{2}$$
$$x = 11$$

This means that Chad has 11 DVDs.

Determine how many DVDs Shereen has by substituting 11 for x in the expression $x + 8$.
$$x + 8$$
$$= 11 + 8$$
$$= 19$$

This means that Shereen has 19 DVDs. These numbers also satisfy the equation $x + (x + 8) = 30$.

Check:
$$x + (x + 8) = 11 + 11 + 8$$
$$= 30$$

Your Turn 6

If Miriam has 12 more CDs than Sabrina and together they have 44 CDs, how many CDs does each person have?

PRACTICE EXERCISES

Solve the following equations.

1. $5y + 4 = 14$

2. $-3h + 5 = -13$

3. $6p - 2 = 40$

4. $-3s - 8 = -14$

5. $5f + 1 = 41$

6. $3q + 4 = 40$

7. $-2p + 7 = -35$

8. $-8s + 3 = -45$

9. $9g - 4 = 59$

10. $6h - 7 = 65$

11. $-6t - 2 = -14$

12. $-2m - 7 = -19$

318

13. Eight more than two times a number is sixteen. What is the number?

14. Seven more than four times a number is thirty-five. What is the number?

15. Four more than five times a number is twenty-four. What is the number?

16. The sum of three consecutive numbers is 45. What are the numbers?

Lesson 4   EQUATIONS IN THE FORM $\dfrac{x}{a} + b = c$

NOTES

Equations in the form $\dfrac{x}{a} + b = c$ are two-step equations, and they involve dividing a variable by a number, and then adding or subtracting a number. To solve for the unknown, first apply the opposite operation to the number being added or subtracted. Then, the resulting one-step equation can be solved by multiplication.

Example

Solve $\dfrac{x}{2} + 4 = 12$.

Solution

To isolate the variable x, first isolate the term that contains the variable. This requires that 4 be subtracted from both sides of the equation.

$$\frac{x}{2} + 4 = 12$$

$$\frac{x}{2} + 4 - 4 = 12 - 4$$

$$\frac{x}{2} = 8$$

Now this is a one-step equation. The variable can be isolated by multiplying both sides by 2.

$$\frac{x}{2} \times 2 = 8 \times 2$$

$$x = 16$$

Your Turn 1

Solve $\dfrac{w}{7} + 6 = 10$.

Example

Solve $\dfrac{w}{-5} + 7 = 10$.

Solution

To isolate the variable w, first subtract 7 from both sides of the equation.

$$\frac{w}{-5} + 7 = 10$$

$$\frac{w}{-5} + 7 - 7 = 10 - 7$$

$$\frac{w}{-5} = 3$$

$$\frac{w}{-5} \times -5 = 3 \times (-5)$$

$$w = -15$$

Your Turn 2

Solve $\dfrac{f}{-8} + 9 = 15$.

Example

Solve $\dfrac{d}{6} - 3 = 2$.

Solution

To isolate the variable d, first add 3 to both sides of the equation.

$$\frac{d}{6} - 3 = 2$$

$$\frac{d}{6} - 3 + 3 = 2 + 3$$

$$\frac{d}{6} = 5$$

$$\frac{d}{6} \times 6 = 5 \times 6$$

$$d = 30$$

Your Turn 3

Solve $\dfrac{g}{3} - 6 = 2$.

Example

Solving $\dfrac{p}{-4} - 6 = 0$.

Solution

To isolate the variable p, first add 6 to both sides of the equation.

$$\frac{p}{-4} - 6 = 0$$

$$\frac{p}{-4} - 6 + 6 = 0 + 6$$

$$\frac{p}{-4} = 6$$

$$\frac{p}{-4} \times (-4) = 6 \times (-4)$$

$$p = -24$$

Your Turn 4

Solve $\dfrac{n}{10} - 6 = -1$.

PRACTICE EXERCISES

Solve the following equations.

1. $\dfrac{m}{3} + 1 = 10$

2. $\dfrac{r}{-7} + 6 = 8$

3. $\dfrac{v}{9} - 4 = 3$

4. $\dfrac{e}{-2} - 5 = 0$

5. $\dfrac{k}{7} + 3 = 9$

6. $\dfrac{y}{2} + 4 = 13$

7. $\dfrac{a}{4} + 3 = 10$

8. $\dfrac{n}{-4} + 10 = 11$

9. $\dfrac{c}{-8} + 4 = 9$

10. $\dfrac{e}{3} - 2 = 5$

11. $\dfrac{k}{7} - 5 = 7$

12. $\dfrac{u}{-3} - 8 = 1$

13. $\dfrac{v}{-6} - 4 = 0$

REVIEW SUMMARY

- One-step algebra equations can be solved by performing one operation to both sides of the equation to isolate the variable.
- Addition and subtraction are opposite operations, and multiplication and division are opposite operations.
- To solve equations in the form $ax = b$, apply the opposite operation to both sides of the equation, which in this case will always be division.
- To solve equations in the form $\dfrac{x}{a} = b$, apply the opposite operation to both sides of the equation, which in this case will always be multiplication.
- Two-step algebra equations require two operations to be performed in order to isolate the variable.
- To solve two-step equations, do the opposite operation to the addition or subtraction first in order to isolate the term with the variable, then do the opposite operation to the multiplication or division second.
- Performing the addition or subtraction operation on a two-step equation turns it into a one-step equation, which can be solved like any other one-step equation.
- To solve equations in the form $ax + b = c$, first apply the opposite operation to the number being added or subtracted, then solve the resulting one-step equation by division.
- To solve equations in the form $\dfrac{x}{a} + b = c$, first apply the opposite operation to the number being added or subtracted, then solve the resulting one-step equation by multiplication.
- Solving word problems involving linear equations requires the correct equation be established from the information provided in the question, then the proper techniques to be applied to the equation in order to solve for the unknown value.

PRACTICE TEST

Solve.

1. $3l = 36$

2. $7k = 28$

3. $-12n = 84$

4. $-5b = 65$

5. $4k = -32$

6. $6n = -72$

7. $-5h = -55$

8. $-8r = -104$

9. $\dfrac{t}{4} = 9$

10. $\dfrac{k}{6} = 14$

11. $\dfrac{h}{-7} = -7$

12. $\dfrac{k}{-5} = -8$

13. $\dfrac{q}{-13} = 5$

14. $\dfrac{n}{-6} = 7$

15. $\dfrac{r}{-12} = 6$

16. $\dfrac{c}{5} = -27$

17. $\dfrac{k}{12} = -10$

18. The product of negative eleven and a number is one hundred twenty-one. What is the number?

19. The product of twenty-one and a number is eighty-four. What is the number?

20. A number divided by –16 is 2. What is the number?

21. A number divided by 7 is –8. What is the number?

Solve.

22. $7t + 2 = 30$

23. $6u + 8 = 50$

24. $-9f + 5 = -103$

25. $-4t + 7 = -53$

26. $3y - 4 = 20$

27. $5v - 8 = 17$

28. $-2c - 3 = -19$

29. $-12m - 2 = -14$

30. Five more than three times a number is seventeen. What is the number?

31. Seven more than six times a number is nineteen. What is the number?

327

32. Three less than four times a number is twenty-five. What is the number?

33. Nine less than eight times a number is seventy-nine. What is the number?

Solve.

34. $\dfrac{j}{5} + 7 = 15$

35. $\dfrac{a}{3} + 6 = 10$

36. $\dfrac{y}{-2} + 4 = 8$

37. $\dfrac{m}{-6} + 2 = 7$

38. $\dfrac{s}{8} - 6 = 6$

39. $\dfrac{k}{4} - 8 = 12$

40. $\dfrac{r}{-6} - 8 = 0$

41. $\dfrac{l}{-7} - 2 = 3$

PROBABILITY

When you are finished this unit, you will be able to...
- create tree diagrams and tables to illustrate probability
- express probability as a fraction
- calculate probability using the basic probability formula
- calculate the probabilities of two or more events occurring at the same time
- use the order of operations to solve problems involving probabilities

PREREQUISITE SKILLS AND KNOWLEDGE

Prior to starting this unit, you should be able to...
- write fractions in lowest terms
- add, subtract, multiply, and divide integers
- multiply fractions

Lesson 1 TREE DIAGRAMS AND TABLES

Probability is the likelihood of an event happening. If two or more events are happening at the same time and the result of each event does not affect the outcome of any other event, these are called **independent events**.

For example, if a pair of standard dice are thrown at the same time, the result on one die has no affect on the result of the other. These are independent events.

When determining the probability of an event happening, it is useful to show all the possible outcomes. All the possible outcomes are called the **sample space**. The two main ways that a sample space can be shown is using a table or a tree diagram.

Example

Consider rolling a die and spinning the spinner shown. Make a table and a tree diagram showing all the possible outcomes, and then list all the possible outcomes.

Solution

The table of all possible outcomes is as shown:

		Die					
		1	**2**	**3**	**4**	**5**	**6**
Spinner	**a**	1a	2a	3a	4a	5a	6a
	b	1b	2b	3b	4b	5b	6b
	c	1c	2c	3c	4c	5c	6c
	d	1d	2d	3d	4d	5d	6d

The tree diagram of all possible outcomes is as shown:

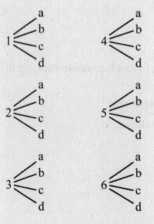

The outcomes (sample space) are 1a, 1b, 1c, 1d, 2a, 2b, 2c, 2d, 3a, 3b, 3c, 3d, 4a, 4b, 4c, 4d, 5a, 5b, 5c, 5d, 6a, 6b, 6c, and 6d.

A desired outcome is referred to as a **favourable outcome**.
The probability of independent events can be calculated using the
probability formula:

$$P(\text{favourable outcome}) = \frac{\text{favourable outcomes}}{\text{total possible outcomes}}$$

Example

Two coins are tossed at the same time.

a) Determine the total number of possible outcomes using a tree diagram.

Solution

The tree diagram showing all possible outcomes will look as shown:

```
        H     H, H
   H  <
        T     H, T

        H     T, H
   T  <
        T     T, T
```

Therefore, there are 4 possible outcomes: HH, HT, TH and TT.

b) Find $P(\text{H, H})$.

Solution

There are four possible outcomes. Only one of the possible outcomes
involves tossing two heads, HH.

$$P(\text{favourable outcome}) = \frac{\text{favourable outcomes}}{\text{total possible outcomes}}$$

$$P(H,H) = \frac{1}{4}$$

The answer is $\frac{1}{4}$.

c) Find $P(\text{at least one T})$.

Solution

There are four possible outcomes, three of which involve tossing at
least one tail, HT, TH and TT.

$$P(\text{favourable outcome}) = \frac{\text{favourable outcomes}}{\text{total possible outcomes}}$$

$$P(\text{at least one T}) = \frac{3}{4}$$

The answer is $\frac{3}{4}$.

Probabilities written as
fractions should be in
lowest terms unless the
question indicates
otherwise.

Your Turn 1

Consider a regular deck of 52 playing cards. There are four suits in a regular deck, with 13 cards in each suit: clubs, spades, hearts, and diamonds. Half the deck are black cards, and the other half are red cards. The 13 cards in each suit are A, 2, 3, 4, 5, 6, 7, 8, 9, 10, jack, queen, and king.

a) Find P(heart).

b) Find P(any red card).

c) Find P(any king).

d) Find P(any numbered card).

PRACTICE EXERCISES

Use the following information to answer the next five questions.

A student tosses a regular die.

1. Find $P(2)$.

2. Find P(even number).

3. Find P(a number less than 5).

4. Find $P(8)$.

5. Find P(not a three).

Use the following information to answer the next four questions.

A student draws a card from a regular deck of cards.

6. Find $P(7)$.

7. Find P(face card).

8. Find P(odd numbered card).

9. Find P(black).

Use the following information to answer the next four questions.

A student put each letter in the word MATHEMATICS on a separate piece of paper, placed them in a bag, and randomly picked one out.

10. Find P(M).

11. Find P(vowel).

12. Find P(consonant).

13. Find P(M or T).

14. Draw a spinner that would make all of the following probabilities true.

$P(\text{grey}) = \dfrac{1}{2}$, $P(\text{black}) = \dfrac{1}{4}$, $P(\text{white}) = \dfrac{1}{4}$

Use the following diagram to answer the next four questions.

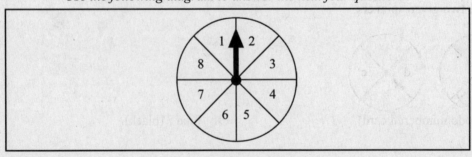

15. Find P(odd number).

16. Find P(4).

334

17. Find *P*(more than 2).

18. Find *P*(not 3).

19. A pair of dice are tossed at the same time. If one die is blue and the other is red, draw a table to show the all the possible outcomes.

Draw a tree diagram for the following events, and then list all the possible outcomes.

20. Toss a coin and roll a die.

21. Spin the two given spinners.

Lesson 2 *OUTCOMES OF INDEPENDENT EVENTS*

There are two methods that can be used to determine the total number of possible outcomes of two or more independent events.

Method 1
Create a table of values or a tree diagram, then count all possible outcomes.

Method 2
Multiply the number of outcomes of each event together.

Example
Sarah spins the given spinner and rolls a die. How many possible outcomes are there?

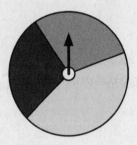

Solution
Method 1
Create a table of values showing all the possible outcomes.

Die	Spinner Colours		
	White	**Black**	**Grey**
1	W, 1	B, 1	G, 1
2	W, 2	B, 2	G, 2
3	W, 3	B, 3	G, 3
4	W, 4	B, 4	G, 4
5	W, 5	B, 5	G, 5
6	W, 6	B, 6	G, 6

The table shows 18 possible outcomes.

Method 2
Multiply the number of outcomes of each event together.

Number of possible outcomes of rolling one die: 6
Number of possible outcomes of spinning the spinner: 3

Total number of possible outcomes: $6 \times 3 = 18$

Example

Arnie flips a coin, spins the given spinner, and rolls a die. How many possible outcomes are there?

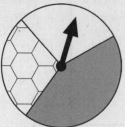

Solution

Method 1

Draw a tree diagram showing all the possible outcomes.

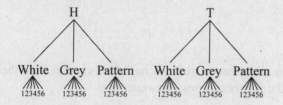

The tree diagram shows 36 possible outcomes.

Method 2

Multiply the number of outcomes of each event together.

Number of possible outcomes of tossing one coin: 2
Number of possible outcomes of spinning the spinner: 3
Number of possible outcomes of rolling one die: 6

Total number of possible outcomes: $2 \times 3 \times 6 = 36$

Your Turn 1

A bag contains one penny, one nickel, and one dime. A die is rolled and a coin is drawn from the bag. How many possible outcomes are there? Show your answer using both methods.

PRACTICE EXERCISES

Use the following diagram to answer the next question.

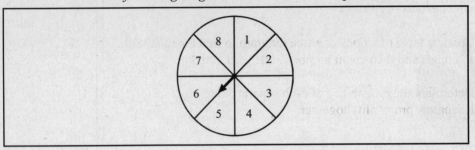

1. Chelsea spins the given spinner and tosses a coin. Use a table to determine the number of possible outcomes.

2. A bag contains one red marble, one blue marble, and one green marble. A marble is chosen from the bag, and a coin is tossed. Use a table to determine the number of possible outcomes.

Use the following diagram to answer the next question.

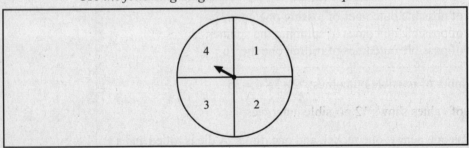

3. Cole tosses a coin, spins the given spinner, and rolls a die. Use a tree diagram to determine the number of possible outcomes.

4. Mark is getting ready for a party. He has 4 suits, 8 ties, and 3 pairs of shoes to choose from. How many possible outcomes are there? Show using multiplication.

Lesson 3   SOLVING PROBLEMS INVOLVING PROBABILITY

There are two methods that can be used to find the probability of two or more independent events occurring.

Method 1: Create a table of values or a tree diagram to find the number of all possible outcomes and then count number of desired outcomes.

Method 2: Determine the probability of each separate outcome and multiply each separate probability together.

Example

The two given spinners are spun at the same time.

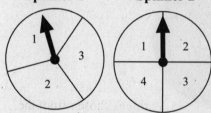

Spinner 1   **Spinner 2**

a) Determine the number of all possible outcomes.

Solution

The table of all possible outcomes is as shown:

Spinner 2	Spinner 1		
	1	2	3
1	1, 1	2, 1	3, 1
2	1, 2	2, 2	3, 2
3	1, 3	2, 3	3, 3
4	1, 4	2, 4	3, 4

The table of values shows 12 possible outcomes.

b) Find $P(1, 1)$.

Solution

The table shows this event occurring once out of 12 events, which can be written as $\dfrac{1}{12}$.

The first value in P(1,1) refers to the outcome in spinner 1 and the second value refers to the outcome in spinner 2.

c) Find $P(3, \text{odd})$.

Solution

The only odd numbers that occur on spinner 2 are 1 and 3. The outcomes that match this are $(3, 1)$ and $(3, 3)$. The table shows this event occurring twice out of 12 events, which can be written as

$$\frac{2}{12} = \frac{1}{6}.$$

d) Find P(sum of 6).

Solution

The only outcomes that add up to six are (2, 4) and (3, 3). The table shows this event occurring twice out of 12 events, which can be written as $\dfrac{2}{12} = \dfrac{1}{6}$.

Your Turn 1

The two given spinners are spun at the same time.

Spinner 1   **Spinner 2**

a) Find P(yellow, brown).

b) Find P(red, green).

c) Find P(not green, not green).

d) Find P(at least one green).

Example

Ian has the following coins in his pocket: 11 quarters, 6 loonies, and 3 toonies. He randomly picks out a coin, replaces it, and then randomly picks out another coin.

a) Find P(quarter, loonie).

Solution

Multiply the probability of each separate outcome together.

There are 11 quarters, 6 loonies and 20 coins in total.

$$P(\text{quarter, loonie}) = \frac{11}{20} \times \frac{6}{20}$$
$$= \frac{66}{400}$$
$$= \frac{33}{200}$$

b) Find *P*(loonie, toonie).

Solution

Multiply the probability of each separate outcome together.

There are 6 loonies, 3 toonies and 20 coins in total.

$$P(\text{loonie, toonie}) = \frac{6}{20} \times \frac{3}{20}$$
$$= \frac{18}{400}$$
$$= \frac{9}{200}$$

c) Find *P*(toonie, quarter).

Solution

Multiply the probability of each separate outcome together.

There are 3 toonies, 11 quarters and 20 coins in total.

$$P(\text{toonie, quarter}) = \frac{3}{20} \times \frac{11}{20}$$
$$= \frac{33}{400}$$

d) Find *P*(quarter, quarter).

Solution

Multiply the probability of each separate outcome together.

There are 11 quarters and 20 coins in total.

$$P(\text{quarter, quarter}) = \frac{11}{20} \times \frac{11}{20}$$
$$= \frac{121}{400}$$

Your Turn 2

What is the probability of rolling an even number on a green, six-sided number cube and a 3 on a red, six-sided number cube?

A **simulation** models a real-life situation using a table or a tree diagram. After the modelling is done, the results can show whether a probability is experimental or theoretical. **Experimental probability** is based on actual results, while **theoretical probability** is a prediction of the possibility of an event occurring.

Example

Hunter is on his way to a hockey game and is interested in how quickly he can get there. There are three sets of traffic lights between his house and the arena. The lights are red or yellow 70% of the time. Hunter is interested in how likely it is that he will encounter three red lights on his way to the arena.

A spinner divided into ten equal sections, seven of them coloured red and the rest coloured green, can be used to model this situation. The spinner is spun three times, with each set of three spins called a *trial*. After 15 trials, Hunter put the information into a table.

Trial	Results			
	First Light	Second Light	Third Light	All Lights Red?
1	G	R	R	No
2	G	G	R	No
3	R	R	R	Yes
4	G	R	G	No
5	G	R	G	No
6	R	G	R	No
7	R	R	G	No
8	R	R	R	Yes
9	G	R	R	No
10	G	G	G	No
11	R	R	R	Yes
12	G	R	R	No
13	G	R	G	No
14	R	G	R	No
15	G	R	G	No

a) What is the experimental probability that all three lights are red?

Solution

The table shows that this outcome occurs three times out of 15 trials, which gives an experimental probability of $\frac{3}{15} = \frac{1}{5}$.

b) What is the theoretical probability that all three lights are red?

Solution

The question says that the lights are red 70% of the time.

This percentage expressed as a fraction is $\dfrac{70}{100} = \dfrac{7}{10}$. To determine the theoretical probability, multiply this fraction by itself three times, for the three sets of traffic lights.

$$\dfrac{7}{10} \times \dfrac{7}{10} \times \dfrac{7}{10} = \dfrac{343}{1\ 000}$$

c) Compare the experimental probability with the theoretical probability. Which is higher?

Solution

The experimental probability as a fraction over 1 000 is $\dfrac{1}{5} = \dfrac{200}{1\ 000}$.

This is lower than the theoretical probability. Therefore, the theoretical probability is higher.

d) How could the accuracy of the experimental probability be improved?

Solution

To improve the accuracy of any experiment, perform more trials. This will eventually give an experimental probability that is close to the theoretical probability.

Your Turn 3

A die was rolled 25 times, and the outcomes were recorded in the table shown.

Number Rolled	1	2	3	4	5	6
Number of Times Rolled	4	5	6	2	4	4

If the same die were rolled 150 times, predict how many times a 4 will be rolled?

PRACTICE EXERCISES

Use the following information to answer the next five questions.

A student spins the given spinner with colours black, grey and white, and rolls a die.

1. Find P(white, 1).

2. Find P(black, even number).

3. Find P(grey, any number).

4. Find P(white, a number greater than 2).

5. Find P(any colour, a number less than 3).

Use the following information to answer the next four questions.

A couple is having twins.

6. Find P(boy, boy).

7. Find P(girl, boy).

8. Find P(at least one girl).

9. Find P(no boys).

Use the following information to answer the next six questions.

> A student tosses a coin and draws a card.

10. Find P(H, red).

11. Find P(T, face card).

12. Find P(T, ace).

13. Find P(H, a number card).

14. Find P(T, 6).

15. Find P(H or T, 7).

Use the following information to answer the next question.

> In an experiment, a number cube was rolled 120 times. The results are recorded in this table.
>
> | Outcome | 1 | 2 | 3 | 4 | 5 | 6 |
> |---|---|---|---|---|---|---|
> | Frequency | 12 | 18 | 25 | 20 | 25 | 20 |

16. What is the probability of rolling a 5?

REVIEW SUMMARY

- Probability is the likelihood of an event happening.
- Independent events are two or more events happening at the same time in which the result of each event does not affect the outcome of any other event.
- Sample space is all the possible outcomes of an event or group of events.
- A sample space can be shown using a table or a tree diagram.
- Probability is calculated using the formula $P(\text{favourable outcome}) = \dfrac{\text{favourable outcomes}}{\text{total possible outcomes}}$.
- Probabilities written as fractions should be in lowest terms unless the question indicates otherwise.
- A simulation models a real-life situation using a table or a tree diagram.
- Experimental probability is based on actual results, while theoretical probability is a prediction of the possibility of an event occurring.

PRACTICE TEST

1. There are 6 boys and 5 girls in a group. A teacher wants to select one boy and one girl for a speech. Make a table to list all the possible outcomes.

2. A bag has one red marble, one blue marble, and one yellow marble. A marble is chosen, and a die is rolled. Make a tree diagram to list all the possible outcomes.

Use the following information to answer the next 3 questions.

A student draws a card from a regular deck of 52 playing cards.

3. Find $P(2)$.

4. Find P(even number).

5. Find P(multiple of 5).

6. A shop has five types of ice cream and three types of juice. In how many ways can an ice cream and a juice be chosen? Create a table to find the solution.

7. A bag contains one red marble, one blue marble, and one green marble. A marble is chosen from the bag, and a die is rolled. How many possible outcomes are there? Create a table to find the solution.

8. A restaurant offers four different drinks and five different sandwiches. What is the possible number of lunches from which to choose? Use multiplication to find the solution.

9. How many two-character codes are possible with eight letters and nine digits? Use multiplication to find the solution.

Use the following information to answer the next three questions.

The two given spinners are spun at the same time.

I   II

What is the probability of the following events happening?

10. Find $P(2, 2)$.

11. Find $P(3, \text{odd})$.

12. Find $P(\text{sum of } 7)$.

Use the following information to answer the next three questions.

A coin is tossed and a die is thrown at the same time.

13. Find $P(\text{even}, H)$.

14. Find $P(\text{odd}, H)$.

15. Find $P(\text{a number greater than } 2, T)$.

16. Laura and Chris are playing a game in which they roll two dice and find the sum. If the sum is 10, Laura wins; if the sum is 5, Chris wins. Who is more likely to win?

17. Richard and Simon are playing a game in which they choose a card from a deck of playing cards. If the card has a letter on it, then Richard wins; if the card has a number on it, then Simon wins. Who is more likely to win?

18. John's lock at school has a three-digit combination. Each digit is a number from 0 to 9. What is the probability that someone could guess his combination in one attempt?

Use the following information to answer the next question.

A tetrahedral die has four triangular sides numbered 1, 2, 3, and 4. The die was rolled 50 times, and the results were recorded in this table.

Outcome	1	2	3	4
Frequency	15	20	10	5

19. Which outcome has an experimental probability of $\frac{1}{5}$?

S N A P

Student Notes and Problems

ANSWERS AND SOLUTIONS

CASTLE ROCK
RESEARCH CORP

DATA REPRESENTATION

Lesson 1—Graphical Representation

YOUR TURN
ANSWERS AND SOLUTIONS

1 Because this information is given with the categories and the number of packages, it is best to display the information on a bar graph. Each category will be represented by one bar, and the height of each bar will represent the number of seed packages sold on that day.

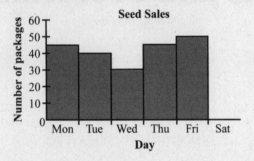

2. Because the choices are given in percentages, it is best to display this information on a circle graph. To figure out the angle for each section, multiply the percentage (as a decimal) by 360. Then, round to the nearest degree.

$$\text{Action} - 16\% = 0.16 \times 360$$
$$= 57.6°$$
$$\doteq 58°$$
$$\text{Thriller} - 14\% = 0.14 \times 360$$
$$= 50.4°$$
$$\doteq 50°$$
$$\text{Romance} - 25\% = 0.25 \times 360$$
$$= 90°$$
$$\text{Comedy} - 31\% = 0.31 \times 360$$
$$= 111.6°$$
$$\doteq 112°$$
$$\text{Horror} - 14\% = 0.14 \times 360$$
$$= 50.4°$$
$$\doteq 50°$$

Now, draw the angles in a circle, and label each section.

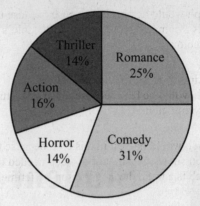

3. Determine how much Melissa earns for each book by making a table. Then, graph the number of books on the x-axis and the dollars earned on the y-axis.

Books Sold	Dollars Earned
1	10
2	20
3	30
4	40
5	50

Plot each point and then join the points to make a line graph, as shown in the following diagram.

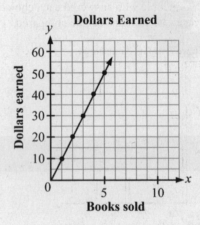

PRACTICE EXERCISES
ANSWERS AND SOLUTIONS

1. A bar graph would be best in this case because the situation is a comparison of a group of people's favourite colours.

3. This case involves approximate numbers, so a pictograph would be best because it shows pictures in an approximation.

5. A line graph would be best in this case because the information shows the amount of sleep needed over time, which is a trend during a person's lifetime.

7. Calculate the angle measure of the losses section based on the percentage of 360 that is being used.
$$26\% \text{ of } 360 = 0.26 \times 360$$
$$= 93.6$$
$$\doteq 94$$

9. Winter
To see which season has the most snow, look at the graph and check which point is the highest: winter.

11. $50 + 13 + 0 + 28 = 91$ cm

13. Since pictographs give an approximation, you can round the 32 schools to 30 and draw three pictures.

15. Use a bar graph because the information is given as the number of people who answered each choice in the survey, and the columns can be compared.

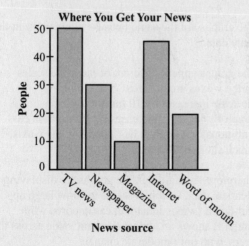

Where You Get Your News

News source

17. Use a line graph because the information is given over five years. A line graph is used for anything that shows trends over a certain period of time.

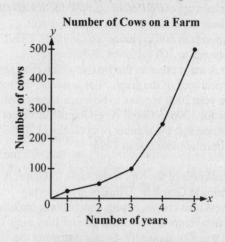

Number of Cows on a Farm

Lesson 2—Ways of Misrepresenting Data

YOUR TURN
ANSWERS AND SOLUTIONS

1. The graphs are the same because they represent the same data.

The graphs appear different because the scales on the y-axes are different. The scale for Graph A increases by 5 million for each level to a total of 30 million. The scale for Graph B increases by 10 million for each level to a total of 50 million.

Graph A shows a sharper increase in the height of the line than graph B.

2. The graphs are the same because they represent the same data.

They are different because they each use a different scale to represent the data. The scale for Graph A starts at zero and increases by five for each level of the scale. The scale for Graph B uses a break to allow for the use of a scale that increases by two hours for each level. On Graph B, the grade 6 does not appear accurately.

Graph A seems to show a shorter range of difference in physical activity than Graph B does, even though the graphs are displaying the exact same data.

3. The graphs are the same because they represent the same data.

The graphs appear different because the scales on the *y*-axes are different. On Graph A, 1 unit corresponds to 100 cyclones; on Graph B, 1 unit corresponds to 300 cyclones. Additionally, Graph A has a break in the *y*-axis, which changes the appearance of the graph. For instance, the bar for the year 2000 appears to be much longer than the bar for 1996 in Graph A, giving the incorrect impression that the number of cyclones in 2000 was almost double that in 1996.

The thickness of the bars is the same in Graph A, but varies in Graph B. Using bars of varying thickness also creates wrong impressions, making some data items appear much greater than they really are. Consequently, Graph B distorts the comparison of the number of cyclones between 2000 and 2004.

4. The graphs are the same because they represent the same data.

They are different because the size of the bars is the same for the years in Graph B, but they are not the same for the years in Graph A. In Graph A, the much larger bar for the year 2000 makes the sales for that year seem much larger, and the much smaller bar for the year 1960 makes the sales for that year seem much smaller.

Using different sized bars can give the false impression that the differences are much larger than they actually are.

5. **a)** Since the line for soccer is the longest, soccer appears to be the most popular sport.

b) Count the number of hockey sticks and tennis rackets displayed. Since there are more tennis rackets than hockey sticks, more students prefer tennis.

c) Yes, the pictograph is misleading. The symbol for each sport represents five students, but the symbols are not all the same size relative to each other. Therefore, soccer appears to be the most popular sport, though it is actually tennis that is the most popular sport.

To make this pictograph more accurate, every symbol used should be of the same size, and when placed on the graph, the spacing between symbols should be the same for each sport.

6. **a)** The two longest lines are produced by basketball and hockey, so they appear to have won the same number of tournaments.

b) Swimming appears to have produced more victories than football because the line for it is longer than the line for football. Football, however, has produced more tournament victories than swimming has.

c) The pictograph is not accurately drawn. There is no legend to explain what each symbol represents, and the symbols are not all the same size relative to each other.

To make this pictograph more accurate, each symbol for each victory should be the same size and should be spaced the same distance apart. There also needs to be a legend below the graph indicating the value of each symbol.

PRACTICE EXERCISES
ANSWERS AND SOLUTIONS

1. The graphs are the same because they represent the same data.

The graphs appear different because the scales on the *y*-axes are different. On Graph A, the scale increases by 10 million cars; on Graph B, the scale increases by 100 million cars. Additionally, Graph A has a break in the *y*-axis, which shortens its length.

Therefore, even though the graphs are displaying identical data, Graph A seems to show large up-and-down swings in annual car imports, while Graph B shows an almost constant value across the years, with only moderate changes.

3. The graphs are the same because they represent the same data.

The graphs appear different because the scales on the *y*-axes are different. On Graph A, the scale increases by 5 bats; on Graph B, the scale increases by 10 bats. Additionally, Graph B has a break in the *y*-axis, which changes the appearance of the graph.

Therefore, the bars in Graph B are much shorter than the corresponding bars in Graph A. This gives the impression that there were fewer bats sighted.

5. Since the line for science fiction is the longest, science fiction appears to be the most popular genre. Since the line for comedy is the shortest, comedy appears to be the least popular.

7. Yes, the pictograph is misleading. The symbol for each genre represents 10 people, but the symbols are not all the same size relative to each other. Therefore, science fiction films appear to be the most popular genre, though by counting the symbols, it is clear that science fiction films are in fact the least popular of the genres.

To make this pictograph more accurate, every symbol used should be the same size, and when placed on the graph, the spacing between symbols should be the same for each genre.

9. Count the number of symbols for each topping. Since there are more pepperoni symbols than mushroom symbols, more students order pepperoni.

Lesson 3—Analysis of Graphs and Data Representation

YOUR TURN
ANSWERS AND SOLUTIONS

1. There are many more people crossing the street than bungee jumping. Therefore, the number of accidents while crossing the street is expected to be greater. The information is misleading.

2. a) The largest group among the women was the group that scored between 5 to 6 points, while the largest group among the men scored higher, between 7 and 8 points.

Most participants scored between 5 and 8 points. More women than men scored in this range.

There were more women than men scoring in the highest range (9 to 10 points) as well as in the lowest range (0 to 4 points).

b)

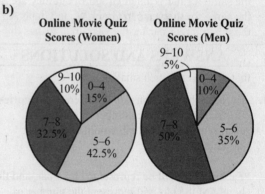

Online Movie Quiz Scores (Women)

Online Movie Quiz Scores (Men)

c) The double bar graph shows the number of participants who scored in each range, while the circle graphs show the percentages of participants who scored in each range.

Observe that the numbers of women and men participants are different. Therefore, comparing the total number of participants in each range is not a correct indicator of performance (since there are many more women participants, their numbers would likely be higher in each range). Using percentages will give a more accurate representation of the relative performances of the two groups. Since circle graphs use percentages, they are the best method to display such data.

PRACTICE EXERCISES
ANSWERS AND SOLUTIONS

1. The number of people who drive within the speed limit, 90 km/h, is far greater than the number who drive at over 120 km/h, which is illegal. Therefore, it is to be expected that there will be a greater number of accidents among cars driving below 90 km/h.

   It is certainly much safer to drive within the speed limit. The information is misleading.

3.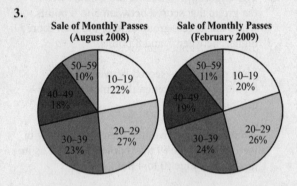

   Sale of Monthly Passes (August 2008)

   50–59 10%
   10–19 22%
   40–49 18%
   30–39 23%
   20–29 27%

   Sale of Monthly Passes (February 2009)

   50–59 11%
   10–19 20%
   40–49 19%
   30–39 24%
   20–29 26%

Practice Test

ANSWERS AND SOLUTIONS

1. Because the data consists of different categories (the seasons) and the number of leaves for each season, a bar graph would be the most suitable choice.

   Each season will be represented by a bar, and the height of the bar will represent the number of leaves for that category.

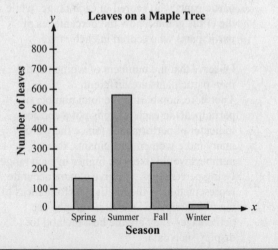

Leaves on a Maple Tree

3. From the graph, you can see that Asad spends the least amount of time burping.

5. Asad sleeps 40% of his time sleeping. There are 24 hours in a day.

   Therefore, he sleeps for $\dfrac{40}{100} \times 24 = 9.6$ hours.

7. Since one sun depicts 2 sunny days, half a sun depicts 1 sunny day.

9. Count the total number of suns shown in the graph. There are $3 + 1 + 3.5 + 2 + 4.5 = 14$ suns.

   Each sun represents 2 sunny days.

   Therefore, in the five months, there were a total of $14 \times 2 = 28$ sunny days.

11. From the graph, that the price was $74 at approximately 11:30 A.M.

13. Since Delna has the highest number of skips, she won the competition. Rashmi came second.

15. The graphs are the same because they represent the same data.

    The graphs appear different because the scales on the x-axes are different, even though the scales on the y-axes are the same. The distance between two consecutive months on the x-axis is much greater for Graph A than for Graph B.

    Therefore, even though the graphs are displaying identical data, Graph B seems to show a greater variation in prices than Graph A for the same time period.

17. The graphs are the same because they represent the same data.

The graphs appear different because the scales on the *y*-axes are different. On Graph A, 1 unit corresponds to 10 years; on Graph B, 1 unit corresponds to 5 years. Additionally, Graph B has a break in the *y*-axis, which changes the appearance of the graph.

For instance, in Graph B, the bar for the elephant is many times longer than the bar for the tiger, giving the incorrect impression that the maximum lifespan of the elephant is over 10 times that of the tiger. In contrast, Graph A gives a more accurate picture of their maximum life spans.

19. Count the number of symbols for each lunch. Since there are more pizza symbols than taco symbols, more students like pizza than tacos.

21. The number of pet dogs is far greater than the number of pet alligators in British Columbia. Therefore, the number of dog bites is expected to exceed the number of alligator bites. The information is misleading.

23. The greatest number of students spent 50 to 59 minutes on their homework.

For class 8A, the time interval 30 to 39 minutes had the least number of students, while for class 8B, it was the time interval 40 to 49 minutes that had the least number of students.

Far fewer students from class 8A than from class 8B spent more than an hour on homework.

For class 8A, most students spent between 40 and 59 minutes on homework; for class 8B, most students spent between 50 and 69 minutes.

25. The double bar graph shows the number of students for each 10-minute time interval, while the circle graphs show the percentages of students for those time intervals.

Note that the numbers of students in the two sections are different. Therefore, comparing absolute numbers of students for each time interval is not a correct indicator of the relative amounts of time spent on homework by the students of the two sections. Using percentages will give a more accurate representation of the relative distribution of students' homework times. Since circle graphs use percentages, they are the best method to display such data.

RATIO, RATE, AND PROPORTIONS

Lesson 1—Ratios

YOUR TURN
ANSWERS AND SOLUTIONS

1. a) There are 3 squares and 8 circles.
Ratio form → 3 : 8
Word form → 3 to 8
Fraction form → $\dfrac{3}{8}$

b) Shapes are being compared.

2. a) There are 5 squares, 1 triangle, and 5 circles.

Ratio form → 5 : 1 : 5
Word form → 5 to 1 to 5

b) Shapes are being compared

3. Convert the units to cents.
4 nickels = 20¢
3 dimes = 30¢

Rewrite the ratio → 20 to 30

Reduce to lowest terms by dividing both terms by 10.
$20 \div 10$ to $30 \div 10$
$= 2 : 3$

In word form, the ratio is 2 to 3.

4. Convert the units to cents.
6 nickels = 30¢
2 dimes = 20¢
2 quarters = 50¢

Rewrite the ratio.
30 : 20 : 50

Reduce to lowest terms by dividing all the terms by 10.
3 : 2 : 5

5. a) In the given statement, "65 Canadians" is the part and "80 Canadians" is the whole.
65 to 80 $\xrightarrow{\text{reduce}}$ $65 \div 5 : 80 \div 5$
$= 13$ to 16

b) Subtract 65 from 80 to determine the Canadians who do not own a car.
$80 - 65 = 15$

The ratio is
$65:15 \xrightarrow{\text{reduce}} 65 \div 5 : 15 \div 5$
$= 13:3$

c) The ratio $13:3$ compares part-to-part—car owners to non-car owners.

The ratio 13 to 16 compares Canadian car owners to total Canadians. It is a part-to-whole ratio.

6. a) Wheat is the first term. Oats is the last term. That ratio of wheat to oats is
$4:2 \xrightarrow{\text{reduce}} 4 \div 2$
$= 2:1$

b) Add the three terms $(4 + 1 + 2 = 7)$ to determine the total.

The ratio of flax to the cereal blend is $1:7$.

7. Calculate the whole by adding the parts.
$24 + 16 = 40$

Write a ratio comparing the part (correct answers) to the whole.
$$\frac{24}{40}$$

Divide the first term by the second term, and then multiply by 100.
$(24 \div 40) \times 100 = 60$

Albert earned 60% on his test.

PRACTICE EXERCISES
ANSWERS AND SOLUTIONS

1. The unit is students.

3. $8:10 \xrightarrow{\text{reduce}} 4:5$
Part-to-part

5. $8:24 \xrightarrow{\text{reduce}} 1:3$
Part-to-whole

7 The ratio in three forms: $13:6$, 13 to 6, $\dfrac{13}{6}$.

Part-to-part

9. The ratio in three forms: $7:20$, 7 to 20, $\dfrac{7}{20}$.

Part-to-whole

11. Convert the nickels and dimes to cents.
6 nickels = 30¢
3 pennies = 3 ¢
6 dimes = 60¢

Write the ratio $\rightarrow$ $30:3:60$

Reduce to lowest terms:
$30 \div 3 : 3 \div 3 : 60 \div 3$
$= 10:1:20$

The ratio in two forms: $10:1:20$, 10 to 1 to 20,
$\dfrac{10}{10} : \dfrac{1}{10} : \dfrac{20}{10}$.

13. There are 15 boys and 30 girls are in science class.
The ratio is $\dfrac{15}{30} \xrightarrow{\text{reduce}} \dfrac{15 \div 15}{30 \div 15} = \dfrac{1}{2}$.

15 Joanne : Alyssa $\rightarrow 32:28 \xrightarrow{\text{reduce}} 32 \div 4 : 28 \div 4$
$= 8:7$

17. Subtract 14 from 20 to determine the number of students that failed the test $(20 - 14 = 6)$.

The ratio of passes to failures is $14:6$.
This ratio simplifies to $7:3$.

19. Add the parts together to determine the whole $(3 + 9 = 12)$.

The ratio of water to solution is
$9:12 \xrightarrow{\text{reduce}} 9 \div 3 : 12 \div 3$
$= 3:4$

Lesson 2—Rates

YOUR TURN
ANSWERS AND SOLUTIONS

1. The rate is 375 works /5 minutes.

   Divide the numeric value of the first term by the numeric value of the second term → $375 \div 5 = 75$.

   Add the units beside the result: 75 words/min.

   John typed 75 words/min (symbolically) or 75 words per min (word form).

2. The question is asking how much money per hour ($/h). The rate is $480.00/6 h.

   Divide the numeric value of the first term by the numeric value of the second term to get the unit rate ($480 \div 6 = 80$), then insert the units.

   The plumber charged $80/h.

3. The rate is 12 kg/4 m.

   Determine the unit rate. Divide the numeric value of the first term by the numeric value of the second term.
   $12 \div 4 = 3$ kg/m

   Multiply the unit rate by the number of metres of pipe being considered.
   3 kg/m × 10 m = 30 kg

   The mass of a 10 m pipe is 30 kg.

PRACTICE EXERCISES
ANSWERS AND SOLUTIONS

1. The fraction $\dfrac{20}{46}$ is a ratio since the units are the same (and thus are not written).

3. The rate is $20.40/43 L.

   Divide the numeric value of the first term by the numeric value of the second term to determine the unit rate.

   $20.40 \div 43 = \$0.474\,418\,604\,7$/L

   Fatima paid $0.47 per litre of gasoline.

5. The rate is 450 mL/10 servings. Calculate the unit rate.
   $450 \div 10 = 45$

   The unit rate is 45 mL/serving.

   Multiply the unit rate by the desired quantity (15 servings).
   45 mL/servings × 15 servings
   = 675 mL

   The amount of chocolate required for 15 servings is 675 mL.

7. The rate is $9.45/5 kg. Calculate the unit rate.
   $9.45 \div 5 = 1.89$
   The unit rate is $1.89/kg.

   Multiply the unit rate by the desired quantity (20 kg).
   $1.89/kg × 20 kg = $37.80

   The cost of 20 kg of tomatoes is $37.80.

Lesson 3—Equivalent Ratios and Proportional Reasoning

YOUR TURN
ANSWERS AND SOLUTIONS

1. There are 6 consonants and 2 vowels. The ratio of consonants to vowels is $\dfrac{6}{2} \xrightarrow[\div 2]{\div 2} \dfrac{3}{1}$.

   The ratios $\dfrac{6}{2}$ and $\dfrac{3}{1}$ are equivalent because they have the same value. The ratio $\dfrac{6}{2}$ is a multiple of $\dfrac{3}{1}$.

2. Answers may vary.
   $\dfrac{2}{3} \xrightarrow[\times 2]{\times 2} \dfrac{4}{6}, \dfrac{2}{3} \xrightarrow[\times 3]{\times 3} \dfrac{6}{9}, \dfrac{2}{3} \xrightarrow[\times 4]{\times 4} \dfrac{8}{12}$

3. **Strategy 1: Equivalent fractions**

$$\frac{6}{14} \xrightarrow[\div 2]{\div 2} \frac{3}{7} \text{ and } \frac{21}{49} \xrightarrow[\div 7]{\div 7} \frac{3}{7}$$

Strategy 2: Cross products

$$\frac{6}{14} = \frac{21}{49}$$
$$6 \times 49 = 21 \times 14$$
$$294 = 294$$

The ratios $\frac{6}{14}$ and $\frac{21}{49}$ are equivalent.

4. **a)** **Strategy 1: Equivalent fractions**

$$\frac{7}{8} \xrightarrow[\times 2]{\times 2} \frac{14}{16}$$

Strategy 2: Cross products

$$\frac{7}{8} = \frac{k}{16}$$
$$7 \times 16 = 8k$$
$$112 = 8k$$
$$\frac{112}{8} = \frac{8k}{8}$$
$$14 = k$$
$$\frac{7}{8} = \frac{14}{16}$$
$$k = 14$$

b) Convert to factions. Set the fractions so they are equal to each other.

$$\frac{3}{5} = \frac{12}{m}$$

Strategy 1: Equivalent fractions

$$\frac{3}{5} \xrightarrow[\times 4]{\times 4} \frac{12}{20}$$

Strategy 2: Cross products

$$\frac{3}{5} = \frac{12}{m}$$
$$3m = 12 \times 5$$
$$3m = 60$$
$$\frac{3m}{3} = \frac{60}{3}$$
$$m = 20$$
$$\frac{3}{5} = \frac{12}{20}$$

$$m = 20$$

5. Set up a proportion of number of cupcakes to grams of sugar.

$$\frac{12 \text{ cupcakes}}{132 \text{ g}} = \frac{6 \text{ cupcakes}}{x \text{ g}}$$

Strategy 1: Equivalent fractions

$$\frac{12}{132} \xrightarrow[\div 2]{\div 2} \frac{6}{66}$$

Strategy 2: Cross products

$$\frac{12}{132} = \frac{6}{x}$$
$$12x = 6 \times 132$$
$$12x = 792$$
$$\frac{12x}{12} = \frac{792}{12}$$
$$x = 66$$
$$\frac{12}{132} = \frac{6}{66}$$

Alice needs 66 g of sugar to make 6 cupcakes.

PRACTICE EXERCISES
ANSWERS AND SOLUTIONS

1. Answers may vary.

$$\frac{2}{2} \xrightarrow[\times 2]{\times 2} \frac{4}{4}, \frac{2}{2} \xrightarrow[\times 3]{\times 3} \frac{6}{6}, \frac{2}{2} \xrightarrow[\times 4]{\times 4} \frac{8}{8}$$

3. Answers may vary.

$$\frac{2}{7} \xrightarrow[\times 2]{\times 2} \frac{4}{14}, \frac{2}{7} \xrightarrow[\times 3]{\times 3} \frac{6}{21}, \frac{2}{7} \xrightarrow[\times 4]{\times 4} \frac{8}{28}$$

5. $\frac{2}{3} \xrightarrow[\times 7]{\times 7} $ **D.** $\frac{14}{21}$

7. $\frac{2}{6} \xrightarrow[\times 4]{\times 4} $ **C.** $\frac{8}{24}$

9. **Strategy 1: Equivalent fractions**

$$\frac{3}{7} \xrightarrow[\times 4]{\times 4} \frac{12}{\mathbf{28}}$$

Strategy 2: Cross products

$$\frac{3}{7} = \frac{12}{r}$$
$$3r = 12 \times 7$$
$$3r = 84$$
$$\frac{3r}{3} = \frac{84}{3}$$
$$r = 28$$
$$\frac{3}{7} = \frac{12}{\mathbf{28}}$$

$$r = 28$$

11. **Strategy 1: Equivalent fractions**

$$\frac{\mathbf{3}}{8} \xleftarrow[\div 3]{\div 3} \frac{9}{24}$$

Strategy 2: Cross products

$$\frac{f}{8} = \frac{9}{24}$$
$$24f = 9 \times 8$$
$$24f = 72$$
$$\frac{24f}{24} = \frac{72}{24}$$
$$f = 3$$
$$\frac{\mathbf{3}}{8} = \frac{9}{24}$$

$$f = 3$$

13. $$\frac{3}{12} \xrightarrow[\div 3]{\div 3} \frac{1}{4}$$
$$\frac{6}{32} \xrightarrow[\div 2]{\div 2} \frac{3}{16}$$
$$\frac{3}{12} \neq \frac{6}{32}$$

15. $$\frac{3}{8} = \frac{24}{64}$$
$$3 \times 64 = 24 \times 8$$
$$192 = 192$$
$$\frac{3}{8} = \frac{24}{64}$$

17. Set up a proportion of Blu-ray discs to total DVDs and Blu-ray discs (1 + 4 = 5).

$$\frac{1}{5} = \frac{v}{440}$$
$$1 \times 440 = 5v$$
$$440 = 5v$$
$$\frac{440}{5} = \frac{5v}{5}$$
$$88 = v$$
$$\frac{1}{5} = \frac{\mathbf{88}}{440}$$

There 88 Blu-ray discs in the video store.

19. Set up a proportion of length to width. Use cross products to solve for w.

$$\frac{3}{5} = \frac{12}{w}$$
$$3w = 12 \times 5$$
$$3w = 60$$
$$\frac{3w}{3} = \frac{60}{3}$$
$$w = 20$$
$$\frac{3}{5} = \frac{\mathbf{12}}{20}$$

When the length is 12 cm the width is 20 cm.

To find perimeter, add the two length values with the two width values.
$$P = 2l + 2w$$
$$= 2(12) + 2(20)$$
$$= 24 + 40$$
$$= 64$$

The perimeter of the picture frame is 64 cm.

21. Set up a proportion of percent to mass. Use cross products to solve for m.

$$\frac{75}{100} = \frac{45}{m}$$
$$75m = 100 \times 45$$
$$75m = 4\ 500$$
$$\frac{75m}{75} = \frac{4\ 500}{75}$$
$$m = 60$$
$$\frac{75}{45} = \frac{100}{\mathbf{60}}$$

Samantha's total mass is 60 kg.

Practice Test

ANSWERS AND SOLUTIONS

1. Since the terms of the ratio have different units (minutes and hours), the first step is to convert the terms into the same units. In this case, minutes are the easiest unit to use.

$1 \text{ h} = 60 \text{ min} \rightarrow 4 \text{ h} = 240 \text{ min}$

Rewrite the ratio.
$45 \text{ min} : 240 \text{ min}$

Remove the units of measure.
$45 : 240$

Reduce the ratio to lowest terms by dividing both terms by their common factor, 15.
$45 \div 15 : 240 \div 15$
$= 3 : 16$

3. The part is 54 students, and the whole is 81 students.

$54 : 81 \xrightarrow{\text{reduce}} 54 \div 27 : 81 \div 27$
$= 2 : 3$

The ratio in word form is 2 to 3.

5. The ratio $2 : 1$ compares part to part—students going to university, to not going to university.

The ratio $2 : 3$ compares part to whole—students going to the university, to total students.

7. Liquid 1 is the first term. Liquid 3 is the last term. The ratio of liquid 1 to liquid 3 is $8 : 5$.

9. The ratio of games won to total number of games played is $12 : 20$.

Reduce to lowest terms:
$12 \div 4 : 20 \div 4$
$= 3 : 5$

The ratio in three forms: $3 : 5$, 3 to 5, $\dfrac{3}{5}$

Since it compares games won and total number of games played, it is a part-to-whole ratio.

11. The ratio is $12 : 6$.

Reduce to lowest terms:
$12 \div 6 : 6 \div 6$
$= 2 : 1$

The ratio in three forms: $2 : 1$, 2 to 1, $\dfrac{2}{1}$

This ratio is part-to-part.

13. The ratio is $50 : 25 : 35$.

Reduce to lowest terms.
$50 \div 5 : 25 \div 5 : 35 \div 5$
$= 10 : 5 : 7$

The ratio in both forms: $10 : 5 : 7$, 10 to 5 to 7.

This ratio is part-to-part.

15. The number of men and women on the fifth floor is 24 and 16.

The ratio of men to women is $24 : 16$.

Reduce to lowest terms:
$24 \div 8 : 16 \div 8$
$= 3 : 2$

The ratio in fraction form is $\dfrac{3}{2}$.

17. There are 24 men on the fifth floor, 10 on the sixth floor, and 42 on the seventh floor.

The ratio is $24 : 10 : 42$.

Reduce to lowest terms:
$24 \div 2 : 10 \div 2 : 42 \div 2$
$= 12 : 5 : 21$

The ratio is $12 : 15 : 21$.

19. The expression $\dfrac{12 \text{ km}}{3 \text{ h}}$ is a rate since the units are different.

21. Answers may vary.

$\dfrac{2}{5} \xrightarrow[\times 2]{\times 2} \dfrac{4}{10} \qquad \dfrac{2}{5} \xrightarrow[\times 3]{\times 3} \dfrac{6}{15} \qquad \dfrac{2}{5} \xrightarrow[\times 4]{\times 4} \dfrac{8}{20}$

23. Strategy 1: Equivalent fractions

$$\frac{4}{7} \xrightarrow[\times 4]{\times 4} \frac{16}{28}$$

Strategy 2: Cross products

$$\frac{4}{7} = \frac{b}{28}$$
$$4 \times 28 = 7 \times b$$
$$112 = 7b$$
$$\frac{112}{7} = \frac{7b}{7}$$
$$16 = b$$
$$\frac{4}{7} = \frac{16}{28}$$

$$b = 16$$

25. Strategy 1: Equivalent fractions

$$\frac{4}{6} \xleftarrow[\div 6]{\div 6} \frac{24}{36}$$

Strategy 2: Cross products

$$\frac{z}{6} = \frac{24}{36}$$
$$36 \times z = 6 \times 24$$
$$36z = 144$$
$$\frac{36z}{36} = \frac{144}{36}$$
$$z = 4$$
$$\frac{4}{6} = \frac{24}{36}$$

$$z = 4$$

27. Tank A has a capacity of 30 L, and is half filled with water. Thus, the volume of water in tank A is $\frac{30}{2}$ or 15 L.

Set up a proportion of tank A to tank B, and then use equivalent fractions and cross products to solve for B.

$$\frac{3}{5} = \frac{15}{B}.$$

Solve by using the equivalent-fractions method.

$$\frac{3}{5} \xrightarrow[\times 5]{\times 5} \frac{15}{25}$$

Solve by using the cross-products method.

$$\frac{3}{5} = \frac{15}{B}$$
$$3 \times B = 5 \times 15$$
$$3B = 75$$
$$\frac{3B}{3} = \frac{75}{3}$$
$$B = 25$$
$$\frac{3}{5} = \frac{15}{25}$$

There are 25 L of water in tank B.

PYTHAGOREAN RELATIONSHIPS

Lesson 1—Exponents and Perfect Squares

YOUR TURN
ANSWERS AND SOLUTIONS

1.

	Read As	Base	Exponent	Factored	Perfect Square
25^2	Twenty-five squared	25	2	25×25	625
19^2	Nineteen squared	19	2	19×19	361
4.2^2	Four decimal two squared	4.2	2	4.2×4.2	4.2 is not a whole number, no perfect square

2. $A_{\text{square}} = s^2$
   $= 8^2 \leftarrow$ read as "eight squared"
   $= 8 \times 8 \leftarrow$ expanded multiplication (factored)
   $= 64 \text{ units}^2 \leftarrow 64$ is a perfect square

3. a) Factors of 4: 1, 2, 4
   Since 4 has 3 factors, it is a perfect square.

   b) Factors of 6: 1, 2, 3, 6
   Since 6 has 4 factors, it is not a perfect square.

c) Factors of 9: 1, 3, 9
   Since 9 has 3 factors, it is a perfect square.

PRACTICE EXERCISES
ANSWERS AND SOLUTIONS

1.

	Read As	Base	Exponent	Factored	Perfect Square
23^2	Twenty-three squared	23	2	23×23	529
15^2	Fifteen squared	15	2	15×15	225
12.9^2	Twelve decimal nine squared	12.9	2	12.9×12.9	Not a perfect square
5.3^2	Five decimal three squared	5.3	2	5.3×5.3	Not a perfect square

3. The side measures are different, so 156 is not a perfect square.

5. The side measures are the same; the area value is a perfect square.

Square the side length to determine the matching perfect square.

7. D.
   $32^2 = 32 \times 32$
   $= 1\ 024 \text{ mm}^2$

9. A.
   $23^2 = 23 \times 23$
   $= 529 \text{ mm}^2$

11. All the shapes are rectangles, so 48 is not a perfect square.

The factors of 48 are: 1, 2, 4, 6, 8, 12, 24, 48.
The number 48 has an even number of factors.

Lesson 2—Squares and Square Roots

YOUR TURN
ANSWERS AND SOLUTIONS

1. a) Factors of 81: 1, 3, 9, 27, 81
Odd number of factors; perfect square; 9 is the square root.

b) Factors of 24: 1, 2, 3, 4, 6, 8, 12, 24
Even number of factors; not a perfect square.

c) Factors of 102: 1, 2, 3, 6, 17, 34, 51, 102
Even number of factors; not a perfect square.

d) Factors of 144: 1, 2, 3, 4, 6, 8, 9, 12, 16, 18, 24, 36, 48, 72, 144.

Odd number of factors; perfect square; 12 is the square root.

2. Draw a square area of 25 units.

The square root is the length of one side of the square, which is 5.
$\sqrt{25} = 5$

3. a) $\sqrt{121} = 11$ because $11 \times 11 = 121$

b) $\sqrt{25} = 5$ because $5 \times 5 = 25$

c) $\sqrt{81} = 9$ because $9 \times 9 = 81$

4. a) Model the stained glass window.

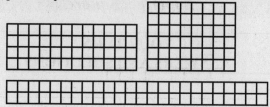

s = squares on side length × unit length
$= 6 \times 2.5$
$= 15$ cm

The side length is 15 cm.

b) Square the length of one side to calculate the area.
$A_{square} = s^2$
$= 15^2$
$= 15 \times 15$
$= 225$ cm^2

The area is 225 cm^2.

c) In question a) the side length calculated is the square root. In question b) the square root is squared to calculate the area.

PRACTICE EXERCISES
ANSWERS AND SOLUTIONS

	Square Root	Perfect Square
1.	2	4
3.	3	9
5.	8	64

7. Factors of 62: 1, 2, 31, 62
Since 62 has an even number of factors, it is not a perfect square.

9. The side length is the same as the square root: 10 units.

Square the side length (10) to determine the perfect square.
10^2
$= 10 \times 10$
$= 100$ units^2

Square root: 10, perfect square: 100

11.

13. The square root of 25 is the length of one side.

$$5^2 = 25$$
$$\sqrt{25} = 5$$

15. $\sqrt{9} = 3$ because $3 \times 3 = 9$

17. $\sqrt{225} = 25$ because $15 \times 15 = 225$

19. Factors of 64: 1, 2, 4, 8, 16, 32, 64
$$\sqrt{64} = 8$$

Square root = 8

21. A. $16 = 4^2 \rightarrow 4 \times 4 = 16$

23. B. $2^2 = 4 \rightarrow 2 \times 2 = 4$

25. Model the quilt.

O	P	O	P
P	O	P	O
O	P	O	P
P	O	P	O

s = squares on side length × unit length
$$= 4 \times 3$$
$$= 12 \text{ dm}$$

The side length is 12 dm.

27. In question 25 the side length, which is the square root, is calculated. In question 26 the side length is squared to calculate the area.

Lesson 3—Square Roots of Imperfect Squares

YOUR TURN
ANSWERS AND SOLUTIONS

1. Begin by using the two perfect squares that are closest to the number in question.

$$\sqrt{64} = 8 \text{ because } 8 \times 8 = 64$$
$$\sqrt{81} = 9 \text{ because } 9 \times 9 = 81$$

On graph paper, draw a square with an area of 64. On the same graph paper, draw an overlapping square with an area of 81.

Since 72 is between 64 and 81, its square root is between 8 and 9. Its side length is $\sqrt{72}$. Since 72 is closer to 64, draw a third overlapping square that is closer to the smaller square.

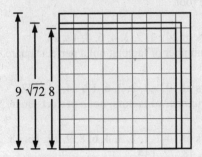

Looking at the model, the square root of 72 is approximately 8.5.

2. a) $\sqrt{66}$ is between $\sqrt{64} = 8$ and $\sqrt{81} = 9$

b) $\sqrt{12}$ is between $\sqrt{9} = 3$ and $\sqrt{16} = 4$

c) The $\sqrt{28}$ is between $\sqrt{25} = 5$ and $\sqrt{36} = 6$, but is closer to $\sqrt{25}$.

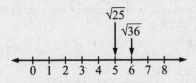

Use guess-and-check to estimate the closest value possible.
$$5.2 \times 5.2 = 27.04 \rightarrow \text{too small}$$
$$5.3 \times 5.3 = 28.09 \rightarrow \text{very close}$$

The approximate square root of 28 is 5.3.

---

3. **Step 1**

The closest perfect squares are 16 ($\sqrt{16} = 4$) and 25 ($\sqrt{25} = 5$).

Step 2

$18 \div 4 = 4.5$

Step 3

$\dfrac{4 + 4.5}{2} = 4.25$

Step 4

$4.25^2 = 4.25 \times 4.25$
$\qquad = 18.0625$

This answer is very close to 18, so steps 2–4 do not need to be repeated.

The approximate square root of 18 is 4.25.

4. Using either method (depending on the calculator), $\sqrt{98}$ appears as $9.899\ 494\ 937$.

The tenths place is one place after the decimal. So, rounded to the tenths place, $\sqrt{98}$ is 9.9.

5. $\sqrt{3.7}$ appears as $1.923\ 538\ 406$.

The hundredths place is two places after the decimal. So, rounded to the hundredths place, $\sqrt{3.7} \doteq 1.92$.

6. Because the field is square, each side must be the same length. The formula for a square area is $A = s^2$.

Determine what number multiplied by itself results in 576. In other words, find the square root of 576. $\sqrt{576} = 24$.

Each side of the field is 24 m long, since $24 \times 24 = 576$.

7. Find $\sqrt{81}$ to determine the side length. $\sqrt{81} = 9$, so each side length is 9 m.

A square has 4 sides. The perimeter of a square is $4 \times s = 4 \times 9 = 36$ m.

The perimeter of the classroom is 36 m, since $9 + 9 + 9 + 9 = 36$ m.

PRACTICE EXERCISES
ANSWERS AND SOLUTIONS

1. Begin by using the two perfect squares that are closest to the number in question.

$\sqrt{25} = 5$ because $5 \times 5 = 25$
$\sqrt{36} = 6$ because $6 \times 6 = 36$

Looking at the model, the square root of 30 is approximately 5.5.

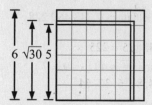

3. $\sqrt{7}$ is between $\sqrt{4} = 2$ and $\sqrt{9} = 3$

5. False

$\sqrt{88}$ is between $\sqrt{81} = 9$ and $\sqrt{100} = 10$

7. True

$\sqrt{55}$ is 7.6157, which is closer 8

9. $\sqrt{104}$, $100 = 10 \times 10$, $121 = 11 \times 11$. Since 104 is much closer to 100 than 121, it will be about 10.2.

11. $\sqrt{171}$, $169 = 13 \times 13$, $196 = 14 \times 14$. Since 171 is much closer to 169 than 196, it will be about 13.1.

13. 5.75

$\sqrt{33}$ is closer to $\sqrt{36} = 6$ than $\sqrt{25} = 5$

Start the guess-and-check at 5.6 or 5.7.
$\quad 5.7 \times 5.7 = 32.49$ too small
$\quad 5.8 \times 5.8 = 33.64$ too large
$5.75 \times 5.75 = 33.0625$ very close

The approximate square root of 33 is 5.75.

15. Estimate: 3.335, Calculator: $3.316\ 624\ 79$

Step 1

The closest perfect square is 9 ($\sqrt{9} = 3$).

Step 2

$11 \div 3 \doteq 3.67$

Step 3

$$\frac{3 + 3.67}{2} = 3.335$$

Step 4

$3.335^2 = 11.122\ 225$

This answer is very close, so steps 2–4 do not need to be repeated.

The approximate square root of 11 is 3.335.

17. Estimate: 7.355, Calculator: 7.348 469 228

Step 1

The closest perfect square is 49 ($\sqrt{49} = 7$).

Step 2

$54 \div 7 \doteq 7.71$

Step 3

$$\frac{7 + 7.71}{2} = 7.355$$

Step 4

$7.355^2 \doteq 54.1$

This answer is very close, so steps 2–4 do not need to be repeated.

The approximate square root of 54 is 7.355.

19. The mat is a square. Each side must be the same length.

The formula for a square area is $A = s^2$.

Determine what number multiplied by itself is 64. In other words, take the square root of 64.
$\sqrt{64} = 8$

The length of each side is 8 m.

21. Take the square root of 16 to find the length of each side: $\sqrt{16} = 4$.

Each small section is 4 km by 4 km.

Lesson 4—Area and Line Segments

YOUR TURN
ANSWERS AND SOLUTIONS

1. **Step 1**
Draw a larger square, following the graph paper lines, that contains the given square.

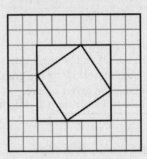

Step 2
Calculate the area of the larger square.
$$A_{\text{large square}} = s^2$$
$$= 5^2$$
$$= 25 \text{ units}^2$$

Step 3
Calculate the area of one of the triangles created by the larger square.
$$A_{\text{triangle}} = \frac{bh}{2}$$
$$= \frac{2 \times 3}{2}$$
$$= \frac{6}{2}$$
$$= 3 \text{ units}^2$$

Multiply the result by 4 to calculate the total area of all four triangles.
$$A_{\text{four triangles}} = A_{\text{triangle}} \times 4$$
$$= 3 \times 4$$
$$= 12 \text{ units}^2$$

Step 4
Subtract the area of the four triangles from the area of the large square.
$$A_{\text{small square}} = A_{\text{large square}} - A_{\text{four triangles}}$$
$$= 25 - 12$$
$$= 13 \text{ units}^2$$

Step 5
Take the square root of the area of the small square to calculate the side length.

Estimate or use a calculator to find the square root: $\sqrt{13} = 3.605\ 551\ 275\ldots$ Round the answer to the tenths place: 3.6 units.

The area of the given square is 13 units^2. The side length of the given square, rounded to the tenths place, is 3.6 units.

2. **Step 1**
Create a square from the given line segment. Then, draw a larger square, following the graph paper lines, that contains the given square.

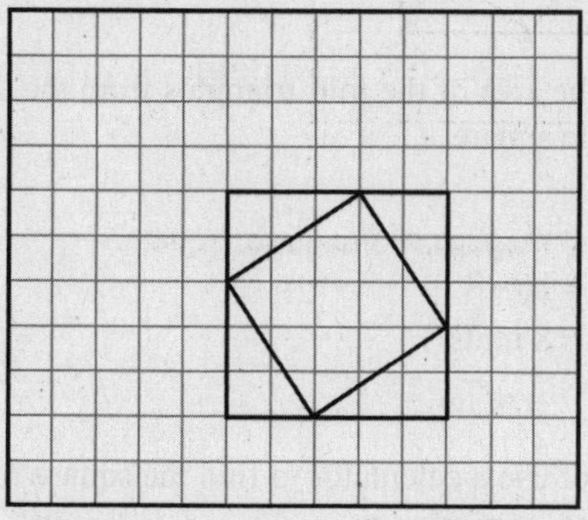

Step 2
Calculate the area of the larger square.

$$\begin{aligned} A_{\text{large square}} &= s^2 \\ &= 5^2 \\ &= 25 \text{ units}^2 \end{aligned}$$

Step 3
Calculate the area of one of the triangles created by the larger square.

$$\begin{aligned} A_{\text{triangle}} &= \frac{bh}{2} \\ &= \frac{2 \times 3}{2} \\ &= \frac{6}{2} \\ &= 3 \text{ units}^2 \end{aligned}$$

Multiply the result by 4 to calculate the total area of all four triangles.

$$\begin{aligned} A_{\text{four triangles}} &= A_{\text{triangle}} \times 4 \\ &= 3 \times 4 \\ &= 12 \text{ units}^2 \end{aligned}$$

Step 4
Subtract the area of the four triangles from the area of the large square.

$$\begin{aligned} A_{\text{small square}} &= A_{\text{large square}} - A_{\text{four triangles}} \\ &= 25 - 12 \\ &= 13 \text{ units}^2 \end{aligned}$$

Step 5
Take the square root of the area of the small square to calculate the side length.

Estimate or use a calculator to find the square root: $\sqrt{13} = 3.605\ 551\ 275\ldots$ Round the answer to the hundredths place: 3.61 units.

The side length of the small square is the length of the given line segment.

Therefore, the length of the line segment, rounded to the nearest hundredth, is 3.61 units.

PRACTICE EXERCISES ANSWERS AND SOLUTIONS

1. $A = 25$ units^2, $s = 5$ units

Step 1
Create a square from the given line segment. Then, draw a larger square, following the graph paper lines, that contains the given square.

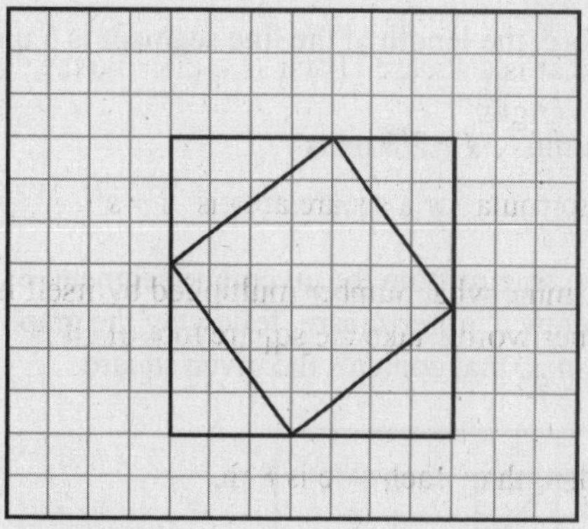

Step 2
Calculate the area of the larger square.

$$\begin{aligned} A_{\text{large square}} &= s^2 \\ &= 7^2 \\ &= 49 \text{ units}^2 \end{aligned}$$

Step 3
Calculate the area of one of the triangles created by the larger square.

$$A_{\text{triangle}} = \frac{bh}{2}$$
$$= \frac{3 \times 4}{2}$$
$$= \frac{12}{2}$$
$$= 6 \text{ units}^2$$

Multiply the result by 4 to calculate the total area of all four triangles.

$$A_{\text{four triangles}} = A_{\text{triangle}} \times 4$$
$$= 6 \times 4$$
$$= 24 \text{ units}^2$$

Step 4
Subtract the area of the four triangles from the area of the large square.

$$A_{\text{small square}} = A_{\text{large square}} - A_{\text{four triangles}}$$
$$= 49 - 24$$
$$= 25 \text{ units}^2$$

Step 5
Take the square root of the area of the small square to calculate the side length.

$$\sqrt{25} = 5 \text{ units}$$

The side length of the small square is the length of the given line segment.

Therefore, the length of the line segment is 5 units.

3. $A = 8 \text{ units}^2$, $s = 2.8$ units

Step 1
Create a square from the given line segment. Then, draw a larger square, following the graph paper lines, that contains the given square.

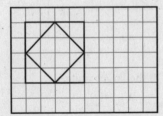

Step 2
Calculate the area of the larger square.

$$A_{\text{large square}} = s^2$$
$$= 4^2$$
$$= 16 \text{ units}^2$$

Step 3
Calculate the area of one of the triangles created by the larger square.

$$A_{\text{triangle}} = \frac{bh}{2}$$
$$= \frac{2 \times 2}{2}$$
$$= \frac{4}{2}$$
$$= 2 \text{ units}^2$$

Multiply the result by 4 to calculate the total area of all four triangles.

$$A_{\text{four triangles}} = A_{\text{triangle}} \times 4$$
$$= 2 \times 4$$
$$= 8 \text{ units}^2$$

Step 4
Subtract the area of the four triangles from the area of the large square.

$$A_{\text{small square}} = A_{\text{large square}} - A_{\text{four triangles}}$$
$$= 16 - 8$$
$$= 8 \text{ units}^2$$

Step 5
Estimate or use a calculator to find the square root: $\sqrt{8} = 2.828\,427\,124$. Round the answer to the tenths place: 2.8 units. The area of the given square is 8 units². The side length of the given square, rounded to the tenths place, is 2.8 units.

5. $A = 5 \text{ units}^2$, $s = 2.2$ units

Step 1
Create a square from the given line segment. Then, draw a larger square, following the graph paper lines, that contains the given square.

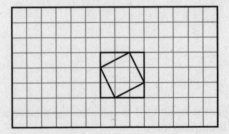

Step 2
Calculate the area of the larger square.

$$A_{\text{large square}} = s^2$$
$$= 3^2$$
$$= 9 \text{ units}^2$$

Step 3

Calculate the area of one of the triangles created by the larger square.

$$\begin{aligned} A_{triangle} &= \frac{bh}{2} \\ &= \frac{1 \times 2}{2} \\ &= \frac{2}{2} \\ &= 1 \text{ unit}^2 \end{aligned}$$

Multiply the result by 4 to calculate the total area of all four triangles.

$$\begin{aligned} A_{four\ triangles} &= A_{triangle} \times 4 \\ &= 1 \times 4 \\ &= 4 \text{ units}^2 \end{aligned}$$

Step 4

Subtract the area of the four triangles from the area of the large square.

$$\begin{aligned} A_{small\ square} &= A_{large\ square} - A_{four\ triangles} \\ &= 9 - 4 \\ &= 5 \text{ units}^2 \end{aligned}$$

Step 5

Take the square root of the area of the small square to calculate the side length.

Estimate or use a calculator to find the square root: $\sqrt{5} = 2.236\ 067\ 977\dots$. Round the answer to the tenths place: 2.2 units.

The side length of the small square is the length of the given line segment.

Therefore the length of the line segment, rounded to the nearest tenths place, is 2.2 units.

Lesson 5—Pythagorean Theorem

YOUR TURN
ANSWERS AND SOLUTIONS

1. **a)** $p = \text{leg}$
    $q = \text{hypotenuse}$
    $r = \text{leg}$

    b) $r = \text{hypotenuse}$
    $s = \text{leg}$
    $t = \text{leg}$

2. Draw a square on each side of the right triangle.

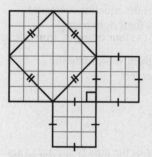

Leg a and leg b are each 3 cm long.

Find the area of each square.

$$\begin{aligned} A_{leg\ a} &= s^2 \\ &= 3^2 \\ &= 9 \text{ units}^2 \end{aligned} \qquad \begin{aligned} A_{leg\ b} &= s^2 \\ &= 3^2 \\ &= 9 \text{ units}^2 \end{aligned}$$

$$\begin{aligned} A_{large\ square} &= s^2 \\ &= 6^2 \\ &= 36 \text{ units}^2 \end{aligned}$$

$$\begin{aligned} A_{triangle} &= \frac{bh}{2} \\ &= \frac{3 \times 3}{1} \\ &= \frac{9}{2} \\ &= 4.5 \text{ units}^2 \end{aligned} \qquad \begin{aligned} A_{four\ triangles} &= A_{triangle} \times 4 \\ &= 4.5 \times 4 \\ &= 18 \text{ units}^2 \end{aligned}$$

$$\begin{aligned} A_{hypotenuse} &= A_{large\ square} - A_{four\ triangles} \\ &= 36 - 18 \\ &= 18 \text{ units}^2 \end{aligned}$$

Add the area of squares created by the two legs to see if they equal the area of the hypotenuse.

$$A_{\text{leg } a} + A_{\text{leg } b} = A_{\text{hypotenuse}}$$
$$9 + 9 = 18$$

The sum of the areas of the two legs ($9 + 9 = 18$ units^2) is the same as the area of the hypotenuse (18 units^2). This proves the Pythagorean theorem.

3. **a)** Substitute the given values into the Pythagorean theorem.
    $$15^2 + 8^2 = 17^2$$
    $$225 + 64 = 289$$
    $$289 = 289$$

    The two sides of the equation are equal. This equation is for a right triangle.

    b) Substitute the given values into the Pythagorean theorem.
    $$15^2 + 9^2 = 17^2$$
    $$225 + 81 = 289$$
    $$306 \neq 289$$

    The two sides of the equation are not equal. This equation is not for a right triangle.

4. **a)** Substitute the given values into the Pythagorean theorem.
    $$a^2 + b^2 = c^2$$
    $$16^2 + 30^2 = 35^2$$
    $$256 + 900 = 1\,225$$
    $$1\,556 \neq 1\,225$$

    The two sides of the equation are not equal. This is not a right triangle.

    b) Substitute the given values into the Pythagorean theorem.
    $$a^2 + b^2 = c^2$$
    $$16^2 + 30^2 = 34^2$$
    $$256 + 900 = 1\,156$$
    $$1\,156 = 1\,156$$

    The two sides of the equation are equal. This is a right triangle.

5. Add the areas of the legs to see if their sum is equal to the area of the hypotenuse. The largest value is always the hypotenuse.
    $$81 + 144 = 225$$
    $$225 = 225$$

    The triangle is a right triangle because the sum of the area of the two legs is equal to the area of the hypotenuse.

6. **a)** Substitute the given values into the Pythagorean theorem.
    $$a^2 + b^2 = c^2$$
    $$5^2 + 12^2 = 13^2$$
    $$25 + 144 = 169$$
    $$169 = 169$$

    The numbers 5-12-13 are a Pythagorean triple because the whole number side lengths satisfy the Pythagorean theorem.

    b) Substitute the given values into the Pythagorean theorem.
    $$a^2 + b^2 = c^2$$
    $$33^2 + 56^2 = 66^2$$
    $$1\,089 + 3\,136 = 4\,356$$
    $$4\,225 \neq 4\,356$$

    The numbers 33-56-66 are not a Pythagorean triple because the whole number side lengths do not satisfy the Pythagorean theorem.

    c) Substitute the given values into the Pythagorean theorem.
    $$a^2 + b^2 = c^2$$
    $$12^2 + 16^2 = 20^2$$
    $$144 + 256 = 400$$
    $$400 = 400$$

    The numbers 12-16-20 are a Pythagorean triple because the whole number side lengths satisfy the Pythagorean theorem.

PRACTICE EXERCISES
ANSWERS AND SOLUTIONS

1.

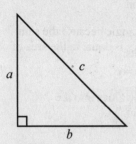

or

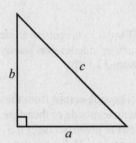

3.

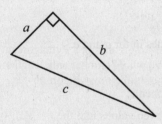

or

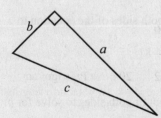

5. Draw a square on each side of the right triangle.

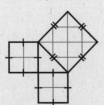

Find the area of each square.

$$A_{\text{leg } a} = s^2 \qquad A_{\text{leg } b} = s^2$$
$$= 2^2 \qquad\qquad = 2^2$$
$$= 4 \text{ units}^2 \qquad = 4 \text{ units}^2$$

$$A_{\text{large square}} = s^2$$
$$= 4^2$$
$$= 16 \text{ units}^2$$

$$A_{\text{triangle}} = \frac{bh}{2} \qquad A_{\text{four triangles}} = 4 \times A_{\text{triangle}}$$
$$= \frac{2 \times 2}{2} \qquad\qquad = 4 \times 2$$
$$= \frac{4}{2} \qquad\qquad = 8 \text{ units}^2$$
$$= 2 \text{ units}^2$$

$$A_{\text{hypotenuse}} = A_{\text{large square}} - A_{\text{four triangles}}$$
$$= 16 - 8$$
$$= 8 \text{ units}^2$$

Add the areas of squares created by the two legs to see if they equal the area of the hypotenuse.

$$A_{leg_a} + A_{leg_b} = A_{hypoteneuse} \qquad A_{leg_a} + A_{leg_b} = A_{hypotenuse}$$
$$4 + 4 = 8$$

The sum of the areas of squares created by the two legs ($4 + 4 = 8$ units^2) is the same as the area of the hypotenuse (8 units^2).

7. Substitute the given values into the Pythagorean theorem.
$$1^2 + 2^2 = 3^2$$
$$1 + 4 = 9$$
$$5 \neq 9$$

This is not a Pythagorean triple because the whole number side lengths do not satisfy the Pythagorean theorem: $5 \neq 9$.

9. Determine whether the two sides are equal.
$$4.5^2 + 6^2 = 7.5^2$$
$$20.25 + 36 = 56.25$$
$$56.25 = 56.25$$

This is a right triangle.

11. Substitute the given values into the equation $a^2 + b^2 = c^2$. The largest number will always be substituted for c in the equation.

$$a^2 + b^2 = c^2$$
$$13^2 + 11^2 = 15^2$$
$$169 + 121 = 225$$
$$290 \neq 225$$

This triangle is not a right triangle.

13. Substitute the given values into the equation $a^2 + b^2 = c^2$. The largest number will always be substituted for c in the equation.

$$a^2 + b^2 = c^2$$
$$5^2 + 12^2 = 13^2$$
$$25 + 144 = 169$$
$$169 = 169$$

The triangle is a right triangle.

Lesson 6—Using the Pythagorean Theorem

YOUR TURN
ANSWERS AND SOLUTIONS

1. Use the Pythagorean Theorem
$$a^2 + b^2 = c^2$$

Label one leg a and the other leg b. Substitute the values into the equation.
$$6^2 + 8^2 = c^2$$

Calculate the exponents.
$$6^2 + 8^2 = c^2$$
$$(6 \times 6) + (8 \times 8) = c^2$$
$$36 + 64 = c^2$$
$$100 = c^2$$

Take the square root of both sides to solve for c.
$$\sqrt{100} = \sqrt{c^2}$$
$$10 = c$$
$$c = 10 \text{ m}$$

The missing side measures 10 m.

2. Use the Pythagorean theorem.
$$a^2 + b^2 = c^2$$

Label one leg a and the other leg b. Substitute the values into the equation.
$$9.5^2 + 7.5^2 = c^2$$

Calculate the exponents.
$$9.5^2 + 7.5^2 = c^2$$
$$(9.5 \times 9.5) + (7.5 \times 7.5) = c^2$$
$$90.25 + 56.25 = c^2$$
$$146.5 = c^2$$

Take the square root of both sides to solve for c.
$$\sqrt{146.5} = \sqrt{c^2}$$
$$12.103\ 718\ 44 = c$$
$$c \doteq 12.1 \text{ cm}$$

The missing side measures 12.1 cm.

3. Label the given sides. The side across from the right angle is the hypotenuse or side c; therefore, $c = 17$ m. One of the legs is given, so label it a or b—they are interchangeable. Solve for the other side.
$$a^2 + b^2 = c^2$$

Substitute the values in for a and c.
$$9^2 + b^2 = 17^2$$

Calculate the exponents.
$$81 + b^2 = 289$$

Solve for b.

Subtract 81 from both sides of the equation to isolate b^2.
$$81 + b^2 - 81 = 289 - 81$$
$$b^2 = 208$$

Take the square root of both sides to solve for b.
$$\sqrt{b^2} = \sqrt{208}$$
$$b = 14.422\ 205\ 1$$
$$= 14.4 \text{ m}$$

Side b is 14.4 m.

4. Draw a diagram.

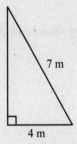

Label the leg that represents the horizontal distance a, and label the hypotenuse, which represents the string, c.

Solve for the missing side, b.

$$a^2 + b^2 = c^2$$
$$4^2 + b^2 = 7^2$$
$$16 + b^2 = 49$$
$$16 + b^2 - 16 = 49 - 16$$
$$b^2 = 33$$
$$\sqrt{b^2} = \sqrt{33}$$
$$b = 5.744\ 562\ 647...$$
$$\doteq 5.7\ \text{m}$$

The kite is 5.7 m up in the air.

5. Draw a diagram. Let the sides be a and b, and let the diagonal line be c.

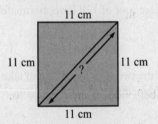

Solve for the length of the line using the Pythagorean theorem.

$$a^2 + b^2 = c^2$$
$$11^2 + 11^2 = c^2$$
$$121 + 121 = c^2$$
$$242 = c^2$$
$$\sqrt{242} = \sqrt{c^2}$$
$$15.556\ 349\ 19... = c$$
$$c \doteq 15.6\ \text{cm}$$

The line across the page is 15.6 cm long.

PRACTICE EXERCISES
ANSWERS AND SOLUTIONS

1. Substitute the given values into the Pythagorean theorem and solve for the missing variable.

$$13^2 + 11^2 = c^2$$
$$169 + 121 = c^2$$
$$290 = c^2$$
$$\sqrt{290} = \sqrt{c^2}$$
$$17.0293\ 863\ 7... = c$$
$$c \doteq 17.0\ \text{m}$$

The missing side length is 17 m.

3. Substitute the given values into the Pythagorean theorem and solve for the missing variable.

$$a^2 + b^2 = c^2$$
$$2^2 + 3^2 = c^2$$
$$4 + 9 = c^2$$
$$13 = c^2$$
$$\sqrt{13} = \sqrt{c^2}$$
$$3.605\ 551\ 275... = c$$
$$c \doteq 3.6\ \text{m}$$

The other side of the garden is 3.6 m long.

5. Draw a diagram.

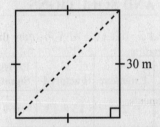

Substitute the given values into the Pythagorean theorem and solve for the missing variable.

$$a^2 + b^2 = c^2$$
$$30^2 + 30^2 = c^2$$
$$900 + 900 = c^2$$
$$1\ 800 = c^2$$
$$\sqrt{1\ 800} = \sqrt{c^2}$$
$$42.426\ 406\ 87... = c$$
$$c \doteq 42.4\ \text{m}$$

The diagonal path is 42.4 m long.

---

7. Draw a diagram.

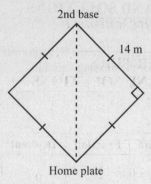

2nd base

14 m

Home plate

Substitute the given values into the Pythagorean theorem and solve for the missing variable.

$$a^2 + b^2 = c^2$$
$$14^2 + 14^2 = c^2$$
$$196 + 196 = c^2$$
$$392 = c^2$$
$$\sqrt{392} = \sqrt{c^2}$$
$$19.798\,989\,87\ldots = c$$
$$c \doteq 19.8 \text{ m}$$

The distance between second base and home plate is 19.8 m.

Practice Test

ANSWERS AND SOLUTIONS

1.

	Read As	Base	Exponent	Factored	Perfect Square
13^2	Thirteen squared	13	2	13×13	169
6^2	Six squared	6	2	6×6	36

3. The side measures are the same, so 1 024 is a perfect square.

5. The side measures are different, so the area value is not a perfect square.

7. Factors of 32: 1, 2, 4, 8, 16, 32
Even number of factors; not a perfect square

9. $\sqrt{64} = 8$ because $8 \times 8 = 64$

11. The side length is the same as the square root: 8 units.

Square the side length to determine the perfect square.
$$8^2 = 64 \text{ units}^2$$

13. D.
$$81 = 9^2 \rightarrow 9 \times 9 = 81$$

15. B.
$$9 = \sqrt{81} \rightarrow 9 \times 9 = 81$$

17. False
The square root of 32 is between $\sqrt{25} = 5$ and $\sqrt{36} = 6$, not $\sqrt{5}$ and $\sqrt{6}$.

19. True
$\sqrt{25} = 5$, $\sqrt{32} \doteq 5.6569$, $\sqrt{36} = 6$.

21. Since $\sqrt{129}$ is closer to $\sqrt{121} = 11$ than $\sqrt{144} = 12$, start the guess-and-check at 11.3 or 11.4.

$11.3 \times 11.3 = 127.69$ too small
$11.4 \times 11.4 = 129.96$ too large
$11.35 \times 11.35 = 128.8225$ very close

Therefore, the square root of 129 is approximately 11.35.

23. B.
Add the square of the two legs together and take the square root of the sum.
$$a^2 + b^2 = c^2$$
$$6^2 + 5^2 = c^2$$
$$36 + 25 = c^2$$
$$61 = c^2$$
$$\sqrt{61} = \sqrt{c^2}$$
$$\sqrt{61} = c$$

25. Substitute the given values into the Pythagorean theorem.

$$a^2 + b^2 = c^2$$
$$10^2 + b^2 = 13^2$$
$$100 + b^2 = 169$$
$$100 + b^2 - 100 = 169 - 100$$
$$b^2 = 69$$
$$\sqrt{b^2} = \sqrt{69}$$
$$b = 8.306\ 623\ 862\ldots$$
$$b \doteq 8.3 \text{ mm}$$

Therefore, the missing length is 8.3 mm.

27. Substitute the given values into the Pythagorean theorem.

$$a^2 + b^2 = c^2$$
$$30^2 + 20^2 = c^2$$
$$900 + 400 = c^2$$
$$1\ 300 = c^2$$
$$\sqrt{1\ 300} = \sqrt{c^2}$$
$$36.055\ 512\ 75\ldots = c$$
$$c \doteq 36.1 \text{ cm}$$

Therefore, the missing length is 36.1 cm.

29. Substitute the given values into the Pythagorean theorem.

$$a^2 + b^2 = c^2$$
$$80^2 + 18^2 = 82^2$$
$$6\ 400 + 324 = 6\ 724$$
$$6\ 724 = 6\ 724$$

The numbers 80-18-82 are a Pythagorean triple because the whole number side lengths satisfy the Pythagorean theorem.

PERCENT

Lesson 1—Representing Percent

YOUR TURN
ANSWERS AND SOLUTIONS

1.

Grid	Percent	Fraction	Decimal
1	50%	$\dfrac{50}{100}$	0.5
2	28%	$\dfrac{28}{100}$	0.28
3	5%	$\dfrac{5}{100}$	0.05

2. Percent form

86 complete squares plus $\dfrac{1}{2}$ a square

$=86.5\%$

Decimal form
The percent is written after the decimal.
$86.5 \div 100 = 0.865$

Fraction form
The numerator is the percent (86.5) over the denominator of 100.

$= \dfrac{86.5}{100}$

3. Place the value of the percentage over a denominator of 100.

$$\dfrac{17\frac{1}{4}}{100}$$

Create an equivalent fraction where the numerator is a whole number.

$$\dfrac{17\frac{1}{4} \times 4}{100 \times 4} = \dfrac{69}{400}$$

The fraction cannot be reduced any further. It is in lowest terms.

Written as a fraction, $17\frac{1}{4}\%$ is $\dfrac{69}{400}$.

4. Change the fractional percent to a decimal percent.

$$94\frac{1}{2}\% = 94.5\%$$

Method 1
Divide the percentage by 100.
$$94.5\% = 94.5 \div 100 = 0.945$$

Method 2
Move the decimal two places to the left.
94.5

$94\frac{1}{2}\%$ as a decimal is 0.945

5. a)

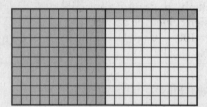

b) 110% means the salesperson sold 10 cars and 10%, or 1 car more.

6. **Method 1**
Divide the percentage by 100.
$$0.085\% = 0.085 \div 100$$
$$= 0.00085$$

Method 2
Move the decimal two places to the left.
0.085

Written as a decimal, 0.085% is 0.00085.

PRACTICE EXERCISES
ANSWERS AND SOLUTIONS

1. Percent form:
Count the number of shaded squares, and write the number in front of the % symbol.
7%

Fraction form:
The percent is the number of squares written over the denominator of 100.

$$\frac{7}{100}$$

Decimal form:
The percentage is the two digits after the decimal.
0.07

When writing a percent as a decimal, it is important to place the last digit in the hundredths place so the whole is still 100.

3. Place the value of the percentage over a denominator of 100.

$$\frac{46\frac{1}{3}}{100}$$

Create an equivalent fraction where the numerator is a whole number.

$$\frac{46\frac{1}{3} \times 3}{100 \times 3} = \frac{139}{300}$$

The fraction cannot be reduced any further. It is in lowest terms.

Written as a fraction, $46\frac{1}{3}\%$ is $\frac{139}{300}$.

5. **Method 1**
Divide the percentage by 100
$$0.61\% = 0.61 \div 100 = 0.0061$$

Method 2
Move the decimal two places to the left.

Written as a decimal, 0.61% is 0.0061.

Lesson 2—Decimals in Percent or Fraction Form

YOUR TURN
ANSWERS AND SOLUTIONS

1. Multiply the decimal number by 100, and place a % sign behind the answer.
$$0.245 \times 100 = 24.5 \rightarrow 24.5\%$$

2. Locate the decimal, and move it two places to the right.

   0.86

   Drop the zero in front of the number and the decimal.

   $0.86 \rightarrow 86$

   Place a % sign behind the answer.

   $\rightarrow 86\%$

3. **Method 1**

   Multiply the decimal by 100. Add the percent sign behind the number.

   $0.935 \times 100 = 93.5\%$

   Method 2

   Move the decimal two places to the right. Add the percent sign behind the number.

   0.935

   $93.5 \rightarrow 93.5\%$

   As a percent, 0.935 is 93.5%.

4. The 4 is in the thousandths place. The denominator is 1 000.

   Remove the decimal and drop the zero.

   The numerator is 124. The fraction is $\dfrac{124}{1\ 000}$.

   Reduce to lowest terms.

   $\dfrac{124}{1\ 000} \xrightarrow[\div 4]{\div 4} \dfrac{31}{250}$

   Written as a fraction, 0.124 is $\dfrac{31}{250}$.

5. The 2 is in the hundredths place. The denominator is 100.

   Remove the decimal. The numerator is 382.

   The fraction is $\dfrac{382}{100}$.

   Reduce to lowest terms.

   $\dfrac{382}{100} \xrightarrow[\div 2]{\div 2} \dfrac{191}{50}$

Convert the improper fraction to a mixed number.

$\dfrac{191}{50} \rightarrow 3\dfrac{41}{50}$

Written as a fraction, 3.82 is $3\dfrac{41}{50}$.

PRACTICE EXERCISES
ANSWERS AND SOLUTIONS

1. Multiply the decimal number by 100, and place a % sign behind the answer.

   $0.68 \times 100 = 68$

   68%

3. Multiply the decimal number by 100, and place a % sign behind the answer.

   $0.7 \times 100 = 70$

   70%

5. Multiply the decimal number by 100, and place a % sign behind the answer.

   $0.08 \times 100 = 8$

   8%

7. Locate the decimal, and move it two places to the right.

   0.73

   Place a % sign behind the answer.

   73%

9. Locate the decimal, and move it two places to the right.

   2.7

   Place a % sign behind the answer.

   270%

11. Locate the decimal, and move it two places to the right.

    0.64

    Place a % sign behind the answer.

    64%

13. The 2 is in the tenths place. The denominator is 10.

    Remove the decimal. The numerator is 2.

    The fraction is $\dfrac{2}{10}$.

Reduce to lowest terms.

$$\frac{2}{10} \xrightarrow[\div 2]{\div 2} \frac{1}{5}$$

15. The 5 is in the hundredths place. The denominator is 100.

Remove the decimal. The numerator is 85.

The fraction is $\frac{85}{100}$.

Reduce to lowest terms.

$$\frac{85}{100} \xrightarrow[\div 5]{\div 5} \frac{17}{20}$$

17. The 5 is in the hundredths place. The denominator is 100.

Remove the decimal. The numerator is 125.

The fraction is $\frac{125}{100}$.

Reduce to lowest terms and express as a mixed number.

$$\frac{125}{100} \xrightarrow[\div 25]{\div 25} \frac{5}{4} = 1\frac{1}{4}$$

19. Multiply the decimal number by 100, and place a % sign behind the answer.
$3.5 \times 100 = 350\%$
$350\% > 35\%$
$3.5 > 35\%$

21. Multiply the decimal number by 100, and place a % sign behind the answer.
$0.5 \times 100 = 50\%$
$50\% > 5\%$
$0.5 > 5\%$

23. Multiply the decimal number by 100, and place a % sign behind the answer.
$0.062 \times 100 = 6.2\%$
$6.2\% < 62\%$
$0.062 < 62\%$

25. The 4 is in the tenths place. The denominator is 10.

Remove the decimal. The numerator is 4.

The fraction is $\frac{4}{10}$.

Reduce to lowest terms.

$$0.4 = \frac{4}{10} \xrightarrow[\div 2]{\div 2} \frac{2}{5}$$
$$\frac{2}{5} = \frac{2}{5}$$
$$0.4 = \frac{2}{5}$$

27. The 6 is in the tenths place. The denominator is 10.

Remove the decimal. The numerator is 26.

The fraction is $\frac{26}{10}$.

Reduce to lowest terms.

$$\frac{26}{10} \xrightarrow[\div 2]{\div 2} \frac{13}{5} = 2\frac{3}{5}$$
$$2\frac{3}{5} > 2\frac{2}{5}$$
$$2.6 > 2\frac{2}{5}$$

Lesson 3—Fractions as Percent or Decimal

YOUR TURN
ANSWERS AND SOLUTIONS

1. Divide the numerator by the denominator.
$3 \div 12 = 0.25$

As a decimal, $\frac{3}{12}$ is 0.25

2.

$3\frac{1}{5} \rightarrow \frac{16}{5}$	Convert $3\frac{1}{5}$ to an improper fraction.
$16 \div 5 = 3.2$	Divide the numerator (16) by the denominator (5).

As a decimal, $3\frac{1}{5}$ is 3.2.

3. **Method 1**
    Convert the mixed number to an improper fraction.
    $$4\frac{13}{20} \rightarrow \frac{93}{20}$$

    Divide the numerator (93) by the denominator (20).
    $93 \div 20 = 4.65$

    Method 2
    Divide the numerator (13) by the denominator (20), and add the whole number (4) to the resulting decimal number.
    $13 \div 20 = 0.65 \rightarrow 4 + 0.65 = 4.65$

4. **Method 1**
    Convert the mixed number to an improper fraction.
    $$5\frac{7}{9} \rightarrow \frac{52}{9}$$

    Divide the numerator (52) by the denominator (9).
    $52 \div 9 = 5.777\ 777\ldots$

    Write the decimal number with bar notation.
    $5.\overline{7}$

    Method 2
    Divide the numerator (7) by the denominator (9), and add the whole number (5) to the resulting decimal number.
    $$7 \div 9 = 0.\overline{7}$$
    $$5 + 0.\overline{7} = 5.\overline{7}$$

5. Divide the numerator by the denominator and multiply the result by 100.
    $24 \div 50 \times 100 = 48$

    Place the % sign behind the answer.
    48%

6.

$\dfrac{4}{7} = \dfrac{x}{100}$	Set up a proportion. The second fraction is the percentage. The numerator is x. The denominator is 100.
$\dfrac{4}{7} = \dfrac{x}{\mathbf{100}}$ $4 \times 100 = 400$	Multiply the numerator of the first fraction by the denominator of the second fraction.
$\dfrac{4}{7} = \dfrac{x}{100}$ $x \times 7 = 7x$	Multiply the numerator of the second fraction by the denominator of the first fraction.

$400 = 7x$ $\dfrac{400}{7} = \dfrac{7x}{7}$ $57.14 = x$	Solve for the missing number by dividing both sides by 7 to isolate the variable.

As a percent, $\dfrac{4}{7}$ is 57.14%.

7. First, convert the mixed number into an improper fraction
    $$2\frac{1}{4} \rightarrow \frac{9}{4}$$

    Method 1
    Divide the numerator by the denominator and multiply the result by 100.
    $9 \div 4 \times 100 = 225 \rightarrow 225\%$

    Method 2
    Set up equivalent fractions.
    $$\frac{9}{4} = \frac{x}{100}$$

    Multiply each numerator by the denominator in the fraction across from it. Solve by isolating the variable, x.
    $$9 \times 100 = x \times 4$$
    $$900 = 4x$$
    $$\frac{900}{4} = \frac{4x}{4}$$
    $$225 = x$$

    Place the % sign behind the answer.
    225%

    As a percent, $2\dfrac{1}{4}$ is 225%.

PRACTICE EXERCISES
ANSWERS AND SOLUTIONS

1. Divide the numerator by the denominator.
    $5 \div 8 = 0.625$

3. Divide the numerator by the denominator.
    $4 \div 25 = 0.16$

5. Divide the numerator by the denominator.
    $9 \div 96 = 0.093\ 75$

7. **Method 1**
Divide the numerator by the denominator and multiply the result by 100.
$3 \div 4 \times 100 = 75 \rightarrow 75\%$

Method 2
Set up equivalent fractions.
$$\frac{3}{4} = \frac{x}{100}$$
$$300 = 4x$$
$$\frac{300}{4} = \frac{4x}{4}$$
$$75 = x$$
$$\frac{3}{4} = 75\%$$

As a percent, $\frac{3}{4}$ is 75%.

9. **Method 1**
Divide the numerator by the denominator and multiply the result by 100.
$3 \div 8 \times 100 = 37.5 \rightarrow 37.5\%$

Method 2
Set up equivalent fractions.
$$\frac{3}{8} = \frac{x}{100}$$
$$300 = 8x$$
$$\frac{300}{8} = \frac{8x}{8}$$
$$37.5 = x$$
$$\frac{3}{8} = 37.5\%$$

As a percent, $\frac{3}{8}$ is 37.5%.

11. Convert the mixed number to an improper fraction.
$$2\frac{1}{2} \rightarrow \frac{5}{2}$$

Method 1
Divide the numerator by the denominator and multiply the result by 100.
$5 \div 2 \times 100 = 250 \rightarrow 250\%$

Method 2
Set up equivalent fractions.
$$\frac{5}{2} = \frac{x}{100}$$
$$500 = 2x$$
$$\frac{500}{2} = \frac{2x}{2}$$
$$250 = x$$
$$2\frac{1}{2} = 250\%$$

As a percent, $2\frac{1}{2}$ is 250%.

13. Divide the numerator by the denominator.
$8 \div 20 = 0.4$
$0.4 > 0.35$

15. Divide the numerator by the denominator.
$2 \div 5 = 0.4$
$$\frac{2}{5} = 0.4$$

17. Divide the numerator by the denominator.
$3 \div 50 = 0.06$
$0.06 = 0.06$

$$\frac{3}{50} = 0.06$$

19. **Method 1**
Divide the numerator by the denominator and multiply the result by 100.
$1 \div 3 \times 100 = 33.\overline{3} \rightarrow 33.\overline{3}\%$

Method 2
Set up equivalent fractions.
$$\frac{1}{3} = \frac{x}{100}$$
$$100 = 3x$$
$$\frac{100}{3} = \frac{3x}{3}$$
$$33.\overline{3} = x$$

$$33.\overline{3}\% = 33.\overline{3}\%$$

21. **Method 1**
Divide the numerator by the denominator and multiply the result by 100.
$15 \div 50 \times 100 = 30 \rightarrow 30\%$

Method 2

Set up equivalent fractions.

$$\frac{15}{50} = \frac{x}{100}$$
$$1500 = 50x$$
$$\frac{1500}{50} = \frac{50x}{50}$$
$$30 = x$$

$$30\% < 33.\overline{3}\%$$

23. Draw a 10×10 grid. Shade in 35 complete squares.

Lesson 4—Percent of a Number

YOUR TURN
ANSWERS AND SOLUTIONS

1. Method 1

Convert the percent to a decimal, and multiply the decimal by the given number.
$$230 \div 100 \times 28 = 64.4$$

230% of 28 is 64.4.

Method 2

Set up a proportion, and solve for the unknown value, x.

$$\frac{x}{28} = \frac{230}{100}$$
$$100x = 6\ 440$$
$$\frac{100x}{100} = \frac{6\ 440}{100}$$
$$x = 64.4$$

230% of 28 is 64.4.

2. Method 1

Convert the percent into a decimal, and multiply the decimal by the given number.
$$0.25 \div 100 \times 325 = 0.8125$$

0.25% of 325 is 0.8125

Method 2

Set up a proportion, and solve for the unknown value, x.

$$\frac{x}{325} = \frac{0.25}{100}$$
$$100x = 81.25$$
$$\frac{100x}{100} = \frac{81.25}{100}$$
$$x = 0.8125$$

0.25% of 325 is 0.8125

3. Method 1

Convert the percent into a decimal, and multiply the decimal by the given number.
$$60 \div 100 \times 60 = 36$$

Stan had 36 correct answers.

Method 2

Set up a proportion, and solve for the unknown value, x.

$$\frac{x}{60} = \frac{60}{100}$$
$$100x = 3\ 600$$
$$\frac{100x}{100} = \frac{3\ 600}{100}$$
$$x = 36$$

Stan answered 36 questions correctly.

4. Method 1

Convert the percent to a decimal number.
$$0.5 \div 100 = 0.005$$

Multiply the decimal number by the given number.
$$0.005 \times 141.2 = 0.706$$

Add the increase in spending to October's spending.
$$141.2 + 0.706 = 141.906$$

Method 2

Set up a proportion, and solve for the unknown by isolating the variable.

$$\frac{x}{141.2} = \frac{100.5}{100}$$
$$100x = 1\ 4190.6$$
$$\frac{100x}{100} = \frac{1\ 4190.6}{100}$$
$$x = 141.906$$

The average Canadian spent $141.91 on bakery products in November.

5. Convert the percent to a decimal number.
$0.9 \div 100 = 0.009$

Multiply the decimal number by the given number.
$0.009 \times 2\ 303\ 200 = 20\ 728.8$

The company had a profit of \$20 728.80

6. Convert the percent to a decimal number.
$168.2 \div 100 = 1.682$

Multiply the decimal number by the given number.
$1.682 \times 110 = 185.02$

Kevin's height is 185.02 cm at 20 years of age.

PRACTICE EXERCISES
ANSWERS AND SOLUTIONS

1. Convert the percent to a decimal, and multiply the result by the given number.
$30 \div 100 = 0.3$
$0.3 \times 45 = 13.5$

3. Convert the percent to a decimal, and multiply the result by the given number.
$0.5 \div 100 = 0.005$
$0.005 \times 22 = 0.11$

5. Convert the percent to a decimal, and multiply the result by the given number.
$1 \div 2 = 0.5 \xrightarrow[\text{whole number}]{\text{add the}} 9.5$
$9.5 \div 100 = 0.095$
$0.095 \times 38 = 3.61$

7. Convert the percent to a decimal, and multiply the result by the given number.
$12 \div 100 \times 504 = 60.48$
$48 \div 100 \times 93 = 44.64$
$60.48 > 44.64$

9. Convert the percent to a decimal, and multiply the result by the given number.
$225 \div 100 \times 330 = 742.5$
$148 \div 100 \times 505 = 747.4$
$742.5 < 747.4$

11. Convert the percent to a decimal, and multiply the result by the given number.
$0.06 \div 100 \times 200 = 0.12$
$0.03 \div 100 \times 400 = 0.12$
$0.12 = 0.12$

13. If the percentage is less than one hundred, the percent of the number will be *smaller* than the given number.

15. If the percentage is greater than one hundred, the percent of the number will be *greater* than the given number.

17. Divide the percentage by 100 and multiply the result by the given number.
$148 \div 100 \times 330 = 488.4$

Since it is impossible to have a partial person, the answer is rounded down. 488 people attend the movie theatre during the holiday season.

Lesson 5—Discounts

YOUR TURN
ANSWERS AND SOLUTIONS

1. a) Calculate the percent of the original number.

Method 1: Division and multiplication
$25 \div 100 \times 29 = 7.25$

Method 2: Cross products
$$\frac{x}{29} = \frac{25}{100}$$
$$100x = 725$$
$$\frac{100x}{100} = \frac{725}{100}$$
$$x = 7.25$$

A 25% discount on a \$29.00 item is a savings of \$7.25.

b) Subtract the discount from the original price.
$\$29 - \$7.25 = \$21.75$

The discounted price of the DVD is \$21.75

2. Calculate the first discount on the original price.

Method 1: Division and multiplication
20% of $60.00
$20 \div 100 \times 60 = 12$

Method 2: Cross products
$$\frac{x}{60} = \frac{20}{100}$$
$$100x = 1\ 200$$
$$\frac{100x}{100} = \frac{1\ 200}{100}$$
$$x = 12$$

The reduced price is $60 - \$12 = \$48$.

Calculate the second discount on the reduced price.

Method 1: Division and multiplication
$10 \div 100 \times 48 = 4.8$

Method 2: Cross products
$$\frac{x}{48} = \frac{10}{100}$$
$$100x = 4\ 800$$
$$\frac{100x}{100} = \frac{4\ 800}{100}$$
$$x = 4.8$$

The reduced price is $\$48.00 - \$4.80 = \$43.20$.

The final price of the shirt is $43.20, before taxes.

PRACTICE EXERCISES
ANSWERS AND SOLUTIONS

---

1. Calculate the 20% increase on the original price

Method 1: Division and multiplication
20% of $49.95
$20 \div 100 \times 49.95 = 9.99$

Method 2: Cross products
$$\frac{x}{49.95} = \frac{20}{100}$$
$$100x = 999$$
$$\frac{100x}{100} = \frac{999}{100}$$
$$x = 9.99$$

The new price is $\$49.95 + \$9.99 = \$59.94$.

Calculate the discount on the new price.

Method 1: Division and multiplication
15% of $59.94
$15 \div 100 \times 59.94 = 8.99$

Method 2: Cross products
$$\frac{x}{59.94} = \frac{15}{100}$$
$$100x = 899.1$$
$$\frac{100x}{100} = \frac{899.1}{100}$$
$$x = 8.99$$

The selling price is $\$59.94 - \$8.99 = \$50.95$.

The selling price $50.94, before taxes.

3. Calculate the first discount on the original price.

Method 1: Division and multiplication
30% of 390
$30 \div 100 \times 390 = 117$

Method 2: Cross products
$$\frac{x}{390} = \frac{30}{100}$$
$$100x = 11\ 700$$
$$\frac{100x}{100} = \frac{11\ 700}{100}$$
$$x = 117$$

The reduced price is $390 - \$117 = \$273$

Calculate the second discount on the reduced price.

Method 1: Division and multiplication
10% of 273
$10 \div 100 \times 273 = 27.30$

Method 2: Cross products
$$\frac{10}{100} = \frac{x}{273}$$
$$100x = 2\ 730$$
$$\frac{100x}{100} = \frac{2\ 730}{100}$$
$$x = 27.30$$

The reduced price is $273.00 - 27.30 = \$245.70$

Caitlin would pay $245.70 for the Camcorder, before taxes.

5. Calculate the first discount on the original price.

Method 1: Division and multiplication
10% of 5 000
$10 \div 100 \times 5\,000 = 500$

Method 2: Cross products
$$\frac{x}{5000} = \frac{10}{100}$$
$100x = 50\,000$
$$\frac{100x}{100} = \frac{50\,000}{100}$$
$$x = 500$$

The reduced price is $\$5\,000 - \$500 = \$4\,500$

Calculate the second discount on the reduced price.

Method 1: Division and multiplication
20% of 4 500
$20 \div 100 \times 4\,500 = 900$

Method 2: Cross products
$$\frac{x}{4\,500} = \frac{20}{100}$$
$100x = 90\,000$
$$\frac{100x}{100} = \frac{90\,000}{100}$$
$$x = 900$$

The second reduced price is
$\$4\,500.00 - \$900.00 = \$3\,600.00$

Calculate the third discount on the second reduced price.

Method 1: Division and multiplication
30% of 3 600
$30 \div 100 \times 3\,600 = 1\,080$

Method 2: Cross products
$$\frac{x}{3\,600} = \frac{30}{100}$$
$100x = 108\,000$
$$\frac{100x}{100} = \frac{108\,000}{100}$$
$$x = 1\,080$$

The third reduced price is
$\$3\,600 - \$1\,080 = \$2\,520$

The final price of the hot tub is $\$2\,520.00$, before taxes.

Lesson 6—Taxes

YOUR TURN
ANSWERS AND SOLUTIONS

1. a) Method 1: Division and multiplication
8% of $75.00
$8 \div 100 \times 75 = 6$

Method 2: Cross products
$$\frac{x}{75} = \frac{8}{100}$$
$100x = 600$
$$\frac{100x}{100} = \frac{600}{100}$$
$$x = 6$$

The tax on a $75.00 shirt is $6.00.

b) Add the tax to the original price.
$6 + 75 = 81$

The shirt, including tax, is $81.00.

2. Calculate the discount on the original price.

Method 1: Division and multiplication
30% of $200.00
$30 \div 100 \times 200 = 60$

Method 2: Cross products
$$\frac{x}{200} = \frac{30}{100}$$
$100x = 6\,000$
$$\frac{100x}{100} = \frac{6\,000}{100}$$
$$x = 60$$

The discounted price is $200 - 60 = 140$.

Calculate the GST on the reduced price.

Method 1: Division and multiplication
5% of $140.00
$5 \div 100 \times 140 = 7$

Method 2: Cross products

$$\frac{5}{100} = \frac{x}{140}$$
$$100x = 700$$
$$\frac{100x}{100} = \frac{700}{100}$$
$$x = 7$$

The total purchase price is the sales price plus the amount of the GST.
$$140 + 7 = 147$$

A $200 jacket on sale for 30% off will cost $147.00 with the taxes included.

PRACTICE EXERCISES
ANSWERS AND SOLUTIONS

1. **Method 1: Division and multiplication**
5% of $125.00
$$5 \div 100 \times 125 = 6.25$$

    Method 2: Cross products
$$\frac{x}{125} = \frac{5}{100}$$
$$100x = 625$$
$$\frac{100x}{100} = \frac{625}{100}$$
$$x = 6.25$$

The tax on a $125.00 coat is $6.25.

3. Calculate the discount on the original price.

    Method 1: Division and multiplication
30% of $30.00
$$30 \div 100 \times 30 = 9$$

    Method 2: Cross products
$$\frac{x}{30} = \frac{30}{100}$$
$$100x = 900$$
$$\frac{100x}{100} = \frac{900}{100}$$
$$x = 9$$

The discounted price is $30 - $9 = $21.

Calculate the GST on the reduced price.

Method 1: Division and multiplication
5% of $21.00
$$5 \div 100 \times 21 = 1.05$$

Method 2: Cross products

$$\frac{x}{21} = \frac{5}{100}$$
$$100x = 105$$
$$\frac{100x}{100} = \frac{105}{100}$$
$$x = 1.05$$

The total purchase price is the sales price plus the amount of the GST.
$$21 + 1.05 = 22.05$$

The $30 pair of jeans on sale for 30% off will cost $22.05 with the sales tax included.

5. Calculate the discount on the original price.

    Method 1: Division and multiplication
40% of $300.00
$$40 \div 100 \times 300 = 120$$

    Method 2: Cross products
$$\frac{x}{300} = \frac{40}{100}$$
$$100x = 12\ 000$$
$$\frac{100x}{100} = \frac{12\ 000}{100}$$
$$x = 120$$

The discounted price is $300 - 120 = $180.00.

Calculate the GST on the reduced price.

    Method 1: Division and multiplication
5% of $180.00
$$5 \div 100 \times 180 = 9.00$$

    Method 2: Cross products
$$\frac{x}{180} = \frac{5}{100}$$
$$100x = 900$$
$$\frac{100x}{100} = \frac{900}{100}$$
$$x = 9.00$$

The total purchase price is the sales price plus the amount of the GST.
$$180 + 9.00 = 189.00$$

The $400 vacuum on sale for 40% off will cost $189.00 with the taxes included.

7. Calculate the PST on the original price.

Method 1: Division and multiplication
7% of $500.00
$7 \div 100 \times 500 = 35$

Method 2: Cross products
$$\frac{x}{500} = \frac{7}{100}$$
$$100x = 3500$$
$$\frac{100x}{100} = \frac{3500}{100}$$
$$x = 35$$

The PST is $35.

Calculate the GST on the original price.

Method 1: Division and multiplication
5% of $500.00
$5 \div 100 \times 500 = 25$

Method 2: Cross products
$$\frac{x}{500} = \frac{5}{100}$$
$$100x = 2\ 500$$
$$\frac{100x}{100} = \frac{2\ 500}{100}$$
$$x = 25$$

The GST is $25.

The total purchase price is the original price plus the amount of the PST and GST.
$500 + $35 + $25 = $560.00

The piece of Indian art will cost $560.00 with the taxes included.

Lesson 7—Commissions

YOUR TURN
ANSWERS AND SOLUTIONS

1. Method 1: Division and multiplication
4.5% of $12 000
$4.5 \div 100 \times 12\ 000 = 540$

Method 2: Cross products
$$\frac{x}{12\ 000} = \frac{4.5}{100}$$
$$100x = 54\ 000$$
$$\frac{100x}{100} = \frac{54\ 000}{100}$$
$$x = 540$$

The salesperson earns $540.00.

PRACTICE EXERCISES
ANSWERS AND SOLUTIONS

1. Method 1: Division and multiplication
30% of $190.00
$30 \div 100 \times 190 = 57$

Method 2: Cross products
$$\frac{x}{190} = \frac{30}{100}$$
$$100x = 5\ 700$$
$$\frac{100x}{100} = \frac{5\ 700}{100}$$
$$x = 57$$

The salesperson earned $57.00 in commission.

3. Method 1: Division and multiplication
3.5% of $280 000
$3.5 \div 100 \times 280\ 000 = 9\ 800$

Method 2: Cross products
$$\frac{x}{280\ 000} = \frac{3.5}{100}$$
$$100x = 980\ 000$$
$$\frac{100x}{100} = \frac{980\ 000}{100}$$
$$x = 9\ 800$$

The real estate salesman earned $9 800.00 in commission.

5. **Method 1: Division and multiplication**
1.2% of $375 000
$1.2 \div 100 \times 375\ 000 = 4\ 500$

Method 2: Cross products
$$\frac{x}{375\ 000} = \frac{1.2}{100}$$
$$100x = 450\ 000$$
$$\frac{100x}{100} = \frac{450\ 000}{100}$$
$$x = 4\ 500$$

The financial advisor earned $4 500.00 in commission in February.

Practice Test

ANSWERS AND SOLUTIONS

1. Percent form:
Count the number of shaded squares and write the number in front of the % symbol.
37%

Fraction form:
The percent is the number of shaded squares written over the denominator of 100.
$$\frac{37}{100}$$

Decimal form:
The percent is written after the decimal.
0.37

3. Percent form:
There are 19 complete squares and $\frac{1}{2}$ a square.

19.5%

Fraction form
The percent is the number of shaded squares written over the denominator of 100.
$$\frac{19.5}{100}$$

Decimal form:
The percent is written after the decimal.
$19.5 \div 100 = 0.195$

5. Change the fractional percent to a decimal percent.
$$22\frac{3}{4}\% = 22.75\%$$

Method 1
Divide the percentage by 100.
$$22.75\% = 22.75 \div 100$$
$$= 0.2275$$

Method 2
Move the decimal two places to the left.
$$22.75 \longrightarrow 0.2275$$

As a decimal, $22\frac{3}{4}\%$ is 0.2275.

7. Multiply the decimal number by 100, and place a % sign behind the answer.
$$0.825 \times 100 = 82.5 \rightarrow 82.5\%$$

9. The 5 is in the hundredths place. The denominator is 100.

Remove the decimal. The numerator is 65.

The fraction is $\frac{65}{100}$.

Reduce to lowest terms.
$$\frac{65}{100} \xrightarrow[\div 5]{\div 5} \frac{13}{20}$$

11. The 2 is in the hundredths place. The denominator is 100.

Remove the decimal. The numerator is 562.

The fraction is $\frac{562}{100}$.

Reduce to lowest terms.
$$\frac{562}{100} \xrightarrow[\div 2]{\div 2} \frac{281}{50}$$

Convert to a mixed number.
$$\frac{281}{50} \rightarrow 5\frac{31}{50}$$

13. Multiply the decimal by 100 and place a % in behind the answer.

$9.0 \times 100 = 900\%$

$900\% > 90\%$

$9.0 > 90\%$

15. The 5 is in the tenths place. The denominator is 10. Remove the decimal. The numerator is 5.

The fraction is $\dfrac{5}{10}$.

Reduce to lowest terms.

$\dfrac{5}{10} \xrightarrow[\div 5]{\div 5} \dfrac{1}{2}$

$\dfrac{1}{2} = \dfrac{1}{2}$

$0.5 = \dfrac{1}{2}$

17. Divide the numerator (3) by the denominator (5).

$3 \div 5 = 0.6$

As a decimal, $\dfrac{3}{5} = 0.6$

19. **Method 1**

Convert the mixed number to an improper fraction.

$7\dfrac{2}{3} \to \dfrac{23}{3}$

Divide the numerator (23) by the denominator (3).

$23 \div 3 = 7.666\ 666\ 666\ldots$.

Write the decimal number with bar notation.

$7.\overline{6}$

Method 2

Divide the numerator (2) by the denominator (3), and add the whole number (7) to the resulting decimal number.

$2 \div 3 = 0.\overline{6} \to 7 + 0.\overline{6} = 7.\overline{6}$.

21. **Method 1: Division and multiplication**

Divide the numerator by the denominator, and multiply the result by 100.

$7 \div 25 \times 100 = 28$

Place the % sign behind the answer.

28%

Method 2: Cross products

Set up equivalent fractions.

$\dfrac{7}{25} = \dfrac{x}{100}$

Multiply each numerator by the denominator in the fraction across from it. Solve by isolating the variable, x.

$7 \times 100 = x \times 25$

$700 = 25x$

$\dfrac{700}{25} = \dfrac{25x}{25}$

$28 = x$

Place the % sign behind the answer.

28%

23. Convert the mixed number into an improper fraction.

$2\dfrac{5}{10} = \dfrac{25}{10}$

Method 1: Division and multiplication

Divide the numerator by the denominator, and multiply the result by 100.

$25 \div 10 \times 100 = 250 \to 250\%$

Method 2: Cross products

Set up equivalent fractions.

$\dfrac{25}{10} = \dfrac{x}{100}$

Multiply each numerator by the denominator in the fraction across from it. Solve by isolating the variable, x.

$25 \times 100 = x \times 10$

$2\ 500 = 10x$

$\dfrac{2\ 500}{10} = \dfrac{10x}{10}$

$250 = x$

Place the % sign behind the answer.

250%

As a percent, $2\dfrac{5}{10}$ is 250%.

25. Convert the mixed number to a decimal.

$$2\frac{2}{5} \rightarrow \frac{12}{5}$$
$$12 \div 5 = 2.4$$

Compare the two numbers.
$$2.4 = 2.4$$
$$2\frac{2}{5} = 2.4$$

27. Method 1: Division and multiplication
Divide the percentage by 100, and multiply the result by the given number.
$$0.5 \div 100 \times 150 = 0.75$$

Method 2: Cross products
Set up equivalent fractions and solve for the unknown variable.

$$\frac{x}{150} = \frac{0.5}{100}$$
$$100x = 75$$
$$\frac{100x}{100} = \frac{75}{100}$$
$$x = 0.75$$

29. Convert the percent to a decimal, and multiply the result by the given number.
$$11 \div 100 \times 400 = 44$$
$$67 \div 100 \times 80 = 53.6$$
$$44 < 53.6$$

11% of 400 < 67% of 80

31. Convert the percentage to a decimal number.
$$175 \div 100 = 1.75$$

Multiply the decimal number by the given number:.
$$1.75 \times 112 = 196$$

The renovated auditorium has 196 seats.

33. Subtract the discount from the original price.
$$\$30 - \$4.5 = \$25.50$$

The discounted price of the shirt is $25.50.

35. Calculate the discount on the original price.

Method 1: Division and multiplication
25% of $300.00
$$25 \div 100 \times 300 = 75$$

Method 2: Cross products

$$\frac{x}{300} = \frac{25}{100}$$
$$100x = 7\ 500$$
$$\frac{100x}{100} = \frac{7\ 500}{100}$$
$$x = 75$$

The discounted price is $300 - \$75 = \$225$.

Calculate the GST on the reduced price.

Method 1: Division and multiplication
5% of $225.00
$$5 \div 100 \times 225 = 11.25$$

Method 2: Cross products

$$\frac{x}{225} = \frac{5}{100}$$
$$100x = 1\ 125$$
$$\frac{100x}{100} = \frac{1\ 125}{100}$$
$$x = 11.25$$

The total purchase price is the sales price plus the amount of the GST.
$$225 + 11.25 = 236.25$$

The $300 television on sale for 25% off will cost $236.25 with the taxes included.

SURFACE AREA

Lesson 1—Three-Dimensional Objects

YOUR TURN
ANSWERS AND SOLUTIONS

1. This net is the two-dimensional representation of the given rectangular prism.

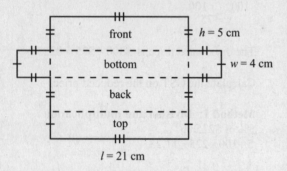

2. This net is the two-dimensional representation of the given triangular prism

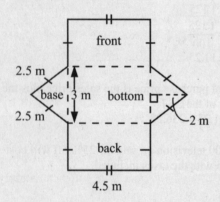

3. This net is the representation of the given cylinder.

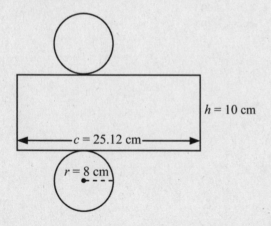

PRACTICE EXERCISES
ANSWERS AND SOLUTIONS

1. A pentagonal pyramid has one pentagon and five triangles.

3. A cylinder has two circles and one rectangle.

4. The 3-D objects that have at least one rectangle include any type of prism, a rectangular pyramid, a square pyramid (a square is a rectangle with four equal sides), and a cylinder (it has a rectangle wrapped around the middle).

5. The three-dimensional objects that contain exactly one rectangle are a cylinder and a rectangular pyramid.

7. This net represents a rectangular prism.

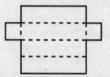

It has 12 edges and 8 vertices.

9. This net represents a cube.

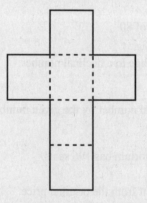

It has 12 edges and 8 vertices.

Lesson 2—Calculating the Surface Area of Prisms

YOUR TURN
ANSWERS AND SOLUTIONS

1. Draw the net for the rectangular prism.

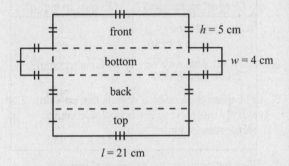

$l = 21$ cm

Find the area of each part of the rectangular prism.

Front and Back	Top and Bottom	Sides
(2 equal rectangles)	(2 equal rectangles)	(2 equal rectangles)
$A = lh$	$A = lw$	$A = hw$
$= 21 \times 5$	$= 21 \times 4$	$= 5 \times 4$
$= 105$	$= 84$	$= 20$
$105 \times 2 = 210$	$84 \times 2 = 168$	$20 \times 2 = 40$

Add the areas together.
$$SA = 210 + 168 + 40$$
$$= 418 \text{ cm}^2$$

The surface area of the given rectangular prism is 418 cm².

2. Draw the net for the triangular prism.

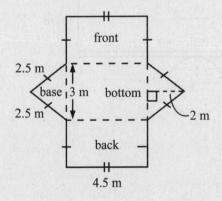

The front and back are the same size because the triangular bases are isosceles triangles.
Find the area of each part of the triangular prism.

Front and Back	Bottom	Sides
(2 equal rectangles)	(rectangle)	(2 equal triangles)
$A = lw$	$A = lw$	$A = \dfrac{bh}{2}$
$= 4.5 \times 2.5$	$= 3 \times 4.5$	$= \dfrac{3 \times 2}{2}$
$= 11.25$	$= 13.5$	$= 3$
$11.25 \times 2 = 22.5$		$3 \times 2 = 6$

Add the areas together
$$SA = 22.5 + 13.5 + 6$$
$$= 42 \text{ m}^2$$

The surface area of the given triangular prism is 42 m².

3. Draw the net that represents the given cube.

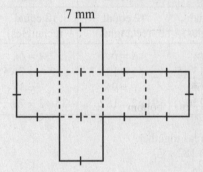

Find the area of one square side, and then multiply by 6.
$$A = lw$$
$$= 7 \times 7$$
$$= 49$$
$$49 \times 6 = 294$$

The surface area of the cube is 294 mm².

4. Len is painting five faces of the cube.

Find the area of one square side and multiply by 5.
$$A = lw$$
$$= 4 \times 4$$
$$= 16$$
$$16 \times 5 = 80$$

Len will need 80 m^2 of paint to cover the sides and top of the container. Since the paint costs $1.99/m^2, multiply the cost of paint by the surface area.
$$80 \times 1.99 = 159.20$$

It will cost Len $159.20 for the paint.

PRACTICE EXERCISES
ANSWERS AND SOLUTIONS

1. Find the area of each part of the rectangular prism.

Front and Back	Top and Bottom	Sides
(2 equal rectangles)	(2 equal rectangles)	(2 equal rectangles)
$A = lw$ $= 13 \times 5$ $= 65$ $65 \times 2 = 130$	$A = lw$ $= 13 \times 7$ $= 91$ $91 \times 2 = 182$	$A = lw$ $= 7 \times 5$ $= 35$ $35 \times 2 = 70$

Add the areas together.
$$SA = 130 + 182 + 70$$
$$= 382 \text{ m}^2$$

The surface area of the given rectangular prism is 382 m^2.

3. Calculate the area of one square face, and multiply it by 6.
$$A = lw$$
$$= 5.3 \times 5.3$$
$$= 28.09$$
$$28.09 \times 6 = 168.54$$

The surface area of the given cube is 168.5 m^2.

5. Since the bases of the prism are composed of equilateral triangles, all three edges are the same measure. This means that the sides are 3 equal rectangles.

Find the area of each part of the triangular prism.

Front, Back, and Bottom	Sides
(3 equal rectangles)	(2 equal triangles)
$A = lw$ $= 25 \times 80$ $= 2\ 000$ $2\ 000 \times 3 = 6\ 000$	$A = \dfrac{bh}{2}$ $= \dfrac{25 \times 18}{2}$ $= \dfrac{450}{2}$ $= 225$ $225 \times 2 = 450$

Add the areas together
$$SA = 6\ 000 + 450$$
$$= 6\ 450 \text{ mm}^2$$

The surface area of the given box is 6 450 mm^2.

Lesson 3—Calculating the Surface Area of Cylinders

YOUR TURN
ANSWERS AND SOLUTIONS

1. Draw the net that represents the cylinder.

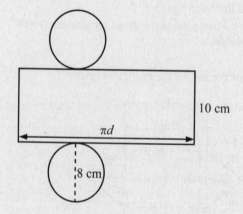

Find the area of each part.

Bases (2 identical circles)	Rectangle
$A = \pi r^2$ $= 3.14 \times 4^2$ $= 3.14 \times 16$ $= 50.24$ $50.24 \times 2 = 100.48$	$A = \pi d \times h$ $= 3.14 \times 8 \times 10$ $= 251.2$

Add the areas together.
$SA = 100.48 + 251.2$
$\quad = 351.68 \text{ cm}^2$

The surface area of the cylinder is 351.68 cm^2.

PRACTICE EXERCISES
ANSWERS AND SOLUTIONS

1. Find the area of each part of the cylinder.

Bases (2 identical circles)	Rectangle
$A = \pi r^2$ $= 3.14 \times \left(\dfrac{4}{2}\right)^2$ $= 3.14 \times 2^2$ $= 3.14 \times 4$ $= 12.56$ $12.56 \times 2 = 25.12$	$A = \pi d \times h$ $= 3.14 \times 4 \times 6$ $= 75.36$

Add the areas together.
$SA = 25.12 + 75.36$
$\quad = 100.48 \text{ m}^2$

The surface area of the given cylinder is 100.48 m^2.

3. Find the area of each part of the rectangular prism.

Front and Back (2 equal rectangles)	Top and Bottom (2 equal rectangles)	Sides (2 equal rectangles)
$A = lw$ $= 25 \times 8$ $= 200$ $200 \times 2 = 400$	$A = lw$ $= 25 \times 10$ $= 250$ $250 \times 2 = 500$	$A = lw$ $= 10 \times 8$ $= 80$ $80 \times 2 = 160$

Add the areas together.
$SA = 400 + 500 + 160$
$\quad = 1\,060$

The surface area of the rectangular prism is 1 060 cm^2.

Find the area of each part of the cylinder.

Bases (2 identical circles)	Rectangle
$A = \pi r^2$ $= 3.14 \times \left(\dfrac{15}{2}\right)^2$ $= 3.14 \times (7.5)^2$ $= 3.14 \times 56.25$ $= 176.625$ $176.625 \times 2 = 353.25$	$A = \pi d \times h$ $= 3.14 \times 15 \times 35$ $= 1\,648.5$

Add the areas together.
$SA = 353.25 + 1\,648.5$
$\quad = 2\,001.75$

The surface area of the cylinder is 2001.75 cm^2.

Find the difference.
$2\,001.75 - 1\,060 = 941.75$

The cylinder has a greater surface area by 941.75 cm^2.

Practice Test

ANSWERS AND SOLUTIONS

1. Find area of square side, and multiply by 6.
$A = lw$
$\quad = 6 \times 6$
$\quad = 36$
$36 \times 6 = 216$

The surface area of the cube is 216 m^2.

3. Find the area of each part of the triangular prism.

Front, Back, and Bottom	Sides
(3 equal rectangles)	(2 equal triangles)
$A = lw$ $= 12 \times 8.0$ $= 96$ $96 \times 3 = 288$	$A = \dfrac{b \times h}{2}$ $= \dfrac{8.0 \times 6.9}{2}$ $= 27.6$ $27.6 \times 2 = 55.2$

Add the areas together.
$$SA = 288 + 55.2$$
$$= 343.2$$

The surface area of the given triangular prism is 343.2 m^2.

5. The book is a rectangular prism.

Find the area of each part of the rectangular prism.

Front and Back	Top and Bottom	Sides
(2 equal rectangles)	(2 equal rectangles)	(2 equal rectangles)
$A = lw$ $= 23 \times 20$ $= 460$ $460 \times 2 = 920$	$A = lw$ $= 23 \times 3$ $= 69$ $69 \times 2 = 138$	$A = lw$ $= 20 \times 3$ $= 60$ $60 \times 2 = 120$

Add the areas together.
$$SA = 920 + 138 + 120$$
$$= 1\ 178$$

The surface area of the given textbook is 1 178 cm^2.

7. Find the area of each part of the triangular prism.

Front, Back, and Bottom	Sides
(3 equal rectangles)	(2 equal triangles)
$A = lw$ $= 8 \times 4$ $= 32$ $32 \times 3 = 96$	$A = \dfrac{bh}{2}$ $= \dfrac{4 \times 3.5}{2}$ $= 7$ $7 \times 2 = 14$

Add the areas together.
$$SA = 96 + 14$$
$$= 110$$

The surface area of the triangular prism is 110 m^2.

9. Find the area of each part of the rectangular prism.

Front and Back	Top and Bottom	Sides
(2 equal rectangles)	(2 equal rectangles)	(2 equal rectangles)
$A = lw$ $= 10 \times 2$ $= 20$ $20 \times 2 = 40$	$A = lw$ $= 10 \times 5$ $= 50$ $50 \times 2 = 100$	$A = lw$ $= 2 \times 5$ $= 10$ $10 \times 2 = 20$

Add the areas together.
$$SA = 40 + 100 + 20$$
$$= 160$$

The surface area of the rectangular prism is 160 cm^2.

FRACTION OPERATIONS

Lesson 1—Multiplying a Fraction by a Whole Number

YOUR TURN
ANSWERS AND SOLUTIONS

1. a) **Method 1: Using a model**
    The multiplication can be expressed by using repeated addition.

    $$4 \times \frac{3}{7} = \frac{3}{7} + \frac{3}{7} + \frac{3}{7} + \frac{3}{7}$$

    Model the fractions using fraction strips.

    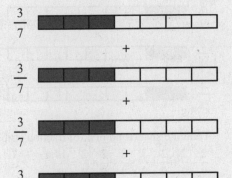

    Total the shaded number of fraction strips.

    $$\frac{3}{7} + \frac{3}{7} + \frac{3}{7} + \frac{3}{7} = \frac{12}{7}$$

    Model the answer, and ensure the final answer is in lowest terms.

    $$\frac{12}{7}$$

    The answer is already in lowest terms.

    $$4 \times \frac{3}{7} = \frac{12}{7}$$
    $$= 1\frac{5}{7}$$

Method 2: Using a diagram of a number line
Model the fractions using a number line.

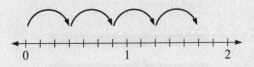

$$\frac{3}{7} + \frac{3}{7} + \frac{3}{7} + \frac{3}{7} = \frac{12}{7}$$
$$= 1\frac{5}{7}$$

Method 3: Showing the multiplication
Multiply the whole number by the numerator, and write the resulting number over the denominator. Ensure the fraction is in lowest terms.

$$\frac{4 \times 3}{7} = \frac{12}{7}$$
$$= 1\frac{5}{7}$$

b) **Method 1: Using a model**
The multiplication can be expressed by using repeated addition.

$$\frac{1}{2} \times 5 = \frac{1}{2} + \frac{1}{2} + \frac{1}{2} + \frac{1}{2} + \frac{1}{2}$$

Model the fractions using fraction strips.

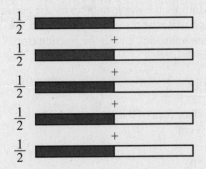

Total the shaded number of fraction strips.

$$\frac{1}{2} + \frac{1}{2} + \frac{1}{2} + \frac{1}{2} + \frac{1}{2} = \frac{5}{2}$$

Model the answer, and ensure the final answer is in lowest terms.

$$\frac{5}{2}$$

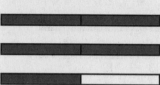

The answer is already in lowest terms.

$$\frac{1}{2} \times 5 = \frac{5}{2}$$
$$= 2\frac{1}{2}$$

Method 2: Using a diagram of a number line

Model the fractions using a number line.

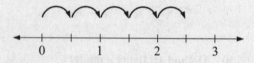

$$\frac{1}{2} + \frac{1}{2} + \frac{1}{2} + \frac{1}{2} + \frac{1}{2} = \frac{5}{2}$$
$$= 2\frac{1}{2}$$

Method 3: Showing the multiplication

Multiply the whole number by the numerator, and write the resulting number over the denominator. Ensure the fraction is in lowest terms.

$$\frac{1 \times 5}{2} = \frac{5}{2}$$
$$= 2\frac{1}{2}$$

c) Method 1: Using a model

The multiplication can be expressed by using repeated addition.

$$7 \times \frac{2}{9} = \frac{2}{9} + \frac{2}{9} + \frac{2}{9} + \frac{2}{9} + \frac{2}{9} + \frac{2}{9} + \frac{2}{9}$$

Model the fractions using fraction strips.

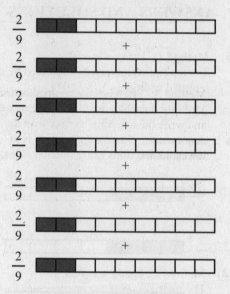

Total the shaded number of fraction strips.

$$\frac{2}{9} + \frac{2}{9} + \frac{2}{9} + \frac{2}{9} + \frac{2}{9} + \frac{2}{9} + \frac{2}{9} = \frac{14}{9}$$

Model the answer, and ensure the final answer is in lowest terms.

$$\frac{14}{9}$$

The answer is already in lowest terms.

$$7 \times \frac{2}{9} = \frac{14}{9}$$
$$= 1\frac{5}{9}$$

Method 2: Using a diagram of a number line

Model the fractions using a number line.

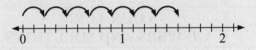

$$\frac{2}{9}+\frac{2}{9}+\frac{2}{9}+\frac{2}{9}+\frac{2}{9}+\frac{2}{9}+\frac{2}{9}=\frac{14}{9}$$
$$=1\frac{5}{9}$$

Method 3: Showing the multiplication

Multiply the whole number by the numerator, and write the resulting number over the denominator. Ensure the fraction is in lowest terms.

$$\frac{7\times2}{9}=\frac{14}{9}$$
$$=1\frac{5}{9}$$

d) **Method 1: Using a model**

The multiplication can be expressed by using repeated addition.

$$\frac{4}{9}\times5=\frac{4}{9}+\frac{4}{9}+\frac{4}{9}+\frac{4}{9}+\frac{4}{9}$$

Model the fractions using fraction strips.

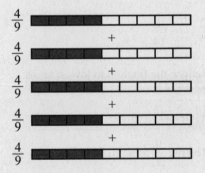

Total the shaded number of fraction strips.

$$\frac{4}{9}+\frac{4}{9}+\frac{4}{9}+\frac{4}{9}+\frac{4}{9}=\frac{20}{9}$$

Model the answer, and ensure the final answer is in lowest terms.

$$\frac{20}{9}$$

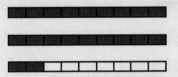

The answer is already in lowest terms.

$$\frac{4}{9}\times5=\frac{20}{9}$$
$$=2\frac{2}{9}$$

Method 2: Using a diagram of a number line

Model the fractions using a number line.

$$\frac{4}{9}+\frac{4}{9}+\frac{4}{9}+\frac{4}{9}+\frac{4}{9}=\frac{20}{9}$$
$$=2\frac{2}{9}$$

Method 3: Showing the multiplication

Multiply the whole number by the numerator, and write the resulting number over the denominator. Ensure the fraction is in lowest terms.

$$\frac{4\times5}{9}=\frac{20}{9}$$
$$=2\frac{2}{9}$$

PRACTICE EXERCISES
ANSWERS AND SOLUTIONS

1. Multiply the whole number by the numerator, and write the resulting number over the denominator.

$$\frac{4 \times 3}{8} = \frac{12}{8}$$

Reduce the fraction to lowest terms.

$$\frac{12 \div 4}{8 \div 4} = \frac{3}{2}$$

Rewrite $\frac{3}{2}$ as a mixed number.

$$\frac{3}{2} \rightarrow 1\frac{1}{2}$$
$$4 \times \frac{3}{8} = 1\frac{1}{2}$$

3. Multiply the whole number by the numerator, and write the resulting number over the denominator.

$$\frac{4 \times 3}{11} = \frac{12}{11}$$

The answer is already in lowest terms.

Rewrite $\frac{12}{11}$ as a mixed number.

$$\frac{12}{11} \rightarrow 1\frac{1}{11}$$
$$\frac{4}{11} \times 3 = 1\frac{1}{11}$$

Lesson 2—Multiplying a Fraction by a Mixed Number

YOUR TURN
ANSWERS AND SOLUTIONS

1. **a)** Change the mixed number to an improper fraction, and multiply by the given fraction.

$$3\frac{3}{7} \rightarrow \frac{24}{7}$$

$$\frac{4}{5} \times \frac{24}{7} = \frac{96}{35}$$

Reduce the fraction to lowest terms.
The fraction is already in lowest terms.

Rewrite $\frac{96}{35}$ as a mixed number.

$$\frac{96}{35} \rightarrow 2\frac{26}{35}$$
$$\frac{4}{5} \times 3\frac{3}{7} = 2\frac{26}{35}$$

b) Change the mixed number to an improper fraction, and multiply by the given fraction.

$$4\frac{1}{2} \rightarrow \frac{9}{2}$$

$$\frac{2}{7} \times \frac{9}{2} = \frac{18}{14}$$

Reduce the fraction to lowest terms.

$$\frac{18 \div 2}{14 \div 2} = \frac{9}{7}$$

Rewrite $\frac{9}{7}$ as a mixed number.

$$\frac{9}{7} \rightarrow 1\frac{2}{7}$$
$$\frac{2}{7} \times 4\frac{1}{2} = 1\frac{2}{7}$$

2. a) Change the mixed number to an improper fraction, and multiply by the given fraction.

$$5\frac{1}{4} \to \frac{21}{4}$$

$$\frac{21 \times 5}{4 \times 8} = \frac{105}{32}$$

Reduce the fraction to lowest terms.
The fraction is already in lowest terms.

Rewrite $\frac{105}{32}$ as a mixed number.

$$\frac{105}{32} \to 3\frac{9}{32}$$
$$5\frac{1}{4} \times \frac{5}{8} = 3\frac{9}{32}$$

b) Change the mixed number to an improper fraction, and multiply by the given fraction.

$$6\frac{1}{4} \to \frac{25}{4}$$

$$\frac{25 \times 7}{4 \times 9} = \frac{175}{36}$$

Reduce the fraction to lowest terms.
The fraction is already in lowest terms.

Rewrite $\frac{175}{36}$ as a mixed number.

$$\frac{175}{36} \to 4\frac{31}{36}$$
$$6\frac{1}{4} \times \frac{7}{9} = 4\frac{31}{36}$$

PRACTICE EXERCISES
ANSWERS AND SOLUTIONS

1. Change the mixed number to an improper fraction, and multiply by the given fraction. Ensure the fraction is in lowest terms.

$$2\frac{2}{7} \to \frac{16}{7}$$

$$\frac{2 \times 16}{3 \times 7} = \frac{32}{21}$$

Reduce the fraction to lowest terms.
The fraction is already in lowest terms.

Rewrite $\frac{32}{21}$ as a mixed number.

$$\frac{32}{21} \to 1\frac{11}{21}$$
$$\frac{2}{3} \times 2\frac{2}{7} = 1\frac{11}{21}$$

3. Change the mixed number to an improper fraction, and multiply by the given fraction. Ensure the fraction is in lowest terms.

$$7\frac{3}{4} \to \frac{31}{4}$$

$$\frac{31}{4} \times \frac{3}{8} = \frac{93}{32}$$

Reduce the fraction to lowest terms.
The fraction is already in lowest terms.

Rewrite $\frac{93}{32}$ as a mixed number.

$$\frac{93}{32} \to 2\frac{29}{32}$$
$$7\frac{3}{4} \times \frac{3}{8} = 2\frac{29}{32}$$

Lesson 3—Dividing a Fraction by a Whole Number

YOUR TURN
ANSWERS AND SOLUTIONS

1. **a)** First, change the whole number to a fraction over 1, and take its reciprocal. Next, multiply the fractions together.

$$5 \to \frac{5}{1} \to \frac{1}{5}$$

$$\frac{3}{4} \div 5 = \frac{3}{4} \times \frac{1}{5}$$
$$= \frac{3}{20}$$

b) First, change the whole number to a fraction over 1, and take its reciprocal. Next, multiply the fractions together.

$$6 \to \frac{6}{1} \to \frac{1}{6}$$

$$\frac{2}{3} \div 6 = \frac{2}{3} \times \frac{1}{6}$$
$$= \frac{2}{18}$$

Reduce the fraction to lowest terms.
$$\frac{2 \div 2}{18 \div 2} = \frac{1}{9}$$

$$\frac{2}{3} \div 6 = \frac{1}{9}$$

c) First, change the whole number to a fraction over 1, and take its reciprocal. Next, multiply the fractions together.

$$7 \to \frac{7}{1} \to \frac{1}{7}$$

$$\frac{1}{5} \div 7 = \frac{1}{5} \times \frac{1}{7}$$
$$= \frac{1}{35}$$

d) First, change the whole number to a fraction over 1, and take its reciprocal. Next, multiply the fractions together.

$$12 \to \frac{12}{1} \to \frac{1}{12}$$

$$\frac{4}{7} \div 12 = \frac{4}{7} \times \frac{1}{12}$$
$$= \frac{4}{84}$$

Reduce the fraction to lowest terms.
$$\frac{4 \div 4}{84 \div 4} = \frac{1}{21}$$

$$\frac{4}{7} \div 12 = \frac{1}{21}$$

PRACTICE EXERCISES
ANSWERS AND SOLUTIONS

1. First, change the whole number to a fraction over 1, and take its reciprocal. Next, multiply the fractions together.

$$5 \to \frac{5}{1} \to \frac{1}{5}$$

$$\frac{1}{3} \div 5 = \frac{1}{3} \times \frac{1}{5}$$
$$= \frac{1}{15}$$

3. First, change the whole number to a fraction over 1, and take its reciprocal. Next, multiply the fractions together.

$$4 \to \frac{4}{1} \to \frac{1}{4}$$

$$\frac{4}{5} \div 4 = \frac{4}{5} \times \frac{1}{4}$$
$$= \frac{4}{20}$$

Reduce the fraction to lowest terms.
$$\frac{4 \div 4}{20 \div 4} = \frac{1}{5}$$

$$\frac{4}{5} \div 4 = \frac{1}{5}$$

Lesson 4—Dividing by a Fraction

YOUR TURN
ANSWERS AND SOLUTIONS

1. Take the reciprocal of the fraction after the division sign.

    $$\frac{2}{9} \rightarrow \frac{9}{2}$$

    Multiply the resulting fractions.

    $$\frac{7}{10} \div \frac{2}{9} = \frac{7}{10} \times \frac{9}{2}$$
    $$= \frac{63}{20}$$
    $$= 3\frac{3}{20}$$

2. Take the reciprocal of the fraction after the division sign.

    $$\frac{3}{4} \rightarrow \frac{4}{3}$$

    Multiply the whole number by the numerator of the reciprocal fraction, leaving the denominator as written.

    $$3 \div \frac{3}{4} = 3 \times \frac{4}{3}$$
    $$= \frac{3 \times 4}{3}$$
    $$= \frac{12}{3}$$
    $$= 4$$

3. Convert the mixed number to an improper fraction.

    $$3\frac{2}{5} \rightarrow \frac{17}{5}$$

    Take the reciprocal of the fraction after the division sign.

    $$\frac{1}{4} \rightarrow \frac{4}{1}$$

    Multiply the resulting fractions together.

    $$3\frac{2}{5} \div \frac{1}{4} = \frac{17}{5} \times \frac{4}{1}$$
    $$= \frac{68}{5}$$
    $$= 13\frac{3}{5}$$

PRACTICE EXERCISES
ANSWERS AND SOLUTIONS

1. Take the reciprocal of the fraction after the division sign.

    $$\frac{4}{5} \rightarrow \frac{5}{4}$$

    Multiply the resulting fractions.

    $$\frac{1}{7} \div \frac{4}{5} = \frac{1}{7} \times \frac{5}{4}$$
    $$= \frac{5}{28}$$

3. Convert the mixed number to an improper fraction.

    $$2\frac{2}{5} \rightarrow \frac{12}{5}$$

    Take the reciprocal of the fraction after the division sign.

    $$\frac{1}{7} \rightarrow \frac{7}{1}$$

    Multiply the resulting fractions together.

    $$2\frac{2}{5} \div \frac{1}{7} = \frac{12}{5} \times \frac{7}{1}$$
    $$= \frac{84}{5}$$
    $$= 16\frac{4}{5}$$

Lesson 5—Using Order of Operations to Solve Problems

YOUR TURN
ANSWERS AND SOLUTIONS

1. Follow the order of operations.

$6 \times \frac{1}{2} = \frac{6 \times 1}{2}$ $= \frac{6}{2}$ $= 3$	First, multiply.

$2 \div \dfrac{5}{3} = 2 \times \dfrac{3}{5}$ $= \dfrac{2 \times 3}{5}$ $= \dfrac{6}{5}$	Divide.
$3 - \dfrac{6}{5} = \dfrac{15}{5} - \dfrac{6}{5}$ $= \dfrac{9}{5}$	Subtract.
$\dfrac{9}{5} \rightarrow 1\dfrac{4}{5}$	Change $\dfrac{9}{5}$ into a mixed number.

$$6 \times \dfrac{1}{2} - 2 \div \dfrac{5}{3} = 1\dfrac{4}{5}$$

2. Follow the order of operations.

$\left(\dfrac{3}{5} - \dfrac{1}{3}\right) = \left(\dfrac{9}{15} - \dfrac{5}{15}\right)$ $= \dfrac{4}{15}$	Evaluate the expression in the brackets first.
$2\dfrac{1}{5} \div \dfrac{4}{15} = \dfrac{11}{5} \div \dfrac{4}{15}$ $= \dfrac{11}{5} \times \dfrac{15}{4}$ $= \dfrac{165}{20}$	Divide.
$= \dfrac{165 \div 5}{20 \div 5}$ $= \dfrac{33}{4}$	Reduce the fraction to lowest terms.
$\dfrac{33}{4} = 8\dfrac{1}{4}$	Change $\dfrac{33}{4}$ into a mixed number.

$$2\dfrac{1}{5} \div \left(\dfrac{3}{5} - \dfrac{1}{3}\right) = 8\dfrac{1}{4}$$

3. Follow the order of operations.

$\left(1\dfrac{1}{8} - \dfrac{2}{3}\right) = \left(\dfrac{9}{8} - \dfrac{2}{3}\right)$ $= \left(\dfrac{27}{24} - \dfrac{16}{24}\right)$ $= \dfrac{11}{24}$	Evaluate the expression in the brackets first.
$2\dfrac{2}{5} \times 1\dfrac{1}{2} = \dfrac{12}{5} \times \dfrac{3}{2}$ $= \dfrac{12 \times 3}{5 \times 2}$ $= \dfrac{36}{10}$	Multiply.
$\dfrac{36}{10} \div \dfrac{11}{24} = \dfrac{36}{10} \times \dfrac{24}{11}$ $= \dfrac{864}{110}$	Divide.
$= \dfrac{864 \div 2}{110 \div 2}$ $= \dfrac{432}{55}$	Reduce the fraction to lowest terms.
$\dfrac{432}{55} = 7\dfrac{47}{55}$	Change $\dfrac{432}{55}$ into a mixed number.

$$2\dfrac{2}{5} \times 1\dfrac{1}{2} \div \left(1\dfrac{1}{8} - \dfrac{2}{3}\right) = 7\dfrac{47}{55}$$

4. Note that three-quarters represents $\dfrac{3}{4}$ and two-thirds represents $\dfrac{2}{3}$.

Here, $\dfrac{3}{4}$ of the land on the farm is used as grazing land for cattle. Therefore, $\left(1 - \dfrac{3}{4}\right)$ land is used to grow crops.

Also, $\dfrac{2}{3}$ of the land for crops is used to grow grain. Therefore, the total land that can be used to grow gain is $\dfrac{2}{3}\left(1 - \dfrac{3}{4}\right)$.

Evaluate $\dfrac{2}{3}\left(1 - \dfrac{3}{4}\right)$.

Follow the order of operations.

$\left(1-\dfrac{3}{4}\right)=\left(\dfrac{4}{4}-\dfrac{3}{4}\right)$ $\qquad =\dfrac{1}{4}$	Evaluate the expression in the brackets first.
$\dfrac{2}{3}\left(\dfrac{1}{4}\right)=\dfrac{2\times1}{3\times4}$ $\qquad =\dfrac{2}{12}$	Multiply.
$=\dfrac{2\div2}{12\div2}$ $=\dfrac{1}{6}$	Reduce the fraction to lowest terms.

One-sixth of the land is used to grow grain.

PRACTICE EXERCISES
ANSWERS AND SOLUTIONS

1. Follow the order of operations.

$12\times\dfrac{1}{3}=\dfrac{12\times1}{3}$ $\qquad =4$	Multiply.
$\dfrac{1}{3}\div\dfrac{11}{8}=\dfrac{1}{3}\times\dfrac{8}{11}$ $\qquad =\dfrac{8}{33}$	Divide.
$=4-\dfrac{8}{33}$ $=\dfrac{4}{1}-\dfrac{8}{33}$ $=\dfrac{132}{33}-\dfrac{8}{33}$ $=\dfrac{124}{33}$	Subtract.
$\dfrac{124}{33}=3\dfrac{25}{33}$	Change $\dfrac{124}{33}$ into a mixed number.

$$12\times\dfrac{1}{3}-\dfrac{1}{3}\div\dfrac{11}{8}=3\dfrac{25}{33}$$

3. Follow the order of operations.

$\left(2\dfrac{1}{8}-\dfrac{4}{5}\right)=\left(\dfrac{17}{8}-\dfrac{4}{5}\right)$ $\qquad =\left(\dfrac{85}{40}-\dfrac{32}{40}\right)$ $\qquad =\dfrac{53}{40}$	Evaluate the expression in the brackets first.
$=5\dfrac{3}{4}\times1\dfrac{1}{3}$ $=\dfrac{23}{4}\times\dfrac{4}{3}$ $=\dfrac{92}{12}$	Multiply.
$\dfrac{92}{12}\div\dfrac{53}{40}=\dfrac{92}{12}\times\dfrac{40}{53}$ $\qquad =\dfrac{3\,680}{636}$	Divide.
$\dfrac{3\,680}{636}+\dfrac{1}{2}=\dfrac{3\,680}{636}+\dfrac{318}{636}$ $\qquad =\dfrac{3\,998}{636}$	Add.
$=\dfrac{3\,998\div2}{636\div2}$ $=\dfrac{1\,999}{318}$	Reduce the fraction to lowest terms.
$\dfrac{1\,999}{318}=6\dfrac{91}{318}$	Change $\dfrac{1\,999}{318}$ into a mixed number.

$$5\dfrac{3}{4}\times1\dfrac{1}{3}\div\left(2\dfrac{1}{8}-\dfrac{4}{5}\right)+\dfrac{1}{2}=6\dfrac{91}{318}$$

5. Follow the order of operations.

$1\dfrac{1}{5} \times 2\dfrac{3}{5} = \dfrac{6}{5} \times \dfrac{13}{5}$ $= \dfrac{78}{25}$	Multiply.
$\dfrac{78}{25} \div \dfrac{1}{5} = \dfrac{78}{25} \times \dfrac{5}{1}$ $= \dfrac{390}{25}$	Divide.
$\dfrac{390}{25} + \dfrac{1}{5} = \dfrac{390}{25} + \dfrac{5}{25}$ $= \dfrac{395}{25}$	Add.
$= \dfrac{395 \div 5}{25 \div 5}$ $= \dfrac{79}{5}$	Reduce the fraction to lowest terms.
$\dfrac{79}{5} = 15\dfrac{4}{5}$	Change $\dfrac{79}{5}$ into a mixed number.

$$1\dfrac{1}{5} \times 2\dfrac{3}{5} \div \dfrac{1}{5} + \dfrac{1}{5} = 15\dfrac{4}{5}$$

PRACTICE TEST
ANSWERS AND SOLUTIONS

1. **Method 1: Using a model**

The multiplication can be expressed by using repeated addition.

$$2 \times \dfrac{5}{7} = \dfrac{5}{7} + \dfrac{5}{7}$$

Model the fractions using fraction strips.

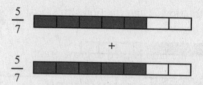

Total the shaded number of fraction strips.

$$\dfrac{5}{7} + \dfrac{5}{7} = \dfrac{10}{7}$$
$$= 1\dfrac{3}{7}$$

Model the answer, and ensure the final answer is in lowest terms.

$$\dfrac{10}{7}$$

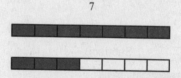

The answer is already in lowest terms.

$$2 \times \dfrac{5}{7} = \dfrac{10}{7}$$
$$= 1\dfrac{3}{7}$$

Method 2: Using a diagram of a number line

Model the fractions using a number line.

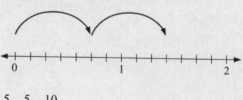

$$\dfrac{5}{7} + \dfrac{5}{7} = \dfrac{10}{7}$$
$$= 1\dfrac{3}{7}$$

Method 3: Showing the multiplication

Multiply the whole number by the numerator, and write the resulting number over the denominator.

$$\frac{5 \times 2}{7} = \frac{10}{7}$$
$$= 1\frac{3}{7}$$

3. **Method 1: Using a model**

The multiplication can be expressed by using repeated addition.

$$\frac{5}{9} \times 3 = \frac{5}{9} + \frac{5}{9} + \frac{5}{9}$$

Model the fractions using fraction strips.

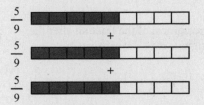

Total the shaded number of fraction strips.

$$\frac{5}{9} + \frac{5}{9} + \frac{5}{9} = \frac{15}{9}$$
$$= 1\frac{6}{9}$$

Model the answer, and ensure the final answer is in lowest terms.

$$\frac{15}{9}$$

The answer is already in lowest terms.

$$\frac{5}{9} \times 3 = \frac{15}{9}$$
$$= 1\frac{6}{9}$$

Method 2: Using a diagram of a number line

Model the fractions using a number line.

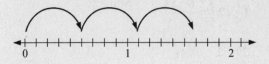

$$\frac{5}{9} + \frac{5}{9} + \frac{5}{9} = \frac{15}{9}$$
$$= 1\frac{6}{9}$$

Method 3: Showing the multiplication

Multiply the whole number by the numerator, and write the resulting number over the denominator.

$$\frac{5 \times 3}{9} = \frac{15}{9}$$
$$= 1\frac{6}{9}$$

5. Change the mixed number to an improper fraction, and multiply by the given fraction.

$$3\frac{2}{7} \rightarrow \frac{23}{7}$$

$$\frac{4}{5} \times \frac{23}{7} = \frac{92}{35}$$

Rewrite $\frac{92}{35}$ as a mixed number.

$$\frac{92}{35} \rightarrow 2\frac{22}{35}$$
$$\frac{4}{5} \times 3\frac{2}{7} = 2\frac{22}{35}$$

7. Change the mixed number to an improper fraction, and multiply by the given fraction.

$$8\frac{3}{4} \rightarrow \frac{35}{4}$$

$$\frac{5}{8} \times \frac{35}{4} = \frac{175}{32}$$

Rewrite $\frac{175}{32}$ as a mixed number.

$$\frac{175}{32} \rightarrow 5\frac{15}{32}$$
$$\frac{5}{8} \times 8\frac{3}{4} = 5\frac{15}{32}$$

9. Change the mixed number to an improper fraction, and multiply by the given fraction.

$$7\frac{1}{4} \rightarrow \frac{29}{4}$$

$$\frac{29}{4} \times \frac{2}{3} = \frac{58}{12}$$

Reduce the fraction to lowest terms.

$$\frac{58 \div 2}{12 \div 2} = \frac{29}{6}$$

Rewrite $\frac{29}{6}$ as a mixed number.

$$\frac{29}{6} \rightarrow 4\frac{5}{6}$$

$$7\frac{1}{4} \times \frac{2}{3} = 4\frac{5}{6}$$

11. First, change the whole number to a fraction over 1, and take its reciprocal. Next, multiply the fractions together.

$$7 \rightarrow \frac{7}{1} \rightarrow \frac{1}{7}$$

$$\frac{1}{4} \div 7 = \frac{1}{4} \times \frac{1}{7}$$
$$= \frac{1}{28}$$

13. First, change the whole number to a fraction over 1, and take its reciprocal. Next, multiply the fractions together.

$$9 \rightarrow \frac{9}{1} \rightarrow \frac{1}{9}$$

$$\frac{7}{11} \div 9 = \frac{7}{11} \times \frac{1}{9}$$
$$= \frac{7}{99}$$

15. First, change the whole number to a fraction over 1, and take its reciprocal. Next, multiply the fractions together.

$$5 \rightarrow \frac{5}{1} \rightarrow \frac{1}{5}$$

$$\frac{9}{13} \div 5 = \frac{9}{13} \times \frac{1}{5}$$
$$= \frac{9}{65}$$

17. Take the reciprocal of the fraction after the division sign.

$$\frac{3}{8} \rightarrow \frac{8}{3}$$

Multiply the whole number by the numerator of the reciprocal fraction, leaving the denominator as written.

$$11 \div \frac{3}{8} = 11 \times \frac{8}{3}$$
$$= \frac{11 \times 8}{3}$$
$$= \frac{88}{3}$$
$$= 29\frac{1}{3}$$

19. Take the reciprocal of the fraction after the division sign.

$$\frac{1}{2} \rightarrow \frac{2}{1}$$

Multiply the resulting fractions.

$$\frac{2}{5} \div \frac{1}{2} = \frac{2}{5} \times \frac{2}{1}$$
$$= \frac{4}{5}$$

21. Convert the mixed number to an improper fraction.

$$2\frac{2}{7} \rightarrow \frac{16}{7}$$

Take the reciprocal of the fraction after the division sign.

$$\frac{1}{7} \rightarrow \frac{7}{1}$$

Multiply the resulting fractions together.

$$2\frac{2}{7} \div \frac{1}{7} = \frac{16}{7} \times \frac{7}{1}$$
$$= \frac{112}{7}$$
$$= 16$$

23. Convert the mixed number to an improper fraction.

$$9\frac{1}{4} \rightarrow \frac{37}{4}$$

Take the reciprocal of the fraction after the division sign.

$$\frac{13}{16} \rightarrow \frac{16}{13}$$

Multiply the resulting fractions together.

$$9\frac{1}{4} \div \frac{13}{16} = \frac{37}{4} \times \frac{16}{13}$$
$$= \frac{592}{52}$$
$$= \frac{148}{13}$$
$$= 11\frac{5}{13}$$

25. Follow the order of operations.

$\left(2\frac{1}{4} \div \frac{1}{2}\right) = \left(\frac{9}{4} \div \frac{1}{2}\right)$ $= \left(\frac{9}{4} \times \frac{2}{1}\right)$ $= \frac{18}{4}$	Evaluate the expression in the brackets first.
$3\frac{1}{2} \times \frac{18}{4} = \frac{7}{2} \times \frac{18}{4}$ $= \frac{126}{8}$	Multiply.
$\frac{126}{8} - \frac{1}{4} = \frac{126}{8} - \frac{2}{8}$ $= \frac{124}{8}$	Subtract.
$\frac{124 \div 4}{8 \div 4} = \frac{31}{2}$	Reduce the fraction to lowest terms.
$\frac{31}{2} = 15\frac{1}{2}$	Change $\frac{31}{2}$ into a mixed number.

$$3\frac{1}{2} \times \left(2\frac{1}{4} \div \frac{1}{2}\right) - \frac{1}{4} = 15\frac{1}{2}$$

27. One-third is represented by $\frac{1}{3}$, and two-thirds is represented by $\frac{2}{3}$.

The expression to represent the total cost is

$$3\left(\frac{1}{3} \times 15\right) + (4 \times 15) + 2\left(\frac{2}{3} \times 15\right).$$

Evaluate this expression using order of operations.

Evaluate the expression in the brackets first.

$$3\left(\frac{1}{3} \times 15\right) + (4 \times 15) + 2\left(\frac{2}{3} \times 15\right)$$
$$= 3(5) + 60 + 2(10)$$
$$= 15 + 60 + 20$$
$$= 95$$

Jake spent $95.

VOLUME

Lesson 1—Calculating the Volume of Prisms

YOUR TURN
ANSWERS AND SOLUTIONS

1. Substitute the known values in the volume formula.
$$V = A_{base} \times h$$
$$= (lw)h$$
$$= 4 \times 21 \times 5$$
$$= 420 \text{ cm}^3$$

2. Substitute the known values in the volume formula.
$$V = A_{base} \times h$$
$$= (lw)h$$
$$= 4 \times 4 \times 4$$
$$= 64 \text{ mm}^3$$

3. Substitute the known values in the volume formula.
$$V = A_{base} \times h$$
$$= \left(\frac{lw}{2} \right) \times h$$
$$= \frac{3 \times 2 \times 4.5}{2}$$
$$= \frac{27}{2}$$
$$= 13.5 \text{ m}^3$$

PRACTICE EXERCISES
ANSWERS AND SOLUTIONS

1. For a rectangular prism, the base is a rectangle, and the height is how high the prism. The height of the prism is 75 cm.

   Substitute the known values in the volume formula.
$$V = A_{base} \times h$$
$$= (lw)h$$
$$= 40 \times 25 \times 75$$
$$= 75\ 000 \text{ cm}^3$$

3. For a triangular prism, the base is a triangle, and the height is how much the prism rises.

   Substitute the known values in the volume formula.
$$V = A_{base} \times h$$
$$= \left(\frac{lw}{2} \right) \times h$$
$$= \frac{5 \times 12 \times 7}{2}$$
$$= \frac{420}{2}$$
$$= 210 \text{ m}^3$$

Lesson 2—Calculating the Volume of Cylinders

YOUR TURN
ANSWERS AND SOLUTIONS

1. Convert the height into millimetres.

   Since 10 mm = 1 cm, 180 mm = 18 cm.

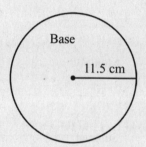

Base

11.5 cm

   The height of the cylinder is 18 cm.
   Substitute the known values in the volume formula.
$$V = \pi r^2 h$$
$$= 3.14 \times (11.5)^2 \times 18$$
$$= 3.14 \times 132.25 \times 18$$
$$= 7\ 474.77 \text{ cm}^3$$

PRACTICE EXERCISES
ANSWERS AND SOLUTIONS

1. Determine the radius of the cylinder.

$$r = \frac{17}{2}$$
$$= 8.5 \text{ m}$$

The height of the cylinder is 24 m.

Substitute the known values in the volume formula.

$$V = \pi r^2 h$$
$$= 3.14 \times (8.5)^2 \times 24$$
$$= 3.14 \times 72.25 \times 24$$
$$= 5\,444.76 \text{ m}^3$$

3. The height of the cylinder is 4.6 mm.

Substitute the known values in the volume formula.

$$V = \pi r^2 h$$
$$= 3.14 \times (1.5)^2 \times 4.6$$
$$= 3.14 \times 2.25 \times 4.6$$
$$= 32.499 \text{ mm}^3$$

Lesson 3—Problem Solving Involving Volumes of Prisms and Cylinders

YOUR TURN
ANSWERS AND SOLUTIONS

1. Substitute the known values in the volume formula.

$$V = A_{base} \times h$$
$$= (lw)h$$
$$= 10 \times 10 \times 25$$
$$= 2\,500 \text{ cm}^3$$

The milk carton can hold 2 500 cm³ of milk.

2. First, find the volume of the larger cylinder as if it were one solid piece. Then, find the volume of the small cylinder cut out of the middle. Finally, subtract the volume of the smaller cylinder from the volume of the larger cylinder.

$$V_{\text{large cylinder}} = \pi r^2 h$$
$$= 3.14 \times (6)^2 \times 15$$
$$= 3.14 \times 36 \times 15$$
$$= 1\,695.6 \text{ cm}^3$$

$$V_{\text{small cylinder}} = \pi r^2 h$$
$$= 3.14 \times (2)^2 \times 15$$
$$= 3.14 \times 4 \times 15$$
$$= 188.4 \text{ cm}^3$$

$$V = V_{\text{large cylinder}} - V_{\text{small cylinder}}$$
$$= 1\,695.6 - 188.4$$
$$= 1\,507.2 \text{ cm}^3$$

The volume of the remaining portion is 1 507.2 cm³.

3. A pop can is a cylinder. Calculate the volume of the cylinder. Then, divide by two because the can is only half full.

Find the length of the radius of the circular base first.

$$r = \frac{6}{2}$$
$$= 3 \text{ cm}$$

$$V = \pi r^2 h$$
$$= 3.14 \times (3)^2 \times 25$$
$$= 3.14 \times 9 \times 25$$
$$= 706.5 \text{ cm}^3$$
$$706.5 \div 2 = 353.25 \text{ cm}^3$$

There is 353.25 cm³ of pop in the half-full can.

PRACTICE EXERCISES
ANSWERS AND SOLUTIONS

1. The fish tank is a rectangular prism. Determine the volume to see how much water it can hold.

   Substitute the known values in the volume formula.
   $$V = A_{base} \times h$$
   $$= (lw)h$$
   $$= 90 \times 75 \times 60$$
   $$= 405\ 000 \text{ cm}^3$$

   The fish tank can hold 405 000 cm³ of water.

3. Determine the volume of the cube to see how many cubic centimetres of peanuts are needed to fill the cube.

   Substitute the known values in the volume formula.
   $$V = A_{base} \times h$$
   $$= (lw)h$$
   $$= 55 \times 55 \times 55$$
   $$= 166\ 375 \text{ cm}^3$$

   Therefore, 166 375 cm³ of peanuts are needed to fill the cube.

Practice Test

ANSWERS AND SOLUTIONS

1. For a rectangular prism, the base is a rectangle, and the height is how high the prism rises. The height of the prism is 5 cm.

   Substitute the known values in the volume formula.
   $$V = A_{base} \times h$$
   $$= (lw)h$$
   $$= 14 \times 7 \times 5$$
   $$= 490 \text{ cm}^3$$

3. Since all six faces of a cube are identical squares, the base is a square and the height is the length of one side of the square. The length, width, and height of the cube are the same.

   Substitute the known values in the volume formula.
   $$V = A_{base} \times h$$
   $$= (lw)h$$
   $$= 31 \times 31 \times 31$$
   $$= 29\ 791 \text{ mm}^3$$

5. Since 1 m = 100 cm, 800 cm = 8 m.
   The height of the cylinder is 8 m.

   Substitute the known values in the volume formula.
   $$V = \pi r^2 h$$
   $$= 3.14 \times (2)^2 \times 8$$
   $$= 3.14 \times 4 \times 8$$
   $$= 100.48 \text{ m}^3$$

7. Since 1 m = 100 cm, 0.125 m = 12.5 cm.
   The height of the cylinder is 12.5 cm.

   Substitute the known values in the volume formula.
   $$V = \pi r^2 h$$
   $$= 3.14 \times (15.8)^2 \times 12.5$$
   $$= 3.14 \times 249.64 \times 12.5$$
   $$= 9\ 798.37 \text{ cm}^3$$

   The cylindrical vessel can hold 9 798.37 cm³ of liquid.

9. First, find the volume of the larger cylinder as if it were one solid piece. Then, find the volume of the small cylinder cut out of the middle. Finally, subtract the volume of the smaller cylinder from the volume of the larger cylinder.

   $$V_{\text{large cylinder}} = \pi r^2 h$$
   $$= 3.14 \times (3)^2 \times 9$$
   $$= 3.14 \times 9 \times 9$$
   $$= 254.34 \text{ m}^3$$

   $$V_{\text{small cylinder}} = \pi r^2 h$$
   $$= 3.14 \times (1)^2 \times 9$$
   $$= 3.14 \times 1 \times 9$$
   $$= 28.26 \text{ m}^3$$

   $$V_{\text{required}} = V_{\text{large cylinder}} - V_{\text{small cylinder}}$$
   $$= 254.34 - 28.26$$
   $$= 226.08 \text{ m}^3$$

   The volume of the remaining portion is 226.08 m³.

INTEGER OPERATIONS

Lesson 1—Multiplying Integers Using Integer Tiles

YOUR TURN
ANSWERS AND SOLUTIONS

1. **Step 1**
Determine how many integers are in the set.

The second integer, (+2), indicates there will be two positive (shaded) tiles in each set.

Step 2
Determine how many sets to draw.

The first integer, (+4), indicates there will be four sets of two positive (shaded) tiles.

Step 3
Calculate the product.

The shade and the number of the tiles represent the product. Eight positive tiles are shown.
The product is (+8).
(+4) × (+2) = (+8)

2. **Step 1**
Determine how many integers are in the set.

The second integer, (−5), indicates there will be five negative (unshaded) tiles in each set.

Step 2
Determine how many sets to draw.

The first integer, (+3), indicates there will be three sets of five negative (unshaded) tiles.

Step 3
Calculate the product.

The shade and the number of the remaining tiles represent the product. Fifteen negative tiles are shown. The product is (−15).
(+3) × (−5) = (−15)

3. **Step 1**
Use the associative property to create a positive multiplier.

(−5) × (+2) is the same as (+2) × (−5).

Step 2
Determine how many integers are in the set.

The second integer, (−5), indicates there will be five negative (unshaded) tiles in each set.

Step 3
Determine how many sets to draw.

The first integer, (+2), there will be two sets of five negative (unshaded) tiles.

Step 4
Calculate the product.

The shade and the number of the tiles represent the product. Ten negative tiles are shown.
The product is (−10).
(−5) × (+2) = (−10)

4. **Step 1**
Determine how many pairs are in the set.

The second integer indicates there will be three zero pairs in each set.

Step 2
Determine how many zero pairs to draw.

The first integer indicates there will be three sets of three zero pairs.

Step 3
Calculate the product

The first integer indicates how many sets to take away, and the second integer indicates which sets to take away. Remove three sets of (–3) tiles.

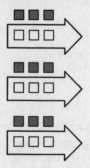

Nine positive tiles remain, meaning the product is (+9).
(–3) × (–3) = (+9)

PRACTICE EXERCISES
ANSWERS AND SOLUTIONS

1. **Step 1**
Determine how many integers are in the set.

The second integer, (+2), indicates there will be two positive (shaded) tiles in each set.

Step 2
Determine how many sets to draw.

The first integer, (+5), indicates there will be five sets of two positive (shaded) tiles.

Step 3
Calculate the product.

The shade and the number of the tiles represent the product. Ten positive tiles are shown. The product is (+10).
(+5) × (+2) = (+10)

3. **Step 1**
Use the associative property to create a positive multiplier.

(–2) × (+6) is the same as (+6) × (–2).

Step 2
Determine how many integers are in the set.

The second integer, (–2), indicates there will be two negative (unshaded) tiles in each set.

□□

Step 3
Determine how many sets to draw.

The first integer, (+6), indicates there are six sets of two negative (unshaded) tiles.

Step 4
Calculate the product.

The shade and the number of the remaining tiles represent the product. Twelve negative tiles are shown. The product is (–12).
(–2) × (+6) = (–12)

5. **Step 1**
Determine how many zero pairs are in the set.

The second integer, (–4), indicates there are four zero pairs in each set.

Step 2
Determine how many sets of zero pairs to draw.

The first integer, (–4), indicates there are four sets of four zero pairs.

Step 3
Calculate the product.

The first integer, (–4), indicates the number of sets to take away. The second integer, (–4), indicates which sets to take away.

Take away 4 sets of (–4) tiles.

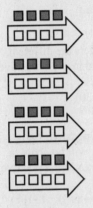

The shade and the number of the remaining tiles represent the sum.

Sixteen positive tiles remain. The product is (+16).
$(–4) \times (–4) = (+16)$

Lesson 2—Multiplying Integers Using Number Lines

YOUR TURN
ANSWERS AND SOLUTIONS

1. The first integer indicates how many lines to draw above the number line, and the second integer indicates the size of each line and the direction. Four lines of 2 will be drawn to the right of zero.

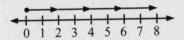

The product is (+8).

2. The first integer indicates how many lines to draw above the number line, and the second integer indicates the size of each line and the direction. Three lines of 5 will be drawn to the left of zero.

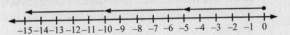

The product is (–15).

3. Use the associative property to create a positive first integer.
$(–2) \times (+5) = (+5) \times (–2)$

The first integer indicates how many lines to draw above the number line, and the second integer indicates the size of each line and the direction. Five lines of (–2) will be drawn to the left of zero.

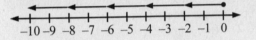

The product is (–10).

4. Since both integers are negative, you can change both integers to positive and still get a correct answer.
$(–3) \times (–3) = (+3) \times (+3)$

The first integer indicates how many lines to draw above the number line, and the second integer indicates the size of each line and the direction. Three lines of 3 will be drawn to the right of zero.

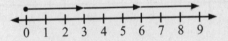

The product is (+9).

PRACTICE EXERCISES
ANSWERS AND SOLUTIONS

1. The first integer indicates how many lines to draw above the number line. Four lines will be drawn. The second integer indicates the size of each line and the direction. Lines with size 5 will be drawn to the right of zero. The correct modelling is shown in the figure.

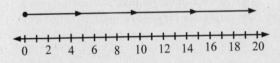

The product is (+20).

3. Use the associative property to create a positive first integer. $(-5) \times (+2) = (+2) \times (-5)$

The first integer indicates how many lines to draw above the number line. Two lines will be drawn. The second integer indicates the size of each line and the direction. Lines with size (-5) will be drawn to the left of zero. The correct modelling is shown in the figure.

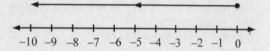

Following the lines from beginning to end shows the product, which is (-10).

5. Since both integers are negative, you can change both integers to positive.
$(-2) \times (-8) = (+2) \times (+8)$

The expression can be modeled just like any other expression with two positive integers.

The first integer indicates how many lines to draw above the number line. Two lines will be drawn. The second integer indicates the size of each line and the direction. Lines with size 8 will be drawn to the right of zero. The correct modelling is shown in the figure.

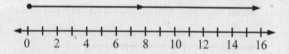

Following the lines from beginning to end shows the product, which is $(+16)$.

Lesson 3—Multiplying Integers Using Expressions

YOUR TURN
ANSWERS AND SOLUTIONS

1. Since the signs of the two integers are the same, multiply the values together and insert a positive sign in front of the product.
$5 \times 8 = 40 \rightarrow (+5) \times (+8) = (+40)$

2. Since the signs of the two integers are the same, multiply the values together and insert a positive sign in front of the product.
$4 \times 9 = 36 \rightarrow (-4) \times (-9) = (+36)$

3. Since the signs of the two integers are different, multiply the values together and insert a negative sign in front of the product.
$4 \times 11 = 44 \rightarrow (+4) \times (-11) = (-44)$

4. Since the signs of the two integers are different, multiply the values together and insert a negative sign in front of the product.
$3 \times 10 = 30 \rightarrow (-3) \times (+10) = (-30)$

5. There is an even number (2) of negative signs, which indicates that the answer will be positive. Multiply the values together and insert a positive sign in front of the answer.
$2 \times 6 \times 3 \times 3 = 108 \rightarrow (+2)(-6)(-3)(+3) = (+108)$

6. There is an odd number (1) of negative signs, which indicates that the answer will be negative. Multiply the values together and insert a negative sign in front of the answer.
$3 \times 5 \times 4 = 60 \rightarrow (-3)(+5)(+4) = (-60)$

PRACTICE EXERCISES
ANSWERS AND SOLUTIONS

1. Multiply the values.

The values are 3 and 7.
$3 \times 7 = 21$

Insert a positive (+) integer sign in front of the product.
$(+3) \times (+7) = (+21)$

3. Multiply the values.

The values are 3 and 6.
$3 \times 6 = 18$

Insert a negative (−) integer sign in front of the product.
$(+3) \times (-6) = (-18)$

5. Multiply the values.

The values are 8 and 7.

$8 \times 7 = 56$
Insert a negative (–) integer sign in front of
the product.
$(+8) \times (-7) = (-56)$

7. Multiply the values.

The values are 5, 4, and 9.
$5 \times 4 \times 9 = 180$

Count the number of negative integer signs.
There is an even number of negative signs (2)
in this expression. Therefore, the solution will
be positive.
$(-5)(+4)(-9) = (+180)$

9. Multiply the values.

The values are 3, 4, 5, and 6.
$3 \times 4 \times 5 \times 6 = 360$

Count the number of negative integer signs.
There is an odd number of negative signs (3) in
this expression. Therefore, the solution will
be negative.
$(-3)(+4)(-5)(-6) = (-360)$

Lesson 4—Dividing Integers Using Integer Tiles

YOUR TURN
ANSWERS AND SOLUTIONS

1. **Step 1**
Rewrite the expression as a multiplication
equation.
$(\_) \times (+4) = (+8)$

Step 2
Draw the integer tiles to represent the
multiplication equation.

(+4) indicates sets of 4 positive (shaded) tiles.
The product is 8 positive (shaded) tiles.

Draw 2 sets of 4 positive tiles to make
8 positive tiles.

Step 3
Calculate the quotient.

The number of sets indicates the missing number.
Adding (+) indicates the integer sign. Two sets of
tiles were added. The quotient is (+2).
$(+8) \div (+4) = (+2)$

2. **Step 1**
Rewrite the expression as a multiplication
equation.
$(\_) \times (-4) = (-8)$

Step 2
Draw the integer tiles to represent the
multiplication equation.

(–4) indicates sets of 4 negative (unshaded) tiles.
The product is 8 negative (unshaded) tiles.

Draw 2 sets of 4 negative tiles to make
8 negative tiles.

Step 3
Calculate the quotient.

The number of sets indicates the missing number.
Adding (+) indicates the integer sign. Two sets of
tiles were added. The quotient is (+2).
$(-8) \div (-4) = (+2)$

3. **Step 1**
Rewrite the expression as a multiplication
equation.
$(\_) \times (-4) = (+8)$

Step 2
Draw the integer tiles to represent the
multiplication equation.

(–4) indicates sets of 4 negative (unshaded) tiles.
The product is 8 positive (shaded) tiles.

Draw 8 zero pairs.

417

Step 3
Calculate the quotient.

Subtract the number of sets to equal the product of the multiplication equation. Two sets of four negative tiles were subtracted to equal (+8).

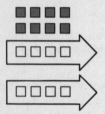

The quotient is (–2).
(+8) ÷ (–4) = (–2)

4. **Step 1**
Rewrite the expression as a multiplication equation.
(_) × (+4) = (–8)

Step 2
Draw the integer tiles to represent the parts of the multiplication equation.

(+4) indicates sets of 4 positive (shaded) tiles. The product is 8 negative (unshaded) tiles.

Draw 8 zero pairs.

Step 3
Calculate the quotient.

Subtract the number of sets to equal the product of the multiplication equation. Two sets of positive tiles were subtracted to equal (–8).

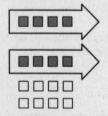

The quotient is (–2).
(–8) ÷ (+4) = (–2)

---

1. Rewrite the expression as a multiplication equation:
(_) × (+3) = (+12)

(+3) indicates sets of 3 positive (shaded tiles). The product is 12 positive (shaded) tiles.

Draw 4 sets of 3 positive (shaded) tiles.

Calculate the quotient.

The number of sets indicates the missing number. Adding (+) indicates the integer sign.

Since there are 4 sets of tiles, the quotient is (+4).
(+12) ÷ (+3) = (+4)

3. Rewrite the expression as a multiplication equation: (_) × (–3) = (+15)

(–3) indicates sets of 3 negative (unshaded tiles). The product is 15 positive (shaded) tiles.

Draw 15 zero pairs.

Subtract the number of sets to equal the product of the multiplication expression.

Five sets of negative tiles were subtracted to equal (+15).

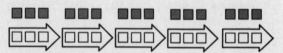

The quotient is (–5).
Therefore, (+15) ÷ (–3) = (–5).

5. Rewrite the expression as a multiplication equation: (_) × (−5) = (+10)

(−5) indicates sets of 5 negative (unshaded tiles). The product is 10 positive (shaded) tiles.

Draw 10 zero pairs.

Subtract the number of sets to equal the product of the multiplication equation.

Two sets of negative tiles were subtracted to equal (+10).

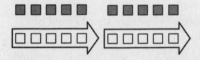

The quotient is (−2).
Therefore, (+10) ÷ (−5) = (−2).

Lesson 5—Dividing Integers Using Number Lines

YOUR TURN
ANSWERS AND SOLUTIONS

1. The first integer shows the size of the line to draw above the number line. The second integer shows the size of the segments the line will be divided into. The correct modelling is shown below.

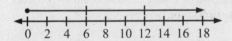

Since the signs of the integers are the same, the answer will be positive. The quotient is (+3).

2. The first integer shows the size of the line to draw above the number line. The second integer shows the size of the segments the line will be divided into. The correct modelling is shown below.

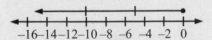

Since the signs of the integers are the same, the answer will be positive. The quotient is (+3).

3. The first integer shows the size of the line to draw above the number line. The second integer shows the size of the segments the line will be divided into. The correct modelling is shown below.

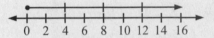

Since the signs of the integers are different, the answer will be negative. The quotient is (−3).

4. The first integer shows the size of the line to draw above the number line. The second integer shows the size of the segments the line will be divided into. The correct modelling is shown below.

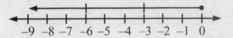

Since the signs of the integers are different, the answer will be negative. The quotient is (−4).

PRACTICE EXERCISES
ANSWERS AND SOLUTIONS

1. The first integer shows the size of the line to draw above the number line. The second integer shows the size of the segments the line will be divided into.

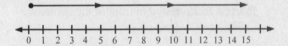

Using the Sign Law, since the integers in the expression are the same, the quotient will be positive. Total the number of segments the line is divided into and insert a positive sign in front. This gives a quotient of (+3).

3. The first integer shows the size of the line to draw above the number line. The second integer shows the size of the segments the line will be divided into.

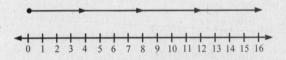

Using the Sign Law, since the integers in the expression are the same, the quotient will be positive. Total the number of segments the line is divided into and insert a positive sign in front. This gives a quotient of (+4).

5. The first integer shows the size of the line to draw above the number line. The second integer shows the size of the segments the line will be divided into.

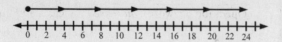

Using the Sign Law, since the integers in the expression are the same, the quotient will be positive. Total the number of segments the line is divided into and insert a positive sign in front. This gives a quotient of (+6).

Lesson 6—Dividing Integers Using Expressions

YOUR TURN
ANSWERS AND SOLUTIONS

1. **Step 1**
Divide the values of the integers.

The values are 54 and 9.
$54 \div 9 = 6$

Step 2
Insert a positive sign in front of the quotient.
$(+54) \div (+9) = (+6)$

2. **Step 1**
Divide the values of the integers.
$49 \div 7 = 7$

Step 2
Insert a positive sign in front of the quotient.
$(-49) \div (-7) = (+7)$

3. **Step 1**
Divide the values of the integers.
$36 \div 12 = 3$

Step 2
Insert a negative sign in front of the quotient.
$(+36) \div (-12) = (-3)$

4. **Step 1**
Divide the values of the integers.
$48 \div 3 = 16$

Step 2
Insert a negative sign in front of the quotient.
$(-48) \div (+3) = (-16)$

PRACTICE EXERCISES
ANSWERS AND SOLUTIONS

1. Divide the values.

The values are 21 and 7.
$21 \div 7 = 3$

Insert a positive (+) integer sign in front of the quotient.
$(-21) \div (-7) = (+3)$

3. Divide the values.

The values are 32 and 4.
$32 \div 4 = 8$

Insert a positive (+) integer sign in front of the quotient.
$(+32) \div (+4) = (+8)$

5. Divide the values.

The values are 21 and 3.
$21 \div 3 = 7$

Insert a negative (–) integer sign in front of the quotient.
$(+21) \div (-3) = (-7)$

7. Divide the values.

The values are 16 and 2.
$16 \div 2 = 8$

Insert a positive (+) integer sign in front of the quotient.
$(+16) \div (+2) = (+8)$

9. Divide the values.

The values are 64 and 8.
$64 \div 8 = 8$

Insert a negative (–) integer sign in front of the quotient.
$(+64) \div (-8) = (-8)$

Lesson 7—Integer Operations

YOUR TURN
ANSWERS AND SOLUTIONS

1. Follow the Order of Operations. Division must be done before addition.
$$= (+30) \div (-5) + (-20) \div (-1)$$
$$= (-6) + (+20)$$
$$= (+14)$$

2. Follow the Order of Operations. Division and multiplication must be done in order from left to right before addition.
$$= (-2) + (-18) \div (+2) \times (-4)$$
$$= (-2) + (-9) \times (-4)$$
$$= (-2) + (+36)$$
$$= (+34)$$

3. Step 1
Identify integer and operation keywords.

Integer keywords: purchased indicates positive; returned indicates negative
Purchased 25 cases $\rightarrow (+25)$
Returned 9 cases $\rightarrow (-9)$

Operation keywords: *used* indicates subtraction

Step 2
Write the expression.
$(+25) - (+9)$

Step 3
Solve
$$(+25) - (+9) = (+25) + (-9)$$
$$= (+16)$$

They drank 16 cases.

4. Step 1
Identify integer and operation keywords.

Integer keyword(s): none, the integers are given: –15 and 9

Operation keyword: *increased* indicates addition

Step 2
Write an expression representing the problem.
$(-15) + (+9)$

Step 3
Solve.
$(-15) + (+9) = (-6)$

The temperature was –6°C by noon.

PRACTICE EXERCISES
ANSWERS AND SOLUTIONS

1. Use the order of operations to simplify.

First, multiply and divide the integers in order from left to right. Then, add the two resulting integers.
$$= (-40) \div (+2) + (+4) \times (+2)$$
$$= (-20) + (8)$$
$$= (-12)$$

3. Perform the division first. Then, the addition and subtraction can be done in order from left to right.
$$= (-9) + (-7) + (-50) \div (+2)$$
$$= (-9) + (-7) + (-25)$$
$$= (-16) + (-25)$$
$$= (-41)$$

5. Division must be done before multiplication. Then, addition and subtraction can be done from left to right.
$$= (+21) \div (+3) \times (+6) + (-64) \div (-8)$$
$$= \left[(+7) \times (+6) \right] + \left[(-64) \div (-8) \right]$$
$$= (+42) + (+8)$$
$$= (+50)$$

7. **Step 1**
Identify integer and operation keywords.

Integer keyword(s): *in her purse* indicates positive
$\$17 \rightarrow (+\$17)$

Operation keyword: *earns* indicates addition

Step 2
Write an expression representing the problem.
$(+\$17) + (\$12)$

Step 3
Solve.
$(+\$17) + (\$12) = (\$29)$

Kelly has $29.

9. Identify integer and operation keywords.

Integer keyword(s): none, the integers are given:
6 and 10

Operation keyword: *in total* indicates
multiplication

Step 2
Write an expression representing the problem.
$(+6) \times (+10)$

Step 3
Solve.
6×10
$= 60$

Hillary paid $60 for the pens.

Practice Test

ANSWERS AND SOLUTIONS

1. **Step 1**
Determine how many integers are in the set.

The second integer (–3) indicates that there are
three negative tiles in each set.

▢▢▢

Step 2
Determine how many sets to draw.

The first integer (+4) indicates there are 4 sets of
3 negative tiles.

▢▢▢
▢▢▢
▢▢▢
▢▢▢

Step 3
Calculate the product.

There are 12 negative tiles shown. Therefore, the
product is (–12).
$(+4) \times (-3) = (-12)$

3. The first integer shows how many lines to draw
above the number line. Two lines will be drawn to
the right of zero.

The second integer shows the size of each line, and
their direction. Lines with size (–3) will be drawn
to the left of zero. The correct modelling is shown.

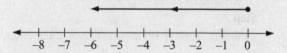

The product is (–6).

5. **Step 1**
Multiply the values.

The values are 5 and 2.
$5 \times 2 = 10$

Step 2
Insert a positive integer sign in front of the product.
$(+5) \times (+2) = (+10)$

422

7. Step 1
Multiply the values.

The values are 9 and 6.
$9 \times 6 = 54$

Step 2
Insert a negative (–) integer sign in front of the product.
$(-9) \times (+6) = (-54)$

9. Step 1
The values are 2, 4, and 6.
$2 \times 4 \times 6 = 48$

Step 2
Count the number of negative integer signs. There is an even number of negative signs (2) in this expression. Therefore, the solution will be positive.
$(-2)(+4)(-6) = (+48)$

11. Step 1
Rewrite the division expression as a multiplication equation.
$(\_) \times (+4) = (+16)$

Step 2
Draw the integer tiles to represent the multiplication equation.

(+4) indicates sets of 4 positive (shaded) tiles. The product is 16 positive (shaded) tiles.

Draw 4 sets of 4 positive tiles.

Step 3
Calculate the quotient.

The number of sets indicates the missing number. Adding (+) indicates the integer sign.

Four sets of tiles were added. The quotient is (+4).
$(+16) \div (+4) = (+4)$

13. The first integer shows the size of the line to draw above the number line. The second integer shows the size of the segments the line will be divided into. The correct modelling is shown.

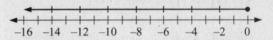

The total number of segments the line is divided into gives the quotient, which is (+8).
Thus, $(-16) \div (-2) = +8$.

15. Step 1
Divide the values.

The values are 45 and 9.
$45 \div 9 = 5$

Step 2
Insert a positive (+) integer sign in front of the quotient.
$(+45) \div (+9) = (+5)$

17. Step 1
Divide the values.

The values are 48 and 4.
$48 \div 4 = 12$

Step 2
Insert a positive (+) integer sign in front of the quotient.
$(-48) \div (-4) = (+12)$

19. Step 1
Divide the values.

The values are 60 and 6.
$60 \div 6 = 10$

Step 2
Insert a negative (–) integer sign in front of the quotient.
$(-60) \div (+6) = (-10)$

21. First, multiply and divide the integers in order from left to right. Then, add the two resulting integers.
$$= (-180) \div (+3) + (+5) \times (+5)$$
$$= (-60) + (+25)$$
$$= (-35)$$

23. To follow the order of operations correctly, the division operation must be done first. Then, the addition and subtraction can be done in order from left to right.

$$= (-19) + (-17) + \underline{(-560) \div (+7)}$$
$$= \underline{(-19) + (-17)} + (-80)$$
$$= (-36) + (-80)$$
$$= (-116)$$

25. After multiplication and division, addition and subtraction can be done from left to right.

$$(+66) \div (+3) \times (+6) + (-120) \div (+10) \times (+2)$$
$$= \left[(+22) \times (+6) \right] + (-120) \div (+10) \times (+2)$$
$$= (+132) + \left[(-120) \div (+10) \right] \times (+2)$$
$$= (+132) + \left[(-12) \times (+2) \right]$$
$$= (+132) + (-24)$$
$$= (+108)$$

27. Step 1
Identify integer and operation keywords.

Integer keyword: *height* indicates positive height of 50 m → 50

Operation keyword: *down* indicates subtraction

Step 2
Write an expression representing the problem.
$(+50) - (+25)$

Step 3
Solve.
$(+50) - (+25) = (+25)$

The change in height was 25 m.

PATTERNS WITH LINEAR RELATIONS

Lesson 1—Graphs of Linear Relations

YOUR TURN
ANSWERS AND SOLUTIONS

1. Step 1
Draw a T-chart.

x	y

Step 2
Pick any values for x. (In this case you are instructed to use values 1 though 5).

x	y
1	
2	
3	
4	
5	

Step 3
Substitute each value of x into the equation and use the Order of Operations to solve for y.

$$3x + 4 = y$$
$$\rightarrow 3(1) + 4 = 7$$
$$\rightarrow 3(2) + 4 = 10$$
$$\rightarrow 3(3) + 4 = 13$$
$$\rightarrow 3(4) + 4 = 16$$
$$\rightarrow 3(5) + 4 = 19$$

Step 4
Complete the table.

x	y
1	7
2	10
3	13
4	16
5	19

2. To isolate y, subtract x from both sides of the equation.
$x + y = 3$
$y = 3 - x$

Step 1
Make a table of values.

x	y
1	2
2	1
3	0
4	−1
5	−2

Step 2
Write the ordered pairs for each point from the table of values.
$(1, 2), (2, 1), (3, 0), (4, -1), (5, -2)$

Step 3
Plot the ordered pairs on the Cartesian plane.

Remember that when the y-value is negative, the point will be below the x-axis.

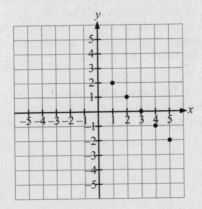

3. These are the main points indicated on the graph:
$(-2, -2), (-1, -1), (0, 0), (1, 1), (2, 2)$

Using these points, create a table of values.

x	y
−2	−2
−1	−1
0	0
1	1
2	2

The pattern indicated is that for every value of x, the corresponding y-value is the same.

PRACTICE EXERCISES
ANSWERS AND SOLUTIONS

1. These are the main points indicated on the graph:
$(0, 2), (1, 4), (2, 6), (3, 8), (4, 10)$

Using these points, create a table of values.

x	y
0	2
1	4
2	6
3	8
4	10

The pattern indicated is that for every value of x, the corresponding y-value is 2 more than two times x.

3. These are the main points indicated on the graph:
$(0, 0), (1, 3), (2, 6), (3, 9), (4, 12)$

Using these points, create a table of values.

x	y
0	0
1	3
2	6
3	9
4	12

The pattern indicated is that for every value of x, the corresponding y-value is three times x.

5. Make a table of values by substituting different values for x.

x	y
0	2
1	6
2	10
3	14
4	18

Write the ordered pairs for each point from the table of values.
(0, 2), (1, 6), (2, 10), (3, 14), (4, 18)

Plot the points on a Cartesian plane and join them by a line.

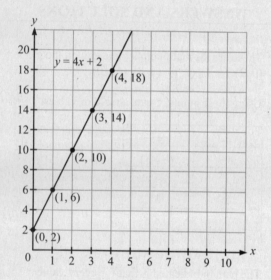

Lesson 2—Patterns with Linear Relations

YOUR TURN
ANSWERS AND SOLUTIONS

1. List the ordered pairs from the table of values.
    (4, 6), (5, 5), (6, 4), (7, 3), (8, 2)

    Graph the ordered pairs.

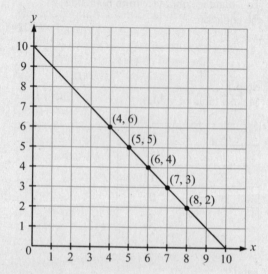

Describe the pattern in words, and then in an equation.

For every x-value, the corresponding y-value is x less than ten. This gives an equation of $y = 10 - x$.

2. a) In Table 1, for every increase of 1 in the x-value, the increase in the y-value is not the same. As well, for every x-value, the corresponding y-value does not increase by the same amount. Since there are no patterns among the values, this is not a linear relation.

    b) In Table 2, for every x-value, the corresponding y-value is twice as large. This would give an equation of $2x = y$. This is a linear relation.

3. **a)** Make a table of values.

Number of Hours	Earnings ($)
1	100
2	190
3	280
4	370
5	460

b) For one hour, including the allowance pay, Oliver earns $100. For each additional, hour he works, his earnings increase by $90. The number of hours and the amount of earnings increase in a regular pattern. This is a linear relation.

c) To determine the linear relation, let x be the number of hours and y be the amount of earnings. The linear relation for this table of values would be $y = 90x + 10$.

d) The amount he earns for 7 hours can be calculated by substituting $x = 7$ in the linear relation and solving for y using the Order of Operations.

$$y = 90x + 10$$
$$= 90(7) + 10$$
$$= 640$$

He will earn $640 for 7 hours of work.

e) To determine how many hours he must work, substitute $y = 550$ into the linear relation and solve for x using the Order of Operations.

$$y = 90x + 10$$
$$550 = 90x + 10$$
$$550 - 10 = 90x + 10 - 10$$
$$540 = 90x$$
$$\frac{540}{90} = \frac{90x}{90}$$
$$6 = x$$

To earn $550, he must work for 6 hours.

PRACTICE EXERCISES
ANSWERS AND SOLUTIONS

1. List the ordered pairs from the table of values.
(1, 2), (2, 5), (3, 8), (4, 11), (5, 14)

Graph the ordered pairs.

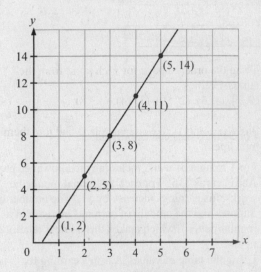

For every x-value, the corresponding y-value is three times x, less one. This would give an equation of $y = 3x - 1$.

3. For every increase of 1 in the x-value, the increase in the y-value is not the same. Since there are no patterns among the values, this is not a linear relation.

5. For every increase of 1 in the x-value, the increase in the y-value is not the same. Since there are no patterns among the values, this is not a linear relation.

7. Make a table of values.

Number of Hats	Cost ($)
1	7
2	9
3	11
4	13
5	15

9. To determine the linear relation, let x be the number of hats and y be the cost of hats. The linear relation for this table of values would be $y = 2x + 5$.

11. To determine how many hats can be ordered, substitute $y = 45$ into the linear relation and solve for x using the Order of Operations.
$$y = 2x + 5$$
$$45 = 2x + 5$$
$$45 - 5 = 2x + 5 - 5$$
$$40 = 2x$$
$$\frac{40}{2} = \frac{2x}{2}$$
$$20 = x$$

For $45, 20 hats can be ordered.

13. For 1 minute of work, including the allowance pay, Aaron earns $16. For each additional minute he works, his earnings increase by $1. The number of minutes and the amount of earnings increase in a regular pattern, which makes this a linear relation.

15. Using the table of values, Aaron's earning for 5 minutes would be $20.

This result could also be obtained from the linear relation by substituting $x = 5$ and solving for y using the Order of Operations.
$$y = x + 15$$
$$= 5 + 15$$
$$= 20$$

Practice Test

ANSWERS AND SOLUTIONS

1. These are the main points indicated on the graph:
$(0, 5), (1, 7), (2, 9), (3, 11), (1, 13)$

Using these points, create a table of values.

x	y
0	5
1	7
2	9
3	11
4	13

The pattern indicated is that for every value of x, the corresponding y-value is 5 more than twice x.

3. These are the main points indicated on the graph:
$(0, 6), (1, 7), (2, 8), (3, 9), (4, 10)$

Using these points, create a table of values.

x	y
0	6
1	7
2	8
3	9
4	10

The pattern indicated is that for every value of x, the corresponding y-value is 6 more.

5. These are the main points indicated on the graph:
$(0, 0), (1, 4), (2, 8), (3, 12), (4, 16)$

Using these points, create a table of values.

x	y
0	0
1	4
2	8
3	12
4	16

The pattern indicated is that for every value of x, the corresponding y-value is four times x.

7. Make a table of values by substituting different values for x.

x	y
1	6
2	5
3	4
4	3
5	2

Write the ordered pairs for each point from the table of values.
$(1, 6), (2, 5), (3, 4), (4, 3), (5, 2)$

Plot the points on a coordinate plane and join them by a line.

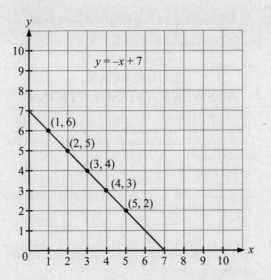

9. In the table, for every x-value, the corresponding y-value is greater by 10. Also, for every increase of 2 in the x-value, there is a corresponding increase of 2 in the y-value. This would give an equation of $y = x + 10$. This is a linear relation.

11. For every increase of 2 in the x-value, the increase in the y-value is not the same. Since there are no patterns among the values, this is not a linear relation.

13. For every x-value, the corresponding y-value is greater by 15. This would give an equation of $x + 15 = y$. This is a linear relation.

15.

Number of Months	Savings ($)
1	50
2	100
3	150
4	200
5	250

17. To determine the linear relation, let x be the number of months and let y be the amount of savings The linear relation for this table of values would be $y = 50x$.

19. Substitute $y = 1\,000$ in the linear relation and solve for x.
$$1\,000 = 50x$$
$$\frac{1\,000}{50} = \frac{50x}{50}$$
$$20 = x$$

Sahara will have saved $1 000 after 20 months.

21. After the first shirt, for every increase of one shirt, the cost increases by 15. The number of shirts and the total cost increase in a regular pattern. This is a linear relation.

23. Substitute $x = 6$ in the linear relation.
$$y = 15(6) - 1$$
$$= 90 - 1$$
$$= 89$$

The total cost for 6 shirts is $89.

25. For every increase of one car sold, earnings increase by 150. The number of cars he sells and the total earnings increase in a regular pattern. This is a linear relation.

27. Substitute $x = 7$ in the linear relation.
$$y = 150(7) + 2\,300$$
$$= 3350$$

Wayne will earn $3 350 if he sells 7 cars in one month.

29. Make a table of values.

Number of Kilometres	Rental Cost ($)
10	42.50
20	45.00
30	47.50
40	50.00
50	52.50

31. To determine the linear relation, let x be the time and let y be the kilometers. The linear relation for this table of values would be $y = 0.25x + 40$.

33. Substitute $y = 80$ in the linear relation and solve for x using the Order of Operations.
$$80 = 0.25x + 40$$
$$80 - 40 = 0.25x$$
$$40 = 0.25x$$
$$\frac{40}{0.25} = x$$
$$160 = x$$

He has to drive 160 kilometres for his rental cost to be $80.

LINEAR RELATIONS

Lesson 1—Equations in the Form $ax = b$

YOUR TURN
ANSWERS AND SOLUTIONS

1. To isolate the variable x, divide both sides of the equation by 3.
$$3x = 21$$
$$\frac{3x}{3} = \frac{21}{3}$$
$$x = 7$$

2. To isolate the variable d, divide both sides of the equation by -4.
$$-4d = 44$$
$$\frac{-4d}{-4} = \frac{44}{-4}$$
$$d = -11$$

3. To isolate the variable y, divide both sides of the equation by 5.
$$5y = -60$$
$$\frac{5y}{5} = \frac{-60}{5}$$
$$y = -12$$

4. To isolate the variable n, divide both sides of the equation by -3.
$$-3n = -33$$
$$\frac{-3n}{-3} = \frac{-33}{-3}$$
$$n = 11$$

5. Set up the one-step equation based on the information given in the problem. Let k stand for the unknown number.
$$6k = -54$$
$$\frac{6k}{6} = \frac{-54}{6}$$
$$k = -9$$

The number is -9.

PRACTICE EXERCISES
ANSWERS AND SOLUTIONS

1. To isolate the variable in q, divide both sides of the equation by 2.

    $2q = 6$

    $\dfrac{2q}{2} = \dfrac{6}{2}$

    $q = 3$

3. To isolate the variable f, divide both sides of the equation by 7.

    $7f = -77$

    $\dfrac{7f}{7} = \dfrac{-77}{7}$

    $f = -11$

5. To isolate the variable y, divide both sides of the equation by 6.

    $6y = 18$

    $\dfrac{6y}{6} = \dfrac{18}{6}$

    $y = 3$

7. To isolate the variable j, divide both sides of the equation by -9.

    $-9j = 90$

    $\dfrac{-9j}{-9} = \dfrac{90}{-9}$

    $j = -10$

9. To isolate the variable v, divide both sides of the equation by 5.

    $5v = -80$

    $\dfrac{5v}{5} = \dfrac{-80}{5}$

    $v = -16$

11. To isolate the variable d, divide both sides of the equation by -9.

    $-9d = -81$

    $\dfrac{-9d}{-9} = \dfrac{-81}{-9}$

    $d = 9$

13. Set up the one-step equation based on the information given in the problem. Let a stand for the unknown number.

    $3a = -18$

    $\dfrac{3a}{3} = \dfrac{-18}{3}$

    $a = -6$

    The number is -6.

Lesson 2—Equations in the Form $\dfrac{x}{a} = b$

YOUR TURN
ANSWERS AND SOLUTIONS

1. To isolate the variable a, multiply both sides of the equation by 4.

    $\dfrac{a}{4} = 9$

    $\dfrac{a}{4} \times 4 = 9 \times 4$

    $a = 36$

2. To isolate the variable f, multiply both sides of the equation by -5.

    $\dfrac{f}{-5} = -6$

    $\dfrac{f}{-5} \times (-5) = (-6) \times (-5)$

    $f = 30$

3. To isolate the variable z, multiply both sides of the equation by -6.

    $\dfrac{z}{-6} = 8$

    $\dfrac{z}{-6} \times (-6) = 8 \times (-6)$

    $z = -48$

4. To isolate the variable w, multiply both sides of the equation by 3.

    $\dfrac{w}{3} = -9$

    $\dfrac{w}{3} \times 3 = (-9) \times 3$

    $w = -27$

5. Set up the one-step equation based on the information given in the problem. Let u stand for the unknown number.

$$\frac{u}{-4} = -8$$

$$\frac{u}{-4} \times (-4) = (-8) \times (-4)$$

$$u = 32$$

The number is 32.

PRACTICE EXERCISES
ANSWERS AND SOLUTIONS

1. To isolate the variable x, multiply both sides of the equation by 5.

$$\frac{x}{5} = 8$$

$$\frac{x}{5} \times 5 = 8 \times 5$$

$$x = 40$$

3. To isolate the variable c, multiply both sides of the equation by 2.

$$\frac{c}{2} = -5$$

$$\frac{c}{2} \times 2 = (-5) \times 2$$

$$c = -10$$

5. To isolate the variable a, multiply both sides of the equation by 7.

$$\frac{a}{7} = 8$$

$$\frac{a}{7} \times 7 = 8 \times 7$$

$$a = 56$$

7. To isolate the variable f, multiply both sides of the equation by -3.

$$\frac{f}{-3} = -12$$

$$\frac{f}{-3} \times (-3) = (-12) \times (-3)$$

$$f = 36$$

9. To isolate the variable w, multiply both sides of the equation by 3.

$$\frac{w}{3} = -81$$

$$\frac{w}{3} \times 3 = (-81) \times 3$$

$$w = -243$$

11. To isolate the variable m, multiply both sides of the equation by -12.

$$\frac{m}{-12} = 4$$

$$\frac{m}{-12} \times (-12) = 4 \times (-12)$$

$$m = -48$$

13. Set up the one-step equation based on the information given in the problem. Let i stand for the unknown number.

$$\frac{i}{2} = -10$$

$$\frac{i}{2} \times 2 = (-10) \times 2$$

$$i = -20$$

The number is -20.

Lesson 3—Equations in the Form $ax + b = c$

YOUR TURN
ANSWERS AND SOLUTIONS

1. To isolate the variable a, first subtract 7 from both sides of the equation.

$$3a + 7 = 22$$
$$3a + 7 - 7 = 22 - 7$$
$$3a = 15$$
$$\frac{3a}{3} = \frac{15}{3}$$
$$a = 5$$

2. To isolate the variable c, first subtract 4 from both sides of the equation.

$$-2c + 4 = 14$$
$$-2c + 4 - 4 = 14 - 4$$
$$-2c = 10$$
$$\frac{-2c}{-2} = \frac{10}{-2}$$
$$c = -5$$

3. To isolate the variable j, first add 6 to both sides of the equation.

$$6j - 6 = 8$$
$$6j - 6 + 6 = 48 + 6$$
$$6j = 54$$
$$\frac{6j}{6} = \frac{54}{6}$$
$$j = 9$$

4. To isolate the variable r, first add 4 to both sides of the equation.

$$-4r - 4 = -40$$
$$-4r - 4 + 4 = -40 + 4$$
$$-4r = -36$$
$$\frac{-4r}{-4} = \frac{-36}{-4}$$
$$r = 9$$

5. Set up the two-step equation based on the information given in the problem. Let x stand for the unknown number.

$$6x - 4 = 44$$
$$6x - 4 + 4 = 44 + 4$$
$$6x = 48$$
$$\frac{6x}{6} = \frac{48}{6}$$
$$x = 8$$

The number is 8.

6. Write the equation, then solve. Let x stand for the number of CDs that Sabrina has, since she owns the smaller amount.

Sabrina $\rightarrow x$

Miriam $\rightarrow x + 12$

Together they have 44 CDs.

Sabrina's CDs + Miriam's CDs = 44 CDs
$$x + (x + 12) = 44$$
$$2x + 12 = 44$$

Solve the equation for x.
$$2x + 12 = 44$$
$$2x + 12 - 12 = 44 - 12$$
$$2x = 32$$
$$\frac{2x}{2} = \frac{32}{2}$$
$$x = 16$$

This means that Sabrina has 16 CDs.

Determine how many CDs Miriam has by substituting 16 for x in the expression $x + 12$.

$$x + 12$$
$$= 16 + 12$$
$$= 28$$

This means that Miriam has 28 CDs.
These numbers also satisfy the equation $x + (x + 12) = 44$.

Check: $x + (x + 12) = 16 + 16 + 12$
$$= 44$$

PRACTICE EXERCISES
ANSWERS AND SOLUTIONS

1. To isolate the variable y, subtract 4 from both sides of the equation.

$$5y + 4 = 14$$
$$5y + 4 - 4 = 14 - 4$$
$$5y = 10$$

Now this is a one-step equation. The variable can be isolated by dividing both sides by 5.

$$\frac{5y}{5} = \frac{10}{5}$$
$$y = 2$$

3. To isolate the variable p, first add 2 to each side of the equation.

$$6p - 2 = 40$$
$$6p - 2 + 2 = 40 + 2$$
$$6p = 42$$

Now this is a one-step equation. The variable can be isolated by dividing both sides by 6.

$$\frac{6p}{6} = \frac{42}{6}$$
$$p = 7$$

5. To isolate the variable f, first subtract 1 from both sides of the equation.

$$5f + 1 = 41$$
$$5f + 1 - 1 = 41 - 1$$
$$5f = 40$$

Now this is a one-step equation. The variable can be isolated by dividing both sides by 5.

$$\frac{5f}{5} = \frac{40}{5}$$
$$f = 8$$

7. To isolate the variable p, first subtract 7 from both sides of the equation.
$$-2p + 7 = -35$$
$$-2p + 7 - 7 = -35 - 7$$
$$-2p = -42$$

Now this is a one-step equation. The variable can be isolated by dividing both sides by –2.
$$\frac{-2p}{-2} = \frac{-42}{-2}$$
$$p = 21$$

9. To isolate the variable g, first add 4 to each side of the equation.
$$9g - 4 = 59$$
$$9g - 4 + 4 = 59 + 4$$
$$9g = 63$$

Now this is a one-step equation. The variable can be isolated by dividing both sides by 9.
$$\frac{9g}{9} = \frac{63}{9}$$
$$g = 7$$

11. To isolate the variable t, first add 2 to both sides of the equation.
$$-6t - 2 = -14$$
$$-6t - 2 + 2 = -14 + 2$$
$$-6t = -12$$

Now this is a one-step equation. The variable can be isolated by dividing both sides by –6.
$$\frac{-6t}{-6} = \frac{-12}{-6}$$
$$t = 2$$

13. Set up the two-step equation based on the information given in the problem. Let p stand for the unknown.
$$2p + 8 = 16$$
$$2p + 8 - 8 = 16 - 8$$
$$2p = 8$$
$$\frac{2p}{2} = \frac{8}{2}$$
$$p = 4$$

The number is 4.

15. Set up the two-step equation based on the information given in the problem. Let x stand for the unknown.
$$5x + 4 = 24$$
$$5x + 4 - 4 = 24 - 4$$
$$5x = 20$$
$$\frac{5x}{5} = \frac{20}{5}$$
$$x = 4$$

The number is 4.

Lesson 4—Equations in the Form $\frac{x}{a} + b = c$

YOUR TURN
ANSWERS AND SOLUTIONS

1. To isolate the variable w, first subtract 6 from both sides of the equation.
$$\frac{w}{7} + 6 = 10$$
$$\frac{w}{7} + 6 - 6 = 10 - 6$$
$$\frac{w}{7} = 4$$
$$\frac{w}{7} \times 7 = 4 \times 7$$
$$w = 28$$

2. To isolate the variable f, first subtract 9 from both sides of the equation.
$$\frac{f}{-8} + 9 = 15$$
$$\frac{f}{-8} + 9 - 9 = 15 - 9$$
$$\frac{f}{-8} = 6$$
$$\frac{f}{-8} \times -8 = 6 \times (-8)$$
$$f = -48$$

3. To isolate the variable g, first add 6 to both sides of the equation.

$$\frac{g}{3} - 6 = 2$$

$$\frac{g}{3} - 6 + 6 = 2 + 6$$

$$\frac{g}{3} = 8$$

$$\frac{g}{3} \times 3 = 8 \times 3$$

$$g = 24$$

4. To isolate the variable n, first add 6 to both sides of the equation.

$$\frac{n}{10} - 6 = -1$$

$$\frac{n}{10} - 6 + 6 = -1 + 6$$

$$\frac{n}{10} = 5$$

$$\frac{n}{10} \times 10 = 5 \times 10$$

$$n = 50$$

PRACTICE EXERCISES
ANSWERS AND SOLUTIONS

1. To isolate the variable m, first subtract 1 from both sides of the equation.

$$\frac{m}{3} + 1 = 10$$

$$\frac{m}{3} + 1 - 1 = 10 - 1$$

$$\frac{m}{3} = 9$$

Now this is a one-step equation. The variable can be isolated by multiplying both sides by 3.

$$\frac{m}{3} \times 3 = 9 \times 3$$

$$m = 27$$

3. To isolate the variable v, first add 4 to both sides of the equation.

$$\frac{v}{9} - 4 = 3$$

$$\frac{v}{9} - 4 + 4 = 3 + 4$$

$$\frac{v}{9} = 7$$

$$\frac{v}{9} \times 9 = 7 \times 9$$

$$v = 63$$

5. To isolate the variable k, first subtract 3 from both sides of the equation.

$$\frac{k}{7} + 3 = 9$$

$$\frac{k}{7} + 3 - 3 = 9 - 3$$

$$\frac{k}{7} = 6$$

Now this is a one-step equation. The variable can be isolated by multiplying both sides by 7.

$$\frac{k}{7} \times 7 = 6 \times 7$$

$$k = 42$$

7. To isolate the variable a, first subtract 3 from both sides of the equation.

$$\frac{a}{4} + 3 = 10$$

$$\frac{a}{4} + 3 - 3 = 10 - 3$$

$$\frac{a}{4} = 7$$

Now this is a one-step equation. The variable can be isolated by multiplying both sides by 4.

$$\frac{a}{4} \times 4 = 7 \times 4$$

$$a = 28$$

9. To isolate the variable c, first subtract 4 from both sides of the equation.

$$\frac{c}{-8} + 4 = 9$$

$$\frac{c}{-8} + 4 - 4 = 9 - 4$$

$$\frac{c}{-8} = 5$$

$$\frac{c}{-8} \times (-8) = 5 \times (-8)$$

$$c = -40$$

11. To isolate the variable k, first add 5 to both sides of the equation.

$$\frac{k}{7} - 5 = 7$$

$$\frac{k}{7} - 5 + 5 = 7 + 5$$

$$\frac{k}{7} = 12$$

$$\frac{k}{7} \times 7 = 12 \times 7$$

$$k = 84$$

13. To isolate the variable v, first add 4 to both sides of the equation.

$$\frac{v}{-6} - 4 = 0$$

$$\frac{v}{-6} - 4 + 4 = 0 + 4$$

$$\frac{v}{-6} = 4$$

$$\frac{v}{-6} \times (-6) = 4 \times (-6)$$

$$v = -24$$

Practice Test

ANSWERS AND SOLUTIONS

1. To isolate the variable l, divide both sides of the equation by 3.

$$3l = 36$$

$$\frac{3l}{3} = \frac{36}{3}$$

$$l = 12$$

3. To isolate the variable n, divide both sides of the equation by –12.

$$-12n = 84$$

$$\frac{-12n}{-12} = \frac{84}{-12}$$

$$n = -7$$

5. To isolate the variable k, divide both sides of the equation by 4.

$$4k = -32$$

$$\frac{4k}{4} = \frac{-32}{4}$$

$$k = -8$$

7. To isolate the variable h, divide both sides of the equation by –5.

$$-5h = -55$$

$$\frac{-5h}{-5} = \frac{-55}{-5}$$

$$h = 11$$

9. To isolate the variable t, multiply both sides of the equation by 4.

$$\frac{t}{4} = 9$$

$$\frac{t}{4} \times 4 = 9 \times 4$$

$$t = 36$$

11. To isolate the variable h, multiply both sides of the equation by –7.

$$\frac{h}{-7} = -7$$

$$\frac{h}{-7} \times (-7) = (-7) \times (-7)$$

$$h = 49$$

13. To isolate the variable q, multiply both sides of the equation by –13.

$$\frac{q}{-13} = 5$$

$$\frac{q}{-13} \times (-13) = 5 \times (-13)$$

$$q = -65$$

15. To isolate the variable r, multiply both sides of the equation by –12.

$$\frac{r}{-12} = 6$$

$$\frac{r}{-12} \times (-12) = 6 \times (-12)$$

$$r = -72$$

17. To isolate the variable k, multiply both sides of the equation by 12.

$$\frac{k}{12} = -10$$

$$\frac{k}{12} \times 12 = (-10) \times 12$$

$$k = -120$$

19. Set up the one-step equation based on the information given in the problem. Let x be the unknown number.

$$21x = 84$$
$$\frac{21x}{21} = \frac{84}{21}$$
$$x = 4$$

The number is 4.

21. Set up the one-step equation based on the information given in the problem. Let y be the unknown number.

$$\frac{y}{7} = -8$$
$$\frac{y}{7} \times 7 = (-8) \times 7$$
$$y = -56$$

The number is -56.

23. To isolate the variable u, first subtract 8 from both sides of the equation.

$$6u + 8 = 50$$
$$6u + 8 - 8 = 50 - 8$$
$$6u = 42$$

Now this is a one-step equation. The variable can be isolated by dividing both sides by 6.

$$\frac{6u}{6} = \frac{42}{6}$$
$$u = 7$$

25. To isolate the variable t, first subtract 7 from both sides of the equation.

$$-4t + 7 = -53$$
$$-4t + 7 - 7 = -53 - 7$$
$$-4t = -60$$
$$\frac{-4t}{-4} = \frac{-60}{-4}$$
$$t = 15$$

27. To isolate the variable v, first add 8 to both sides of the equation.

$$5v - 8 = 17$$
$$5v - 8 + 8 = 17 + 8$$
$$5v = 25$$
$$\frac{5v}{5} = \frac{25}{5}$$
$$v = 5$$

29. To isolate the variable m, first add 2 to both sides of the equation.

$$-12m - 2 = -14$$
$$-12m - 2 + 2 = -14 + 2$$
$$-12m = -12$$
$$\frac{-12m}{-12} = \frac{-12}{-12}$$
$$m = 1$$

31. Set up the two-step equation based on the information given in the problem. Let x be the unknown number.

$$6x + 7 = 19$$
$$6x + 7 - 7 = 19 - 7$$
$$6x = 12$$
$$\frac{6x}{6} = \frac{12}{6}$$
$$x = 2$$

The number is 2.

33. Set up the two-step equation based on the information given in the problem. Let x be the unknown number.

$$8x - 9 = 79$$
$$8x - 9 + 9 = 79 + 9$$
$$8x = 88$$
$$\frac{8x}{8} = \frac{88}{8}$$
$$x = 11$$

The number is 11.

35. To isolate the variable a, first subtract 6 from both sides of the equation.

$$\frac{a}{3} + 6 = 10$$
$$\frac{a}{3} + 6 - 6 = 10 - 6$$
$$\frac{a}{3} = 4$$

Now this is a one-step equation. The variable can be isolated by multiplying both sides by 3.

$$\frac{a}{3} \times 3 = 4 \times 3$$
$$a = 12$$

37. To isolate the variable m, first subtract 2 from both sides of the equation.

$$\frac{m}{-6} + 2 = 7$$

$$\frac{m}{-6} + 2 - 2 = 7 - 2$$

$$\frac{m}{-6} = 5$$

$$\frac{m}{-6} \times (-6) = 5 \times (-6)$$

$$m = -30$$

39. To isolate the variable k, first add 8 to both sides of the equation.

$$\frac{k}{4} - 8 = 12$$

$$\frac{k}{4} - 8 + 8 = 12 + 8$$

$$\frac{k}{4} = 20$$

$$\frac{k}{4} \times 4 = 20 \times 4$$

$$k = 80$$

41. To isolate the variable l, first add 2 to both sides of the equation.

$$\frac{l}{-7} - 2 = 3$$

$$\frac{l}{-7} - 2 + 2 = 3 + 2$$

$$\frac{l}{-7} = 5$$

$$\frac{l}{-7} \times (-7) = 5 \times (-7)$$

$$l = -35$$

PROBABILITY

Lesson 1—Tree Diagrams and Tables

YOUR TURN
ANSWERS AND SOLUTIONS

1. a) There are 13 hearts in a deck of cards. So there are 13 favourable outcomes and 52 total outcomes. Set up the fraction, and reduce.

$$P(\text{heart}) = \frac{13}{52}$$
$$= \frac{1}{4}$$

b) Half the deck are red cards. So there are $26\,(52 \div 2)$ favourable outcomes and 52 total outcomes. Set up the fraction, and reduce.

$$P(\text{any red card}) = \frac{26}{52}$$
$$= \frac{1}{2}$$

c) There are four kings in a deck So there are 4 favourable outcomes and 52 total outcomes. Set up the fraction, and reduce.

$$P(\text{any king}) = \frac{4}{52}$$
$$= \frac{1}{13}$$

d) There are nine numbered cards, with four in each suit, which is 36 in total. So there are 36 favourable outcomes and 52 total outcomes. Set up the fraction, and reduce.

$$P(\text{any numbered card}) = \frac{36}{52}$$
$$= \frac{9}{13}$$

PRACTICE EXERCISES
ANSWERS AND SOLUTIONS

1. There is one 2 on a regular die and six possible numbers. So there are two favourable outcomes and six possible outcomes. Set up the fraction.

$$P(2) = \frac{1}{6}$$

3. The numbers 1, 2, 3, and 4 are less than 5. There are four favourable outcomes and six total outcomes. Set up the fraction, and reduce.

$$P(\text{a number less than} 5) = \frac{4}{6}$$
$$= \frac{2}{3}$$

5. The numbers 1, 2, 4, 5, and 6 are not 3. There are five favourable outcomes and six total outcomes. Set up the fraction

$$P(\text{not a three}) = \frac{5}{6}$$

7. There are 12 face cards in a regular deck. There are 12 favourable outcomes and 52 total outcomes. Set up the fraction, and reduce.

$$P(\text{face card}) = \frac{12}{52}$$
$$= \frac{3}{13}$$

9. Half the cards in a regular deck are black. There are 26 favourable outcomes and 52 total outcomes. Set up the fraction, and reduce.

$$P(\text{black}) = \frac{26}{52}$$
$$= \frac{1}{2}$$

11. There are four vowels in the word *mathematics*. There are four favourable outcomes and 11 total outcomes. Set up the fraction.

$$P(\text{vowel}) = \frac{4}{11}$$

13. There are four letters that are M or T in the word *mathematics*. There are four favourable outcomes and 11 total outcomes. Set up the fraction.

$$P(\text{M or T}) = \frac{4}{11}$$

15. There are four odd numbers on the spinner: 1, 3, 5, and 7. There are four favourable outcomes and eight total outcomes. Set up the fraction and reduce.

$$P(\text{odd number}) = \frac{4}{8}$$
$$= \frac{1}{2}$$

17. The numbers on the spinner that are greater than 2 are 3, 4, 5, 6, 7, and 8. There are six favourable outcomes and eight total outcomes. Set up the fraction and reduce.

$$P(\text{more than 2}) = \frac{6}{8}$$
$$= \frac{3}{4}$$

19.

		Blue Die					
		1	**2**	**3**	**4**	**5**	**6**
	1	1, 1	2, 1	3, 1	4, 1	5, 1	6, 1
	2	1, 2	2, 2	3, 2	4, 2	5, 2	6, 2
Red	**3**	1, 3	2, 3	3, 3	4, 3	5, 3	6, 3
Die	**4**	1, 4	2, 4	3, 4	4, 4	5, 4	6, 4
	5	1, 5	2, 5	3, 5	4, 5	5, 5	6, 5
	6	1, 6	2, 6	3, 6	4, 6	5, 6	6, 6

21.

Grey — a, b, c, d   Ga Ca Wa / Gb Cb Wb / Gc Cc Wc / Gd Cd Wd

Circles — a, b, c, d

White — a, b, c, d

Lesson 2—Outcomes of Independent Events

YOUR TURN
ANSWERS AND SOLUTIONS

1. **Method 1**
   Create a table of values showing all the possible outcomes.

Coins			
Die	**Penny**	**Nickel**	**Dime**
1	P, 1	N, 1	D, 1
2	P, 2	N, 2	D, 2
3	P, 3	N, 3	D, 3
4	P, 4	N, 4	D, 4
5	P, 5	N, 5	D, 5
6	P, 6	N, 6	D, 6

The table shows 18 possible outcomes.

Method 2:
Multiply the number of outcomes of each event together.

Number of possible outcomes of drawing a coin: 3
Number of possible outcomes of rolling a die: 6
Total number of possible outcomes: $6 \times 3 = 18$

PRACTICE EXERCISES
ANSWERS AND SOLUTIONS

1. Create a table of values showing all the possible outcomes.

	Spinner							
Coin	**1**	**2**	**3**	**4**	**5**	**6**	**7**	**8**
H	H, 1	H, 2	H, 3	H, 4	H, 5	H, 6	H, 7	H, 8
T	T, 1	T, 2	T, 3	T, 4	T, 5	T, 6	T, 7	T, 8

The table shows 16 possible outcomes.

3. Draw a tree diagram showing all possible outcomes.

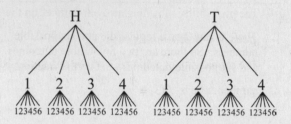

The tree diagram shows 48 possible outcomes.

Lesson 3—Solving Problems involving Probability

YOUR TURN
ANSWERS AND SOLUTIONS

1. Create a table of values showing all the possible outcomes.

	Spinner 1		
Spinner 2	Red	Yellow	Green
Green	Red, Green	Yellow, Green	Green, Green
Purple	Red, Purple	Yellow, Purple	Green, Purple
Brown	Red, Brown	Yellow, Brown	Green, Brown

The table of values shows nine possible outcomes.

a) The table shows this event occurring once out of nine events, which can be written as $\frac{1}{9}$.

b) The table shows this event occurring once out of nine events, which can be written as $\frac{1}{9}$.

c) There are only four events in which neither one of the outcomes is green. The table shows this event occurring four out of nine events, which can be written as $\frac{4}{9}$.

d) The table shows this event occurring five times out of nine events, which can be written as $\frac{5}{9}$.

2. Step 1
Determine the probability of each separate event.

The probability of rolling an even number on the green, six-sided number cube is $P(even) = \dfrac{1}{2}$.

The probability of rolling a 3 on the red, six-sided number cube is $P(3) = \dfrac{1}{6}$.

Step 2
Calculate the probability of the event happening.

Multiply the separate probabilities together.

$$P(\text{even and }3) = \dfrac{1}{2} \times \dfrac{1}{6}$$
$$= \dfrac{1}{12}$$

The probability of rolling an even number on a green, six-sided number cube and a 3 on the red, six-sided number cube is $\dfrac{1}{12}$.

3. Step 1
Calculate the experimental probability of the desired event.

Substitute the values into the probability formula. Reduce if possible.

$$P(\text{favourable outcome}) = \dfrac{\text{favourable outcomes}}{\text{total possible outcomes}}$$
$$P(4) = \dfrac{2}{25}$$

Step 2
Calculate the prediction.

Multiply the resulting probability by the number of die rolls of the predicted event.

$$\dfrac{2}{25} \times \dfrac{150}{1} = \dfrac{300}{25}$$
$$= 12$$

When the die is rolled 150 times, the expected number of times that a 4 will be rolled is 12.

PRACTICE EXERCISES
ANSWERS AND SOLUTIONS

1. There are 18 possible outcomes. The probability of spinning white and rolling 1 is 1 out of 18. Set up the fraction, and reduce if possible.

$$P(\text{white, }1) = \dfrac{1}{18}$$

3. There are 18 possible outcomes. The probability of spinning grey and any number is 6 out of 18: (grey, 1), (grey, 2), (grey, 3), (grey, 4), (grey, 5), and (grey, 6). Set up the fraction, and reduce if possible.

$$P(\text{grey, any number}) = \dfrac{6}{18}$$
$$= \dfrac{1}{3}$$

5. There are 18 possible outcomes. The probability of spinning a colour and rolling a number less than 3 is 6 out of 18: (white, 1), (black, 1), (grey, 1), (white, 2), (black, 2), (grey, 2). Set up the fraction, and reduce if possible.

$$P(\text{a colour, a number less than }3) = \dfrac{6}{18}$$
$$= \dfrac{1}{3}$$

7. The probability of (girl, boy) is 1 out of 4. Set up the fraction.

$$P(\text{girl, boy}) = \dfrac{1}{4}$$

9. Only one outcome (girl, girl) has no boys, so the probability of no boys is 1 out of 4.

$$P(\text{no boys}) = \dfrac{1}{4}$$

11. The probability of tossing tails is 1 out of 2, and the probability of drawing a face card (jack, queen, or king in four different suits) is 12 out of 52.

$$P(\text{T, face card}) = \dfrac{1}{2} \times \dfrac{12}{52}$$
$$= \dfrac{12}{104}$$
$$= \dfrac{3}{26}$$

13. The probability of tossing heads is 1 out of 2, and the probability of drawing a number card (2, 3, 4, 5, 6, 7, 8, 9, 10 in each suit) is 36 numbers out of 52.

$$P(\text{H, a number card}) = \frac{1}{2} \times \frac{36}{52}$$
$$= \frac{36}{104}$$
$$= \frac{9}{26}$$

15. Tossing heads or tails is guaranteed, so the probability is 1 out of 1. There are four 7s in a deck of cards, so the probability is 4 out of 52.

$$P(\text{H or T, 7}) = \frac{1}{1} \times \frac{4}{52}$$
$$= \frac{4}{52}$$
$$= \frac{1}{13}$$

Practice Test

ANSWERS AND SOLUTIONS

1. Make a table.

Girls		Boys					
		1	2	3	4	5	6
	a	1a	2a	3a	4a	5a	6a
	b	1b	2b	3b	4b	5b	6b
	c	1c	2c	3c	4c	5c	6c
	d	1d	2d	3d	4d	5d	6d
	e	1e	2e	3e	4e	5e	6e

The outcomes are 1a, 1b, 1c, 1d, 1e, 2a, 2b, 2c, 2d, 2e, 3a, 3b, 3c, 3d, 3e, 4a, 4b, 4c, 4d, 4e, 5a, 5b, 5c, 5d, 5e, 6a, 6b, 6c, 6d, and 6e.

3. There are four 2s in a deck of 52 cards. There are 4 favourable outcomes and 52 total outcomes. Set up the fraction, and reduce.

$$P(2) = \frac{4}{52}$$
$$= \frac{1}{13}$$

5. Multiples of 5 are 5 and 10 and there are four cards of each number. There are 8 favourable outcomes and 52 total outcomes. Set up the fraction, and reduce.

$$P(\text{multiple of 5}) = \frac{8}{52}$$
$$= \frac{2}{13}$$

7. Create a table of values showing all the possible outcomes.

Die	Marble Colour		
	Red	Blue	Green
1	1, R	1, B	1, G
2	2, R	2, B	2, G
3	3, R	3, B	3, G
4	4, R	4, B	4, G
5	5, R	5, B	5, G
6	6, R	6, B	6, G

The table shows 18 possible outcomes.

9. Use multiplication.
Number of possible outcomes of choosing a letter: 8
Number of possible outcomes of choosing a number: 9

Total number of possible outcomes: $8 \times 9 = 72$

11. The odd numbers that occur on spinner 2 are 1, 3 and 5. The possible outcomes are (3, 1) and (3, 3), and (3, 5). The table shows this event occurring 3 out of 20 events. Set up the fraction.

$$P(3, \text{ odd}) = \frac{3}{20}.$$

13. Create a table of values showing all the possible outcomes.

Die	Coin	
	H	**T**
1	1, H	1, T
2	2, H	2, T
3	3, H	3, T
4	4, H	4, T
5	5, H	5, T
6	6, H	6, T

The table of values shows 12 possible outcomes.

The even numbers on a die are 2, 4 and 6. The possible outcomes are (2, H), (4, H), and (6, H). The table shows this event occurring 3 times out of 12 events. Set up the fraction and reduce.

$$P(\text{even, H}) = \frac{3}{12}$$
$$= \frac{1}{4}$$

15. The numbers greater than 2 are 3, 4, 5, and 6. Therefore, the possible outcomes are (3, T), (4, T) (5, T), and (6, T). The table shows this event occurring 4 out of 12 events. Set up the fraction and reduce.

$$P(\text{a number greater than 2, T}) = \frac{4}{12}$$
$$= \frac{1}{3}$$

17. When choosing a card, there are 52 possible outcomes. Richard's possibilities for choosing a letter are A, J, Q, and K in each of four sets. Therefore, the number of possible outcomes is 16.

Thus, the probability of Robert choosing a card with a letter on it is $\frac{16}{52} = \frac{4}{13}$.

Simon's possibilities for choosing a number are 2, 3, 4, 5, 6, 7, 8, and 9 in each of the four sets.

Therefore, the number of possible outcomes is 32. The probability of Simon choosing a card with a number is $\frac{32}{52} = \frac{8}{13}$.

Simon's probability is higher, meaning he has a better chance of winning.

19. The total possible number of outcomes is 50 since the die was rolled 50 times.

Determine the probability of rolling a 1.

$$P(1) = \frac{15}{50}$$
$$= \frac{3}{10}$$

Determine the probability of rolling a 2.

$$P(2) = \frac{20}{50}$$
$$= \frac{2}{5}$$

Determine the probability of rolling a 3.

$$P(3) = \frac{10}{50}$$
$$= \frac{1}{5}$$

Determine the probability of rolling a 4.

$$P(4) = \frac{5}{50}$$
$$= \frac{1}{10}$$

The only outcome with an experimental probability of $\frac{1}{5}$ is rolling a 3.

Credits

Every effort has been made to provide proper acknowledgement of the original source and to comply with

copyright law. However, some attempts to establish original copyright ownership may have been unsuccessful.

If copyright ownership can be identified, please notify Castle Rock Research Corp so that appropriate corrective action can be taken.

Some images in this document are from www.clipart.com, copyright (c) 2011 Jupiterimages Corporation.

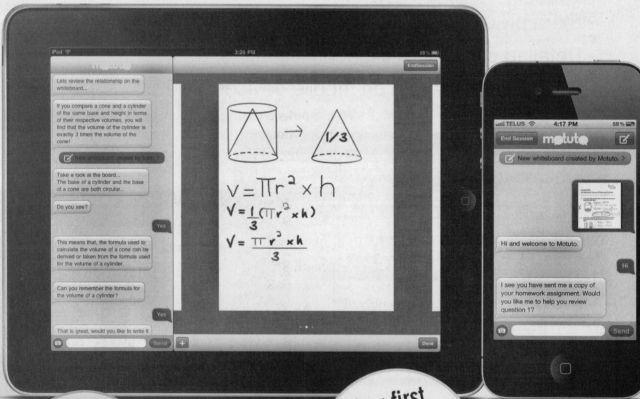